THE
TRIUMPH
OF
SCIENCE
AND
REASON 1660-1685

THE NEW AMERICAN NATION SERIES

Edited by HENRY STEELE COMMAGER *and*
RICHARD B. MORRIS

* *In preparation*

THE TRIUMPH OF SCIENCE AND SCIENCE AND REASON 1660-1685

BY FREDERICK L. NUSSBAUM

BY FREDERICK L. NUSSBAUM

HARPER TORCHBOOKS

THE UNIVERSITY LIBRARY

HARPER & ROW, PUBLISHERS ⬦ NEW YORK AND EVANSTON

TO CECIL

My Good Companion

THE TRIUMPH OF SCIENCE AND REASON 1660-1685

Copyright 1953 by Harper & Row, Publishers, Incorporated
Printed in the United States of America

*This book was originally published in 1953 by Harper &
Brothers in The Rise of Modern Europe series, edited by
William L. Langer.*

First HARPER TORCHBOOK edition published 1962 by Harper
& Row, Publishers, Incorporated, New York and Evanston.

Library of Congress catalog card number: 52-7295

TABLE OF CONTENTS

MAP

ILLUSTRATIONS

The illustrations, grouped in a separate section, will be found following page 112.

INTRODUCTION

OUR age of specialization produces an almost incredible amount of monographic research in all fields of human knowledge. So great is the mass of this material that even the professional scholar cannot keep abreast of the contributions in anything but a restricted part of his general subject. In all branches of learning the need for intelligent synthesis is now more urgent than ever before, and this need is felt by the layman even more acutely than by the scholar. He cannot hope to read the products of microscopic research or to keep up with the changing interpretations of experts, unless new knowledge and new viewpoints are made accessible to him by those who make it their business to be informed and who are competent to speak with authority.

These volumes, published under the general title of *The Rise of Modern Europe,* are designed primarily to give the general reader and student a reliable survey of European history written by experts in various branches of that vast subject. In consonance with the current broad conception of the scope of history, they attempt to go beyond a merely political-military narrative, and to lay stress upon social, economic, religious, scientific and artistic developments. The minutely detailed, chronological approach is to some extent sacrificed in the effort to emphasize the dominant factors and to set forth their interrelationships. At the same time the division of European history into national histories has been abandoned and wherever possible attention has been focused upon larger forces common to the whole of European civilization. These are the broad lines on which this history as a whole has been laid out. The individual volumes are integral parts of the larger scheme, but they are intended also to stand as independent units, each the work of a scholar well qualified to treat the period covered by his book. Each volume contains about fifty illustrations selected from the mass of contemporary pictorial material. All noncontemporary illustrations have been excluded on principle. The bibliographical note appended to each volume is designed to facilitate further study of special aspects touched upon in the text. In general every effort has been made to give the reader a clear idea of the main movements in European history, to embody the monographic contributions of research workers, and to present the material in a forceful and vivid manner.

The early twentieth century marked the end of an intellectual epoch that began in the period covered by the present volume of the series. For it was Newton, following upon Descartes, who established the concepts upon which western thought rested until the theory of relativity opened up yet wider horizons to the human mind. Professor Nussbaum, writing of what is generally thought of as the more "glorious" part of the long reign of Louis XIV, has relegated the Sun King and his contemporaries to a subordinate position in his narrative. He has, instead, centered attention on the brilliant achievements in science and art, on the progressive development of political theory and organization, on the broadening and deepening of religious life, and on the continuing evolution of the modern capitalist economy. For him the incessant wars of the later seventeenth century were anachronistic, a residue of a more primitive culture and even at the time quite out of keeping with the phenomenal attainments of the European mind in other fields. Whether or not one is willing to accept this interpretation, the challenge it presents to established notions would in itself be enough to make this a provocative and stimulating contribution to European history.

WILLIAM L. LANGER

PREFACE

THE problem of the historian is somewhat that of the portraitist, to see the prime element of the character structure of the past that he is attempting to portray and to use it to achieve unity in his story. The custom of our historiography has been to organize European history around political activity and conflict. That is justifiable, if not necessary, in narrating the history of the states, since they are political structures. In a history of Europe it is neither justifiable nor necessary. Europe is a culture complex, of which politics is a phase, but only a phase.

In the history of Europe in the seventeenth century, it is being increasingly recognized, the prime element of the character structure is the new mentality for which "Cartesianism" and "the baroque" are the most convenient names. One distinguished historian of science says flatly that to understand even the intellectualism of the time, it is necessary to begin with the baroque, while another, equally distinguished, declares that the intellectual revolution of the seventeenth century was the greatest development in world history since the emergence of Christianity.

Either formulation seemed attractive and adequate as a theme upon which to develop the history of Europe between 1660 and 1685. I can only say that for me the problem seemed most manageable with Cartesianism as the theme and that the choice did not seem to involve any contradiction except when I had to deal with the irrational disorganization of power with reference to the society as a whole and the anarchistic conflicts between the states. The dictum of the Unesco charter, "War begins in the minds of men," falls short as a comment on the seventeenth-century situation and requires amendment. The intellectualism with which the Europeans undertook the mastery of the rest of their world was not extended to the problem of their relations as Europeans with each other.

Otherwise the rationalism, purposiveness and dynamism that we call Cartesian marked the whole range of European life. In thought and in art, in science and in religion, in economy and in society, Europe in this period began a revolutionary process the momentum of which is not even yet spent. The authority of the past was rejected as the source of learning and wisdom, as the sanction of power, as the limit of social action, and even as the central fact of religion.

Such is the Europe I have tried to portray—a Europe in revolt from the limiting conditions of its past and prepared to live by its own sanctions.

It is a pleasure to acknowledge the kindly assistance of colleagues and friends. Professor Bertram Morris of the University of Colorado and Professor Paul Crissman of the University of Wyoming suggested useful modifications of the formulation of the general intellectual setting. Dr. William H. Clohessy of Lehigh University saved me from some pitfalls in the field of science and Dr. Cyclone Covey of Wheaton College contributed valuably to my idea of the baroque. I owe much to the sympathetic encouragement of Professor Milton Nahm of Bryn Mawr College and to Judge Thurman Arnold. Newberry Library, the Library of Congress, Widener Library and the library of the University of California furnished me working home and generous service for months on end. The University of Wyoming generously favored me with release from teaching, leaves and grants. Professor William L. Langer as editor bore more than an ordinary burden of controlling a hasty pen, correcting errors and demanding clarity.

FREDERICK L. NUSSBAUM

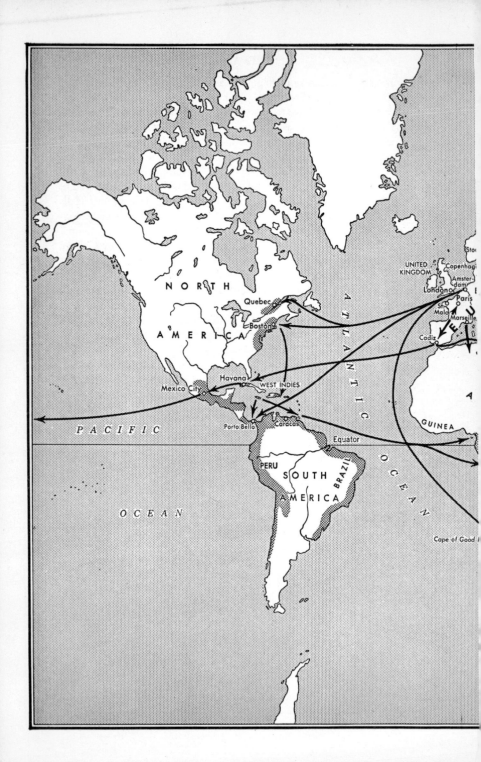

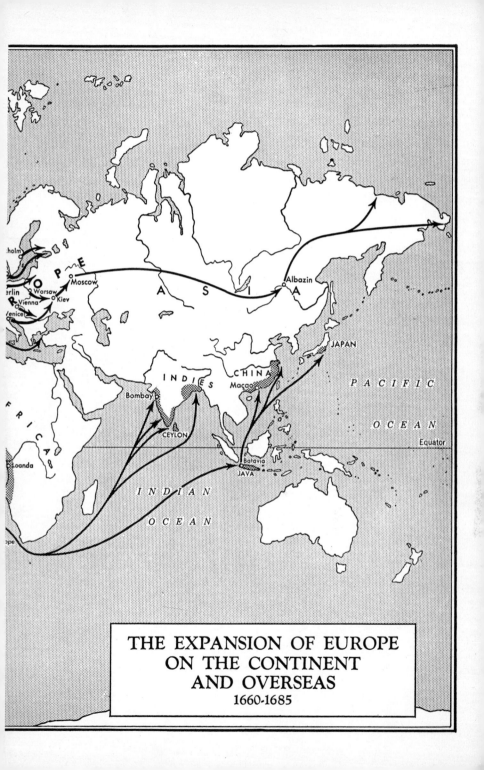

THE EXPANSION OF EUROPE
ON THE CONTINENT
AND OVERSEAS
1660-1685

Chapter One

COSMOS: A NEW HEAVEN AND A NEW EARTH

I. THE CARTESIAN REVOLUTION

In 1660 Europe was in revolution. At no time in its brief history as a society had any generation stood to the future with an orientation so distinct from that of its ancestors.

For two thousand years, the pattern of men's thoughts about themselves and about the world had been the pluralistic and qualitative scheme of the universe devised by the ancient Greeks. In this scheme, as inherited by the Europeans from the Romans and the Arabs, anything could happen, even miracles. Life could come by spontaneous generation. The phoenix could rise anew from its ashes. In the form of scholasticism, the words of the ancient philosophers and scientists had become involved with the word of God, so that it was the function of natural science to serve theology.

The revolution of the seventeenth century overthrew this ancient way of thought. The material world was dissociated from the world of God and assumed to be rational, so that it could be apprehended and mastered by observation and measurement. The revolution attained definitive expression in two works which remained for three centuries the fundamental charters of the European mind: the *Discours sur la méthode de bien conduire la raison et chercher la vérité dans les sciences* of René Descartes and the *Philosophiae naturalis principia mathematica* of Isaac Newton.

In the *Discourse on Method* (1637), Descartes had organized the method of free inquiry by which the Europeans were to develop the control of nature. He had reversed Copernicus, who had displaced the earth as the center of the universe: there Descartes had put man—alone, intangible, percipient—with only his "mind" to grasp and master his world. To find an unchallengeable basis from which to proceed, he had put aside all that authority, even the authority of his senses, told him and thus arrived at what, it seemed to him, could not be doubted: *"Cogito ergo sum"*—"I think, therefore I exist." From this irreducible starting point, he had proceeded to reconstruct the universe. According to him, it was double: a world of experience and a world beyond experience. In the world beyond experience, God existed since, for Descartes, the thinking man could derive from no other source such concepts as eternity and omnipotence, which were beyond his experience. Experience was confined to a world of phenomena, which could be comprehended only by their "primary qualities." For Descartes, these were extension and motion, which could be formulated as clear and distinct ideas, that is, in mathematical terms. "Secondary qualities," which could not be measured and were not clear and distinct ideas, were to be ignored.

Descartes did not succeed in establishing the connection of the mind with the world of extension and motion—it remained for John Locke to initiate that problem—or in making clear and distinct its connection with the world beyond experience. Nevertheless, he succeeded in defining a universe in which the human reason was supreme. In the world beyond experience it led to the knowledge of God. In the world of experience, by wholly different methods, free from involvement with tradition and authority, it could lead, as Descartes saw, to mastery of the material world: "We might thus render ourselves the lords and possessors of nature."[1]

In the latter decades of the century, Cartesianism spread over Europe like a tidal wave, engulfing and sweeping along followers, critics and opponents together, far beyond the limits which Descartes himself had fondly hoped to set to the forces that impelled him. The skepticism which he limited to the facts of the physical world was promptly recognized by the theologians for the danger it was to their structure of authority in the world of faith and morals. Cartesianism was denounced and persecuted by Calvinists, Lutherans and Catholics. Descartes died in exile and in 1663 his works were put on the Index. Yet within half a century after his death, the whole intellectual world of Europe was using Cartesian methods to solve Cartesian problems. *"Cartesius philosophorum nostri saeculi facile princeps."* Thus in 1692 the *Acta eruditorum* recognized the sovereignty of Descartes.

The profound necessity of Cartesianism is manifest in the two great minds of the age who consciously held away from it and condemned it. Pascal, who never wearied of disparaging Descartes, was ultimately reduced to an even bolder assertion of man's loneliness in the universe. The existence of God, he declared, was a good bet! The monstrous wager, whatever Pascal as a devout seeker of God intended by it, was the ultimate expression of a skepticism that surpassed the provisional skepticism of Descartes. As Pascal himself remarked, Descartes "could not help mak-

[1] *Discours sur la méthode*, Part VI.

ing God give a fillip to set the world in motion." [2] For Descartes, God was at least a necessity, if a minimal one; for Pascal, God might be an uncertainty. The Promethean dualism of Pascal's thought is illustrated by his opposition of man and the universe: "Even if the universe should crush him, man would still be nobler than that which kills him, because he knows he dies: and of the advantage which the universe has over him, the universe knows not at all." The genius of the utterance is not distant from the genius of the *"Cogito ergo sum."*

For very different reasons, Newton disapproved of Descartes as heartily as did Pascal. Like the latter, he repudiated the responsibility for generalized thinking in the form of metaphysics. "I do not make hypotheses," was his haughty equivalent to Pascal's "We hold that all philosophy is not worth an hour's trouble." The revolution in physics of our own generation and the end of the long and beneficent reign of Newton make it possible to recognize that the massive solidity and comprehensiveness which for two centuries seemed to render his system the last word possible in the science of nature is based, although he would have denied it, on the work of the great mathematical physicists who had preceded him. In spite of their irrelevance to mathematics and experience, he retained the Greek notions of essence and substance.[3] With naïve unconsciousness, on the other hand, he adopted the main features of the metaphysics of Descartes. The dualistic rationalism which his mighty example imposed upon the world finally overthrew Aristotelianism and became the predominant world view of modern times. It was Cartesianism, ambiguously and incompletely developed.[4]

The deeply religious Newton "had an eye upon such principles as might work with considering men, for the belief in a Deity." [5] He encouraged Richard Bentley to apply the Newtonian system to the refutation of atheism and another follower, Dr. Craig, to write a *Theologiae christianae principia mathematica* (1699). For Newton, as for Descartes and Pascal, not only the empirical problems of physics but the existence of God were problems to be solved by reason. For the scientist as for the religionist and the philosopher, the dualism of mind and matter, of reason and experience, was a necessity.

---

[2] Morris Bishop, *Pascal, the Life of Genius*, 75 *et passim*. Emile Faguet, *Dix-septième siècle: études littéraires* (28th ed., Paris, 1903), 23, makes much more of the place of God in the system of Descartes.

[3] J. Dewey, *The Quest for Certainty* (New York, 1929), 119–20.

[4] E. A. Burtt, *The Metaphysical Foundations of Modern Physical Science* (London, 1932), 236–37.

[5] Sir Isaac Newton, *Four Letters to Dr. Bentley, in Proof of a Deity* (London, 1756).

The victory of Cartesianism was in no way more manifest than in its diffusion among the religious orthodox. It was evident in the most Catholic texts of philosophy even when written by the most anti-Cartesian of priests. Not only the *Logique* of Port Royal, but the *Traités* of Bossuet and Fénelon were marked by the Cartesian spirit.[6] Bossuet recognized that in the emphasis on the authority of reason there were "the seeds of more than one heresy." Danger or no danger, for a man of Bossuet's time and intellectual level, only Cartesian terms would express his problems. It was, however, Nicolas Malebranche (1638-1715), a priest of the Oratory, who appropriated Cartesianism for Christianity and made it what it remained in the eighteenth and most of the nineteenth century, the essential weapon of the polemic against deism, materialism, atheism and ethical naturalism.[7]

From his first contact with Descartes to the end of his long career, Malebranche[8] more than any other individual symbolized the achievement of supremacy by Cartesianism as the form of the European mind. One day in 1664, still somewhat uncertain of his course, he bought and read Descartes's *Traité de l'homme*. It was an illumination, akin to the conversion of Saul of Tarsus. Thenceforth he knew his master and his destiny: he would be at once Cartesian and Christian. He would reconcile religion and reason. The completeness of his own surrender to this compulsion, which was to fill the rest of his life, had its counterpart in the viceroyalty which he exercised in the name of his master over the fashionable as well as over the learned. His works went through many editions. He was the center of industrious controversies, especially with Arnauld, the great Jansenist. In spite of a retiring disposition, he was sought out by aspiring younger men from all over Europe. Legend has it that his end was hastened by the insistence of Berkeley, the then young English philosopher, upon consulting him. His fame spread as far as China. His would-be followers went beyond him and his last work, in the year of his death, was a stout reaffirmation of the belief in freedom of the human will which some of his disciples supposed he had done away with.

[6] E. Faguet, *op. cit.*, 64.

[7] A. G. Balz, "Cartesian Refutations of Spinoza," *Philosophical Review*, 46 (1937), 461–84. See also, P. Hazard, "Les Rationnaux, 1670–1700," *Révue de littérature comparée*, 12 (1932), 677–711.

[8] E. Faguet, *op. cit.*, Essay 11. The principal works of Malebranche are *La récherche de la vérité* (1674–75); *Traité de la nature et de la grace* (1680); *Méditations chrétiennes* (1683); *Traité de l'amour de Dieu* (1697); *Entrétien d'un philosophe chrétien avec un philosophe chinois* (1708); *Réceuil de tous les réponses à M. Arnaut* (1709); *Réflexions sur les prémonitions physiques* (1715).

Cartesianism seemed to Malebranche the perfect instrument with which to destroy the assumption that there was a separation between reason and religion. He set himself the mission of reconciling the pretended differences and of presenting the true religion as the true philosophy by processes of rational evidence. For Malebranche, God functioned in the form of general volitions and not by particularities, under the compulsions of his own wisdom. He was unable to avoid a conduct consistent with the character of his attributes, that is, in Cartesian terms, rational and free from contradictions. He could only establish occasional causes and ministers to act in a secondary relation to His will, whose function was also established once and for all. Unlike his critics—Arnauld, Fénelon, Bossuet—Malebranche did not recognize that, in subordinating God to His order and wisdom, he was taking away not only His privilege of arbitrariness, but even His excuse for existence. Unlike Bayle, emergent at the end of our period, he did not recognize that the initial mystery at the base of all religion was by definition beyond the range of the rational function. God was the *locus* of ideas, the source from which we derive all our ideas of Him, of the universe and of ourselves. Rational evidence was the perfect light to which Malebranche aspired with a mystic fervor, because for him, as a Catholic Cartesian, reason was a perfect instrument, even of mystery. His successors in the field of Christian evidences down to Paley were one long line of witnesses to the power of Cartesianism in European culture.

With Spinoza the ambiguously established dualism of Descartes was displaced by a boldly asserted unity of God and man, mind and matter, in a pantheistic universe. Spinoza was impossible for a Manichean Europe. For the Europeans, the meaning of existence, the reality of man, the reality of nature, the reality of God depended upon the dualism which Descartes maintained. Thus it was that the "God-drunken" Spinoza was rejected by the Europeans of his time and of the succeeding generations as an atheist and accepted only by later generations for whom the world was ceasing to have meaning and a God.

Baruch de Spinoza (1632–1677) was a Jew of the Sephardic congregation of Amsterdam, cast out from the congregation at the age of twenty-four because it had become impossible for him to live within the orthodox Jewish framework of life. Apparently he had been highly trained in Jewish law and philosophy, and though he had gone to the Gentiles for Latin and physics, the "new learning" of the seventeenth century, he retained his heritage as a Jew. It was his life task to unite the authentically monotheistic Hebrew God—eternal, unchangeable, one—with the Greek tradition of intellectualism and naturalism and with the method and conclusions of modern science.[9]

Spinoza began with Cartesianism. His first published work was *The Principles of Cartesian Philosophy* (1663). His *Tractatus brevis de Deo et homine, eiusque felicitate,* which was not published until 1862, shows a very considerable derivation from Descartes. His own distinctive picture of the world emerged in the *Tractatus theologico-politicus* (1670), the only one of his principal works published in his lifetime, and the *Ethica,* published together with his correspondence and some fragments as the *Opera posthuma* in the year of his death. The departure from Descartes was definitive by the time of the *Tractatus theologico-politicus.* For Spinoza, God was not (as Pascal said of Descartes) a mere device to get his universe started. Spinoza's God was all-inclusive. In the rational universe which he assumes—"The order and connection of ideas is one with the order and connection of things"—God was the ultimate expression and manifestation of reason, functioning organically throughout the universe and including all of it, perfect and imperfect, as part of the single whole of things. Things were not really things at all, but one or another of different "modes" by which *The Thing* was expressed.

The relationship between the doctrines of Descartes and those of Spinoza is a matter of continued reinterpretation. It is possible, and it is even important for this structure, to recognize in Spinozism a revised and systematized Cartesianism. For Europeans of the succeeding generations, however, Descartes and Spinoza stood opposed, Descartes as defender of the faith, Spinoza as the exponent of atheism.[10] The Europeans accepted Descartes and rejected Spinoza. As "Christianized" by Malebranche, Cartesianism evaded the terrible conclusion that God is all and that we, indistinguishably from the rest of the universe, have no independent existence but are only aspects of Him. The whole experimental disposition of the Europeans in exploring their universe was antagonistic to Spinoza's unquestioning faith that the logical order and connection of ideas is one with the order and connection of things.[11] The preservation of the dualism kept the way open for the untraditional, the unconventional, the unexpected—that is to say, for the projectors, the inventors and the discoverers. By rejecting Spinoza and retaining Descartes, Europe could keep its God while it unmade and remade its material world at will.

[9] J. Dewey, *op. cit.,* 56.
[10] A. G. Balz, *op. cit.,* 461–84.
[11] J. Dewey, *op. cit.,* 57.

II. THE DISCOVERY OF SCIENCE

The Cartesian faith in man's power to know and to understand operated powerfully to turn men's hopes and interests from religion to science. Unfortunately for our purpose here, we have as yet no social history of science and, indeed, no history of science that corresponds even to the low standards of what we call political history.[12] A king with sufficient military power may enter upon a course of imperialist conquest that proves in the end to be only inane folly; he remains nevertheless a subject for political history. The variant and unsuccessful forms of scientific pursuit, on the other hand, however much they manifest the will of the European to conquer the lands of science, command but little attention in the general histories of science. In an ideal scheme of things past, the victory of Newtonianism, like, say, the rise of Holland in the early seventeenth century, must take into account the alternative possibilities which the Europeans rejected—the unsuccessful rivals and competitors, as well as the allies who, through the preceding decades and centuries, were developing the problem and the instrumentalities to the point where Newton's genius as mathematician found effective application and theory.

The operational form of the revolution to which Descartes had given such significant expression was the exploration, discovery and manipulation of the external world in the patterns which the seventeenth century taught us to call science. The word itself is a prime symbol of the revolution. Up to this period, *scientia* was knowledge, with as near as may be the same generalized connotations. Descartes appropriated the old symbol to serve in the restricted and specialized sense in which it has served ever since.[13] Pascal and his associates established it as usage and toward the end of the century the French Academy gave it place in its *Dictionnaire* as "the certain and evident knowledge of things by their causes." In the English language, despite Bacon's earlier approximation to Descartes's use, the term in this sense was hardly naturalized until the eighteenth century. In the German language, *"Wissenschaft"* still more slowly displaced the older term *"Kunst."* [14] Descartes's success in making a new

---

[12] But see B. Hessen, "The Social and Economic Roots of Newton's *Principia"* (in *Science at the Crossroads,* London, 1931), a Marxian interpretation; and G. N. Clark, *Science and Social Welfare in the Age of Newton* (New York, 1937), equally "social" but an admirable corrective to Hessen; Abel Ray, "Histoire de la science ou histoire des sciences," *Archeion,* 12 (1930), 1–4. A particular exception to my statement must be made for the excellent work of H. Butterfield, *The Origins of Modern Science* (London, 1950).

[13] *Discours de la Méthode, Oeuvres,* VI, 18.

[14] Preserved Smith, *A History of Modern Culture* (3 vols., New York, 1930 ff.), I, 153–54.

symbol throws some light on the social function of philosophy and of his philosophy in particular. He made a place in the general scheme of things for an intellectual activity which dissociated itself from metaphysics and historical studies, and an essential part of his achievement was giving it a name. It is useless to criticize so successful an achievement, but a historian (or a metaphysician or a poet) may well protest at the arrogance of the appropriation. Indeed, the scientists themselves are now confronted with the problem of adjustment to the improper implications of the symbol and of distinguishing between their measurements and actual knowledge.[15] Another word, less portentous and less durable than "science," needs to be recognized as also a substantial semantic monument of this revolution. This is the word "virtuoso." It had with reference to the general field of scientific activity almost the same significance we now give it in the restricted field of musical technique, except that it did not connote specialization. The virtuoso was one who spent much effort and time in observing nature, collecting materials and seeking results that were beyond the range of ordinary experience.[16]

The scientist of the seventeenth century was rarely the specialist he has since become. If a Leeuwenhoek could confine himself to his "glasses" and a Picard could find himself fully occupied with the Paris Observatory, the virtuoso generally held to a versatile and nonspecialized outlook. Especially characteristic was the disposition to subordinate scientific study as we now know it to theological investigation. Descartes and Malebranche avowed that their sole purpose was to verify the truths of the Christian religion. Pascal regarded his interest in physical phenomena as a derogation from his religous contemplations. Newton put the bulk of his effort, not into the *Principia* and the *Opticks,* but into his studies of the Trinity and of the prophetic books of the Bible, especially the Book of Daniel and the Apocalypse. Boyle was thoroughly devout. In his *Christian Virtuoso* (1690) he formulated his personal reconciliation of science and religion. When he died, he left fifty pounds a year to establish a lectureship defending the Christian religion against infidels. Richard Bentley, the first lecturer on this foundation, received considerable aid from Newton, who was at the same time sympathetically promoting John Craig's proposed *Principia mathematica* of Christianity.

---

[15] See especially, John Dewey, *op. cit.;* Joseph Needham, *The Skeptical Biologist* (London, 1930).
[16] C. S. Duncan, *The New Science and English Literature in the Classical Period* (Menasha, Wis., 1913), ch. III *et passim;* W. E. Houghton, Jr., "The English Virtuoso in the Seventeenth Century," *Journal of the History of Ideas,* III (1942), 51–73; 190–219.

III. SCIENCE AS SOCIAL FORM

The advancement of science was in large part the function of an elite. As far as the general population was concerned, then as now it was little aware of the problem of the scientist. The people who read books and saw plays, in their more serious moments with a Milton or a Vondel, took their grave pleasures in terms of the classical Greek mythology with hardly a taint of even Ptolemaic cosmology. Milton in his youth met Galileo but it does not appear that the contact was fruitful. Milton had, indeed, found an infinite universe without abandoning the old science. The cosmology of the *Paradise Lost* was still Ptolemaic. Even the poets who were themselves virtuosos, like Cowley, who in 1661 published a very advanced *Proposition for the Advancement of Learning,* and Edmund Waller, who was also interested in science, found only classical images to express the new ideas. Dryden, who was a member of the Royal Society, clung to Ptolemaic phraseology. Samuel Butler's *Hudibras* ridiculed with utter abandon every new theory of the physical order of the universe. Andrew Marvell scoffed at the atomic theory, the telescopic observations of the sun, the experiments in blood transfusion. Thomas Shadwell's *The Virtuoso* (1676) made the scientist in the person of Sir Nicholas Gimcrack a figure of farce.[17] In the more sophisticated atmosphere of Paris, Molière made the jargon of the laboratory part of the absurdity of the bourgeois who would be a gentleman. On the other hand Boyle had a wide popular appeal and many of his books went at once into several editions. His *Spring and Weight of the Air* aroused great general interest. No less than five tracts commenting upon and criticising his observations were published in the next two years.[18]

The old hypotheses did not "fall without noise," as William Wooton hoped. Even Robert Boyle clung to the problems of the alchemists. In 1675 he produced a paper on the transmutation of metals—"the degradation of gold"—which commanded the intense interest of Isaac Newton.[19] The *Scepsis scientifica* of Joseph Glanvill (1665), one of the best formulations of the intellectual position of the scientist, had its roots in theology: Adam did not need to be skeptical, but his fallen descendents do.[20] Otto von Guericke, in spite of his lively experimentalism, showed his adherence to antiquated notions by his definition of air as an exhalation of

---

[17] C. S. Duncan, *op. cit., passim.*

[18] J. F. Fulton, *A Bibliography of the Honorable Robert Boyle* (Oxford, 1931).

[19] L. T. More, "Boyle as Alchemist," *Journal of the History of Ideas,* II (1941), 61–76.

[20] John Owen, introductory essay, page xxii, to his edition of Joseph Glanvill, *Scepsis scientifica* (London, 1885).

water, earth and other substances.[21] The belief in magic, witchcraft, spirits and astrology persisted even in unexpected places. Sir Thomas Browne formally, if defensively, avowed his belief in all of them. Even in his *Vulgar Errors* (1646) he still clung to a "sober, regulated astrology" and the Ptolemaic system. Henry More, the Cambridge Platonist, stoutly defended the validity of evidence given in witch trials in his *Antidote to Atheism*. Joseph Glanvill, in his *Philosophia pia* (1671), his *Essays on Several Important Subjects in Philosophy and Religion* (1676), and especially in his *Sadducismus triumphatus* (1681), developed an earnest argument, based on the Bible and tales of ghosts and witches, that disbelief in witchcraft leads logically to disbelief in God.

The credulity of Glanvill and More was openly attacked by John Webster in *The Displaying of Supposed Witchcraft* (1677), which "utterly denied and disproved" all of the supposed manifestations. The actual persecution of witches had greatly diminished and the more significant outbursts after 1660 occurred in relatively remote regions such as Scotland, where 150 cases were tried in 1661, Dalecarlia in Sweden, where 84 adults and 15 children were burned in 1669, and in Massachusetts Bay and Connecticut where 14 persons were executed. In general, the belief in witchcraft and the practice of persecution were declining. The relatively high discipline of the Inquisition, both Roman and Spanish, made it possible for Clement VII and Gregory XV to reform the procedure and to mitigate the punishments. The Spanish Inquisition in 1657 issued instructions that, without denying the existence of the crime, made conviction difficult. In 1672 Colbert directed French magistrates to receive no accusations of sorcery. The Great Elector radically revised the treatment of witchcraft and in 1674 the juristic faculty of Mainz, to which his courts referred a case, spoke out in a notable opinion against the whole structure. Spinoza in his *Short Treatise* (1660) and Hobbes in two chapters of the *Leviathan* had denied the intellectual basis of witchcraft. The end of witch-burning did not come until the late eighteenth century, but the gradual spread of the scientific spirit and the development of a critical attitude toward evidence involved the steady obsolescence and disappearance from the minds of educated men of the belief in witchcraft.

The scientific revolution had been so rapid that in spite of the high development of critical capacity, the disappearance of the last remnants of old-fashioned credulity lagged behind.

Although the scientific spirit was restricted to a small minority, it is

---

[21] Mario Gliozzi, *Archeion*, 13 (1931), 191–200.

obvious that more people, and people in larger and more specifically adapted units of association, worked at science. In the first decades of the century, Galileo and Kepler had ignored each other. By the end of the century, the social organization of science had developed to such a point that the work of Newton became known almost instantly throughout western Europe. Unfortunately, no census or *Who's Who in Science* exists to give us any idea of the number of inglorious Galileos or mute Harveys who were the contemporaries and associates of Newton and Huygens, of Swammerdam and Malpighi. Obviously, the interest in science had spread during the half-century to a larger part of the population and to many different sorts of people. Kings like Louis XIV and Charles II, their great ministers and servants like Colbert and Pepys, princes like the duke of Orleans and Leopold de' Medici, statesmen like John de Witt, gentlemen like Cornelius Huygens and Robert Boyle, bourgeois like Otto von Guericke and Leeuwenhoek, university men like Newton and Malpighi, were only conspicuous examples of a company that in every corner of Europe, either as professionals or as busy amateurs, concerned themselves with telescopes or microscpoes, with air pressures or with chemical processes.

Like the musicians and the literary men, the scientists formed societies. In a sense, the habit of association among human beings has no history: man is a gregarious animal. Nevertheless, the principle of association varies widely in time and in space. From this general point of view it is obvious that important new forms of association were developing in the late sixteenth and seventeenth centuries. The older forms of association— the church, the village, the town, the gild, the lordship, even the court— were nonspecialized. The new religious orders illustrate the change that was taking place. In contrast to the old orders, they were being organized with reference to specific functions, the Oratorians with reference to preaching, the order of St. Vincent de Paul with reference to charitable work, and so on. Even within so generalized an order as the Benedictines, such specializations as that of Saint Maur manifested the same disposition.

The association of scientists on the basis of their common interest in experiment and measurement dates well back into the sixteenth century. Baptista della Porta gathered about him a group which helped him perform the experiments recorded in his book on *Natural Magic*. More famous was the Accademia dei Lincei, founded at Rome in 1601 by Duke Federigo Cesi, of which Galileo was a member. The wide-flung correspondence systems carried on in the earlier decades of the century by

Nicolas-Claude Fabri de Peiresc (1580–1637) from Aix-en-Provence, by Marin Mersenne (1588–1648), and in the later decades by Henri Justel (1620–1693) constituted informal bonds of association among scientists all over Europe. In 1660 some societies of local range and generally of brief duration were already in existence. In Paris, the Montmor Academy had brought together in loose association some of the circle of Mersenne. Pascal was associated with a different group, otherwise unidentified, which he called "the Paris Academy." [22] In 1657 some disciples of Galileo, under the protection and with the participation of Leopold de' Medici, brother of the grand duke, formed the Accademia del Cimento (or Academy of Experiment), which during its short life of ten years carried out some valuable research in barometrics and heat. At the University of Rostock, Joachim Jungius organized the Societas Erneutica for the purpose of "seeking truth in reason and experiment and freeing the sciences from sophistry, in order to get demonstative certainty and to multiply useful inventions." As it was suspected of Rosicrucianism, this society lived only a few years. From small beginnings in the little town of Schweinfurt, a group of physicians under the leadership of Lorenz Bausch expanded gradually until by 1677 they had become an imperial society publishing annual reports of the research of their members. The Philosophical Society of Oxford, the leading spirit of which was Dr. Prat, carried on an active correspondence with the Dublin Society and with the Royal Society.[23]

In 1660 the Royal Society was organized by a group of scientists in London. In 1666 the French Academy of Sciences was established by Colbert. These two organizations, both of which were destined to play major roles in the development of science, differed widely in organization and operation.

In 1645, at the suggestion of Theodor Haak, a German who had been associated with the circle about Mersenne, a group of London virtuosos began meeting at Gresham College. When a number of this group migrated to Oxford in 1648 they associated with the Oxford Society. Those that remained in London ceased to meet after 1655, but at the Restoration resumed their meetings. Presently, reinforced by the return of some of their associates from Oxford, they resolved to organize formally (November 28, 1660).

Within two years, the group had been given a charter by the king and

[22] C. H. Boudhors, "L'académie parisienne," *Révue d'histoire littéraire de la France*, 36 (1929), 231–41.

[23] R. T. Gunther, *Early Science at Oxford* (12 vols., Oxford, 1920–1939), XII, Parts II and III.

assumed the name and the form which it has retained to this day. Charles II was by way of being a virtuoso himself and had his own chemical laboratory, for which he is known from time to time to have made considerable expenditures. It does not appear that he had in mind to give the Society anything more substantial than moral support. During its early years, it was often pinched for funds, but the merchants and businessmen who joined its ranks were willing to venture "considerable sums of money to put in practice what some of our members have contrived." Private philanthropy of a systematic kind began to be attracted early in the history of the Society and it was able to acquire some revenue by public performances. As the Society became popular, some of the members, including Hooke and Wren, formed a secret inner circle, the Royal Society Club.

Unlike the Royal Society, the French Academy of Sciences was established as an agency of the royal government. When the Montmor Academy went to pieces as a result of personal frictions, Melchisedec Thevenot, a diplomatic agent of Mazarin and close friend of Magalotti, secretary of the Accademia del Cimento, for two years attempted to carry on as Maecenas of a selected group, but soon found the financial burden too great. Through one of Colbert's connections who took an interest in his group, he suggested to Colbert that the enterprise be given a more lasting form under the approval of the king. A similar suggestion had reached Colbert earlier from the Montmor Academy, in the form of a discourse by Sorbière, undoubtedly carefully prepared by some of the leading spirits of the body. Adrien Auzout, who was member of both groups, strongly urged the need of a properly equipped public observatory in a letter dedicating to Louis XIV his *Ephéméride du comète de 1664*. Huygens' papers, too, contain a *projet de la compagnie des sciences et des arts* which he apparently received early in 1665. The *projet* was characterized by the free inclusiveness of the Royal Society, both as to membership and as to program.[24]

The actual form of the Academy, however, was more bureaucratic. According to Duhamel,[25] the original plan was for a general assembly with several sections, devoted respectively to physics and mathematics, history and literature, but the plan ultimately adopted was more restricted, with particular emphasis on mathematics, astronomy and physics. The limited number of members appointed to the Academy were chosen from various

[24] H. Brown, *Scientific Organizations in Seventeenth Century France 1620–1680* (Baltimore, 1934), 135–36.
[25] *Regiae scientarum academiae historia* (1700).

parts of Europe, as well as from France, and were put on salary as functionaries with regular duties. Many of the leading spirits of the Montmor Academy were omitted. Huygens was brought from Holland to function as what might be called leading member, an honor which he shared apparently without jealousy when Cassini was brought from Italy to conduct the observatory, which was generously supported by Colbert and became a correspondingly important part of the Academy's activity.[26] If the bureaucratic organization of the French Academy perhaps gave less encouragement than the Royal Society to individual achievement, it nevertheless furnished the machinery for some magnificent co-operative work. Thus the establishment of the map of France, which required extensive surveys in France itself, voyages to the West Indies, South America and Africa, and elaborate collaboration between the astronomers, the mathematicians and the cartographers, covered decades and eventuated in an achievement of the highest order. It was almost a century before England had a similar registration of the English metes and bounds.[27]

Scientific journalism developed in close relationship with the societies. In Paris, the *Journal des sçavans* made its appearance under the auspices of one X. Denis de Sallo on January 5, 1665.[28] It was a weekly consisting of a sheet and a half of large type and gave notices of books, literary gossip and scientific developments all over Europe. The *Journal* promptly made enemies, the most important of whom were the Jesuits. De Sallo was forced to suspend publication and to surrender the direction, but the installation of the Abbé Gallois as editor satisfied the Jesuits and the *Journal* was able to continue. In England, the concentration of the function of correspondence had made a heavy burden for Henry Oldenberg, the secretary of the Royal Society. When the *Journal* appeared, the officers of the Society promptly took up the question of a similar venture and on March 6, 1665, the first number of the *Philosophical Transactions* was on sale. It was published once a month in English and once in three months in Latin. In 1672 the Cartesian *conférencier* Jean-Baptiste Denis began to publish a series of *Mémoires et conférences sur les arts et sciences,* as a sort of supplement to the *Journal,* but only fourteen numbers were published. The *Collegium naturae curiosorum* of Schweinfurt, especially after its reorganization in 1670, was in form an association of subscribers to support the *Miscellanea curiosa sive ephemerides medico-physici.* The

[26] See especially Francis Vernon to Henry Oldenberg, Paris, May 11 and May 14, 1669, Royal Society, Guard Books, Nos. 5, 6, quoted by Harcourt Brown, *op. cit.,* 158–59.

[27] Lloyd A. Brown, *The Story of Maps* (Boston, 1949), 171–249.

[28] Betty T. Morgan, *Histoire du Journal des Sçavans depuis 1665 jusqu'en 1701* (Paris, 1929).

Acta eruditorum, founded at Leipzig in 1682, was more inclusive than any of these others, including departments of theology, law and philosophy as well as the natural sciences. Pierre Bayle's *Nouvelles de la république des lettres* in its brief life of three years (1684–1687) was the starting point of a large number of popular scientific journals. The *Giornale de' litterati de Roma,* edited by Angiolo Ricci, a corresponding member of the Accademia del Cimento, was published in Rome for its first twelve years, then transferred to Parma and in 1692 to Modena.

IV. THE CONCEPT OF THE PHYSICAL

At the heart of the scientific revolution of the seventeenth century was the emergent concept of the physical—of a material something, existing independently of the observer and underlying, essentially unchanged, the various changes in the form of things, such as fusion, solution and chemical reaction. The concept reached maturity only in the nineteenth century and, with the development of the quantum theory and relativity, seems to be approaching the end of its function. In the seventeenth century it was only beginning to take form. It was the fundamental note of Descartes's dualism. It was noticeable in the mental process by which William Harvey came to recognize that the large amount of blood put out by the heart must in some way be accounted for. The spirits, the essences, the real qualities of the schoolmen were not so much denied as pushed aside from the problem of the scientist by the definition of the field which the Galileos, the von Helmonts, the Boyles and the Newtons were making as they worked. In his *Origine of Forms and Quantities* (Oxford, 1667) Boyle formulated the distinction in terms that reflect the tentative and essentially negative state of the concept in his day:

I also forbear to answer arguments that however vehemently and subtly urged by many of the modern Schoolmen of the Roman Catholick communion, are either confessedly, or at least really built upon some Theological Tenets of theirs, which being opposed by the Divines of other Churches and not left unquestioned by some acute ones of their own, would not be proper to be solemnly taken notice of by me, *whose business in this Tract is to discourse of Natural things as a naturalist,* without invading the Province of Divines by intermeddling with the Supernatural Mysteries, such as those upon which divers of the Phisico-Theological Tenets of the Schoolmen, especially about Real Qualities and the Separableness of Accidents from Subjects of Inhesion, are manifestly, if not also avowedly grounded.[29]

[29] Quoted by R. B. Fulton, "Robert Boyle and His Influence," *Isis,* 18 (1932), 93. The italics are the present author's.

In Boyle's own work, especially in his failure to make the final step to the discovery of oxygen, it is possible to recognize a certain incompleteness in his notion of the physical. Nevertheless, by his influence on Locke and other contemporaries, Boyle did as much as anyone to destroy the medieval idea that qualities could be treated as entities, and to establish the sphere of physical investigation as the realm of matter. His *Sceptical Chymist* of 1680 and Nicolas Lémery's *Course in Chymistry* (1686) were the great turning points. In the latter there is not a word to be found about "directive spirits, archaei or non-material quintessences." [30] In the field of chemistry the promising beginnings of the seventeenth century were held up by the delusive victory of "vitalism" and spirits in the form of the "phlogiston" theory of Stahl and Hoffman of Halle.

The physical was susceptible of measurement and it was a major sign of their groping for the sense of the physical that the Europeans were finding it necessary and possible to measure to a degree of accuracy thitherto unknown. Accuracy of measurement was remarkably advanced by improvement of old devices and methods and by new inventions. As early as 1550 some investigators were using scales accurate to within one-tenth of a grain, in contrast to the Greco-Roman scales, the minimum error of which was nearly one grain. In the middle of the seventeenth century the necessary error was reduced to five-hundredths and even to three-hundredths of a grain (cf. the present-day figure .00015 grain). The best Roman and early European clocks had an error of one thousand seconds per day. The invention of the pendulum clock by Huygens reduced this to ten seconds, and within less than a century further refinements reduced the error to a little less than one-tenth of a second. [31] A highly motivated form of measurement and one that might be said to have changed the form of economic motivation had been spreading among the Europeans since the fourteenth century: double-entry bookkeeping, which corresponded to the needed kind of measurement in that it was objective and measured something existing independently of the observer. Even so qualitative an art as music was reduced to measurement by Mersenne.

Society itself became material for measurement. Generalized and abstracted as matter had been, "man" became something to be determined by the registration in terms of number of his "primary qualities" of extension and motion. In the preface of his *Political Arithmetick* (1690) Sir William Petty thus formulated the new ideal:

[30] J. Needham, *The Sceptical Biologist, op. cit.*, 25.

[31] H. T. Pledge, *Science since 1500* (London, 1940), 70, 126; G. N. Clark, *op. cit.*, 79, note.

Instead of using only comparative and superlative Words, and intellectual Arguments, I have taken the Course (as a Specimen of the Political Arithmetic I have long aimed at) to express myself in terms of Number, Weight, or Measure; to use only Arguments of Sense, and to consider only such Causes as have visible Foundations in Nature; leaving those that depend on the mutable Minds, Opinions, Appetites and Passions of particular Men, to the Consideration of Others.

Petty, like the scientists, was hardly aware that his mathematical units fell short of actual men and women. "Real men and women were treated in law and government as if they were imaginary bodies." [32]

As a basis for quantitative studies, Petty urged the institution of an analytical census. In the absence of such a census, Petty's friend John Graunt (1620-1674), a London haberdasher, had done pioneer work in analyzing the statistical indications furnished by the London Bills of Mortality, official reports by the clerks of the parishes, listing burials and christenings. Graunt's pioneer work was statistically naïve—he did not realize that statistical variations would be wider in a small unit than in a large one—but his analysis, fortified by comparative studies of other communities in England and of continental towns, laid the foundations for the objective study of population.

Petty made important extensions of the methods of Graunt in his *Political Arithmetick* (finished in 1676, though not published until 1690) and in his shorter *Essays in Political Arithmetick* (1683-1687), which include intensive calculations of the population of London, of England and Wales, and of foreign towns. In his *Political Anatomy of Ireland* (1691) he formulated his idea of the data that a proper demography should utilize. Population should be numbered not only as a whole but by classes, religion, and occupation, age, marital state and origin. The pioneer work of Graunt and Petty was carried a step further by Gregory King (1648-1712), whose *Natural and Political Observations and Conclusions Upon the State and Condition of England* appeared just a few years after our period (1696). The application of these statistics to the problem of life insurance and annuities began very promptly, indeed, with Graunt himself, and, somewhat developed by other studies in Holland, was temporarily standardized by Edmund Halley in 1693.

Although history had no place for the quantitative empiricism that was revolutionizing science, it too was affected by the development of Cartesian rationalism. The bulk of historical writing, it is true, was per-

EFFECT ON HISTORICAL STUDY

[32] Lewis Mumford, *The Culture of Cities* (New York, 1938), 93.

sonal reminiscence rather than scientific analysis. Prominent participants in great affairs wrote contemporary history to justify themselves and their parties. Cardinal de Retz (1613–1679) in his *Mémoires* told the story of the Fronde without much concern for the actual facts when they were inconvenient. The earl of Clarendon, after Charles II dismissed him as lord chancellor, devoted his remaining years to writing a *History of the Rebellion and Civil Wars in England* which, in combination with his autobiography, presents a picture essentially personal of the great movement of which he had been a part. In the field of confessional history, a more rational tone, obviously Cartesian, became manifest with the *Histoire des variations des églises protestantes* of Jacques Bénigne Bossuet (1627–1704) and the *History of the Reformation of the Church of England* (1679) of Gilbert Burnet. Both at least sought to rise above the slogans of the parties and to portray the social character of a historical development independently of the merits or demerits of individuals. With even more objectivity, but with little historical sense, Pufendorf, the great international lawyer, wrote his *Einleitung zu der Historie der vornehmsten Reichen und Staaten* (1682–1686) and his later histories of Sweden and Brandenburg in terms of record rather than interpretation.

It was, however, not in history-writing as such, but in the methods of critical analysis that the study of history began to respond to the scientific revolution. The "sciences auxiliary to history," as they are still called, received their organization in this period. The great collections of materials, the *Acta sanctorum* of the Bollandists and the *Annales ordinis S. Benedicti* of the Benedictine Jean Mabillon (1632–1707), in progress during our period, required objective methods of determining the data and provenance of documents and the genealogical and geographical relations of individuals on a grand scale. In short, these seventeenth-century monks systematized the criticism of sources to such a point that Leibniz could reproach the scientists of his time with the greater exactness of historical research. Jean Mabillon, the great scholar of the Benedictine order of Saint Maur, established the modern methods of analyzing and testing documents in his *De re diplomatica* (1681).[33] Charles Du Fresne Du Cange (1610–1688), a government official, made the first dictionary of medieval Latin, the *Glossarium ad scriptores mediae et infimae latinitatis* (3 vols., Paris, 1678) which the Saint-Maurians revised and greatly enlarged in the next century.

---

[33] E. Fueter, *Histoire de la historiographie moderne* (1914), 387; E. de Broglie, *Mabillon et la société de l'Abbaye de Saint-Germain de Près à la fin du dix-septième siècle* (1664–1707).

Cartesianism in history was carried to a high point by Richard Simon, an Oratorian learned in many languages. His *Critical History of the Old Testament* (1678) went far beyond the rationalistic criticism of Spinoza and Hobbes.[34] Simon demonstrated that the Hebrew writings, like other oriental writings, were the product of a series of writers through different periods, and not the exclusive work of the reputed authors. Like the work of the Abbé d'Aubignac, who was in similar fashion demonstrating the composite authorship of the *Iliad* and the *Odyssey,* Simon's work was to remain without influence. Bossuet, scandalized by such radical conclusions, had the *Histoire critique* suppressed, and it survived only in the English and Dutch translations.

The advance of the disposition to measure involved radical refinement of the older mathematics, which as late as Bruno and Kepler was still oriented to Pythagorean, nonphysical objectives. Through the earlier decades of the seventeenth century the schools and universities had been spreading the techniques of mathematics as measurement.[35] The counting board had been displaced by the "algorism"—arithmetic—which the Europeans had inherited from the Arabs. At the higher levels, mathematics had become an instrument of analysis. Logarithms, slide rules and computing machines had been invented to facilitate large-scale computation. The analytical geometry of Descartes and John Wallis (1616–1703), and the work of Pascal, of Cavalieri (1598–1647) and of Isaac Barrow, Newton's teacher and predecessor at Cambridge, had furnished the materials for the two geniuses, Newton and Leibniz, to organize as the calculus.

[margin note: EFFECT ON MATHEMATICS]

The history of their respective approaches to the calculus is little known. Their conflicting claims to priority gave rise to a bitter dispute and even to a mutual boycott between English and French mathematicians. Newton had used his calculus of fluxions as early as 1666 but, although it was presumably essential in the development of the *Principia mathematica,* gave no public account of it until 1693. Meanwhile, in 1675, Leibniz had arrived at the calculus of infinitesimals and, in 1684, had published it. For men of ordinary gifts, neither organization was practicable until Lagrange in the next century systematized the symbols and procedures. Regardless of personal merits in the case and even of the relative merits of the two methods, the European world had been supplied with a mathe-

[margin note: CALCULUS]

---

[34] H. Margival, *Essai sur Richard Simon et la critique biblique au XVIIe siècle* (Paris, 1900); A. Rébelliau, *Bossuet, historien du protestantisme;* see also below, p. 185.

[35] F. W. Kokomoor, "The Teaching of Elementary Geometry in the Seventeenth Century," *Isis,* 11 (1928), 85–110.

matics adequate to the problems of the world of extension and motion which Descartes had posited.

V. THE ACHIEVEMENTS OF THE NEW SCIENCE

Although it is beyond the function of this book to portray in detail the great scientific achievements of our period, a succinct summary may serve to indicate its extraordinary range and significance. It was the springtime of modern science: Boyle and Huygens, Malpighi and Picard, Swammerdam and Redi, are names that join with the portentous name of Newton to mark the orientation of the European mind to its most characteristic concerns.

CHEMISTRY Robert Boyle (1627–1691) and Robert Hooke (1635–1703) raised the basic questions of chemistry. The activities of the alchemists, the metallurgists and the iatrochemists had been productive of much useful information, but the problem was the critical reconstruction of the concepts, and for this task Hooke and Boyle did the basic work. The radical defect in the old chemistry was the confusion about what was to be considered as an "element." Undertaking "as a philosopher" to consider chemistry, Boyle quickly came to the conclusion that the traditional four elements were too few to account for the known phenomena. His definition of elements deserves to be quoted: ". . . certain primitive and simple or perfectly unmingled bodies, which, not being made of any other bodies, or of one another, are the ingredients out of which all those called perfectly mixed bodies are immediately compounded and into which they are ultimately resolved." The concept thus formulated was the basis upon which Lavoisier a century and a half later founded his work. Boyle himself missed discovering oxygen only because he did not use the results he had attained with full logicality. He knew that the fire was not wholly satisfactory as a means of analysis because something disappeared with the smoke and some "odd substance" in the air was lost when a candle was burned in an airtight container. Some experiments with respiration brought him to the verge of discovery along another path.[36]

Robert Hooke, who had been Boyle's assistant, made a further step at which Boyle had hesitated and assimilated respiration to combusion, showing that essential to both is "the volatile nitrous substance which is contained in the air." Richard Lower (1630–1691) carried Hooke's work one step further and showed that the "production of the scarlet color of

---

[36] A. Wolf, *A History of Science, Technology and Philosophy in the Sixteenth and Seventeenth Centuries* (New York, 1935), 337.

arterial blood must be attributed wholly . . . to the particles of air insinuating themselves into the blood." [37] John Mayow (1643–1679) is sometimes represented as having anticipated Lavoisier and Priestley, but seems rather to have been only an effective collator of the work of Boyle, Hooke and Lower.[38]

Like Boyle, the great Dutch medical teacher F. Sylvius (1614–1672) made a great, though not nearly successful attempt to banish mysticism from chemistry. He held that animal and human bodies were primarily chemical. He tried to identify what we would call organic and inorganic chemistry and formulated the "affinity" of acids and bases and their union in "salts," which are neither. It was as a teacher of physiology that he established the distinction "acid-alkaline" as a substitute for the older terms, "phlegmatic," "bilious," and the rest.

Like the problem of chemistry, the problem of biology was that of developing workable concepts for distinctions and relations. To this end our period saw some very substantial contributions, especially in the field of botany. Cesalpino (1519–1603) had begun the transition to classification based on functional differences. In 1620 Kaspar Bauhin (1560–1624) made a faltering approach to binomial nomenclature by organizing species into genera. Joachim Jungius (1587–1657) had created a scientific terminology adequate to describe the parts and processes of plants in his *Isagoge phytoscopia* (1678). In our period, the principal contributions were those of John Ray (1628–1705), whose *Historia plantarum* (1684–1704) was the first work to enumerate the great natural groups or orders of plants. A rather more artificial classification, devised by Tournefort (1656–1708), came to dominate the botanical field until displaced by that of Linnaeus. In close association with Francis Willughby, Ray applied to birds and fishes the same principles of classification. In his *Historia plantarum,* he laid down the principle that "forms which are different in species always retain their specific natures, and one species does not grow from the seed of another species." [39]   The work of the taxonomists was enlarged and facilitated by the vast increase in the amount of materials available to them. Ray and Willughby had helpers all over England and traveled about Europe collecting. Tournefort traversed Europe and the Near East. The great trading companies were much used as a means of acquiring new plans and animals from distant lands. Botanical gardens and zoological gardens were established in increasing numbers. The Dutch

[handwritten margin notes: BIOLOGY; CLASSIFICATION]

---

[37] *Tractatus de corde* (1669), 166; quoted by A. Wolf, *op. cit.,* 343.
[38] T. S. Patterson, "John Mayow," *Isis,* 15 (1931), 47–96, 504–46.
[39] A. Wolf, *op. cit.,* 407.

governor of Malabar, Hendrick Adrien van Reede tot Drakenstein, published a great botanical encyclopedia of the Malabar coast, prepared by a commission consisting of his regular staff doctor and some missionaries, who enlisted the help of native artists and an advisory commission of Brahmans.[40]

In anatomy and physiology the traditional dependence on Galen had been ended by the work of Vesalius, Servetus, Fabricius and Harvey. Many important results were attained by the microscopists of our period that were hardly exploited till the nineteenth century because of lack of adequate theory. Thus Hooke and Malpighi were quite familiar with cells as features of plant tissue, without attributing to them the general significance given them later. Jan Swammerdam (1637–1680), son of a merchant who had collected by means of his connections in colonial trade the largest private museum of plants and animals in Amsterdam, developed a technique of microscopic study of insects that long remained unrivaled. With Athanasius Kircher, he was the first to see the red corpuscles (1658, published 1738). Malpighi completed Harvey's discovery of the circulation of the blood by finding the capillary system. The greatest microscopist, however, was Anton van Leeuwenhoek (1632–1723), who was primarily a virtuoso of lens production. Leeuwenhoek was the first man to set eyes on protozoa, bacteria and spermatozoa. Although Swammerdam and Francesco Redi (1627–1697) challenged the notion of spontaneous generation, the theoretical consequences of these great discoveries were lost in a long battle over the question of preformationism and in a dispute as to whether the male or the female was the only factor in generation.[41] Somewhat similarly, the highly significant work of Thomas Willis (fl. 1662–1675), who came close to the modern concept of the subconscious, was lost by the development of the less sophisticated but more attractive theories of John Locke.[42] Of significance beyond the field of botany was the definition of sexuality in plants by Nehemiah Grew (*Anatomy of Plants*, 1682) and Rudolph Jakob Camerarius (*Letter on the Sex of Plants*, 1694).

PHYSICS   The central problem of the period was the central problem of science, the operation of forces in nature in relation to matter. In spite of the revolutionary work of Galileo, Torricelli, Pascal and their contemporaries,

[40] *Hortus malabaricus,* 12 vols. (1678–1703).

[41] George Sarton, "The Discovery of the Mammalian Egg and the Foundation of Modern Embryology," *Isis,* 16 (1931), 315–78.

[42] J. Vinchon and J. Vie, "Un maître de neuro-psychiatrie au XVIIᵉ siècle," *Annales medico-psychologiques,* 86 (1928), 109–44.

large areas of fundamental work remained to be done. The problem of impact was systematically examined by a commission of the Royal Society. Huygens arrived at Newton's third law—action and reaction are equal— and even approached the principle of the conservation of energy and, at one point, arrived at a kind of relativity. Boyle enunciated his well-known law that the volume of gases varies inversely according to the pressure, or, in other words, that *pv* is constant. Before and after 1660 Christian Huygens was making the profound studies of the pendulum which took such significant practical form in his pendulum clock and theoretical form in his *Horologium oscillatorium* (1673).

The physics of light—optics—became especially important with the large and growing place of the telescope and microscope in scientific activity. Important in itself, it illustrates how the greatest minds of the time, like Huygens and Newton, were handicapped in groping their way— our way—to what have become the commonplaces of everyday physics.

At the beginning of our period, Francesco Maria Grimaldi (1618–1663), a Jesuit professor at Bologna, made the first announcement of a wave theory of light in his posthumous *Physico-mathesis de lumine, coloribus et iride* (Bologna, 1665). In his *Micrographia* Hooke developed a similar theory. Olaus Römer, a Dane, upset the current belief in the infinite velocity of light. Huygens utilized Römer's finite velocity to make a synthesis of the known optical phenomena, which he communicated to the French Academy in 1678 and published in 1690 as the *Traité de la lumière*. In this work he made the capital advance of analyzing a wave front into wavelets, but, because he had only longitudinal waves in mind, it was left to Newton to think of transverse waves and thus explain the phenomenon of polarization. In 1666, by resynthesizing white light from the prismatic ribbon, Newton had completed the work of Marci (1595–1667), who had analyzed white light by means of the prism and shown that each monochromatic section is indivisible.

The long discussion of the theory of color between Newton and Huygens brought out the considerable divergence between Baconian and Cartesian method. After extended correspondence, Newton laid down his terms for its continuance:

And therefore I could wish that all objections were suspended, taken from hypothesis or any other heads than these two: Of showing the insufficiency of experiments to determine these quaere's or prove any other part of my theory, by assigning the flaws and defects in any conclusions drawn from them; or of producing other experiments which directly contradict me, if any such may seem to occur. For if the experiments, which I urge, be defective, it cannot be difficult to show the defects; but if valid, then by proving the theory they must render all objections invalid.[43]

Every step in development of Newton's theories presented itself to his mind as the direct and naked revelation of experience. On the other hand, as a Cartesian, Huygens persisted in regarding the results of Newton's experiments as "hypotheses."

In the field of heat, Francis Bacon had approached the modern idea that heat is motion, but his ideas were not very clear. In our period Robert Boyle formulated the idea much more exactly in a treatise, *Of the Mechanical Origin of Heat and Cold* (1675), although he continued to regard cold also as something positive and to speak of "atoms of fire." Mariotte (1679) discovered that radiant heat was separable from light. Otto von Guericke, the inventor of the air pump, carried out many experiments concerning the relation of air to our perception of sounds.

In electrical science, little important advance was made on the work of John Gilbert during the seventeenth century, but Guericke first recognized and described the phenomenon of repulsion and also built the first machine for generating electrical charges.

VI. THE PRINCIPIA MATHEMATICA

In 1687 the Royal Society published the *Philosophiae naturalis principia mathematica* of Isaac Newton. This epochal work, which was destined to serve as the frame of reference for physics and other sciences for more than two centuries, was itself a synthesis of advances made during the two preceding centuries. The problem of a universal force had been implicit in Nicholas of Cusa's assertion of infinity. Leonardo da Vinci had arrived at Newton's first and third laws, although the inadequacy of early sixteenth-century mathematics had made any extended development of these laws an impossibility.[44] Galileo's experiments two generations before Newton had shown that the problem of astronomy was to show what force made the planets revolve in closed curves about the sun rather than travel in straight lines into outer space.[45] Among Newton's contemporaries, Huygens had deduced from Kepler's third law that a central force varying as to the square of the radius would have been needed to keep a planet in an elliptical orbit. In the Royal Society itself, of which Newton was a not very devoted member from 1672, Wren, Hooke and

---

[43] *Philosophical Transactions*, No. 85 (1672), pp. 5004–7, quoted by L. Rosenfeld, "La théorie des couleurs de Newton et ses adversaires," *Isis*, 9 (1927), 44–65.

[44] H. T. Pledge, *op. cit.*, 15.

[45] A. Wolf, *op. cit.*, 148.

Halley had come to much the same point. In 1674 Hooke had published *An Attempt to Prove the Annual Motion of the Earth from Observations,* the three conclusions of which show that he had come as near to a solution as is possible without mathematical equipment superior to what was then available to him.[46] He asserted that every heavenly body attracts to its center every other heavenly body, that every moving body moves in a straight line until deflected therefrom by some force and that the attraction between two bodies is greater the nearer they are together.[47]

When Hooke became cosecretary (with Dr. Nehemiah Grew) of the Royal Society, in the attempt to elicit some contribution from Newton who was already immersed in the (to him) much more important problems of scriptural prophesy, he asked Newton for an expression of his thought on Hooke's "hypothesis or opinion . . . of compounding the celestial movements of the planets of a direct motion towards the central body." The writing of the *Principia* itself came about very directly from the concern of Hooke, Halley and Wren with the problem. They already held the conviction that bodies attracted each other, that the attraction was inversely proportional to the square of the distance between them and that it could be proved from Kepler's third law (that the paths of the planets were elliptical). In one of their conferences in January, 1684, Hooke alleged that "upon the principle all the laws of the celestial motions were to be demonstrated and that he himself had done it." [48]

Whether from unwillingness to reveal his secret, as he alleged, or from inability, Hooke failed to produce his proofs. In August, 1684, Halley discussed the situation with Newton and was amazed to find that Newton held the same view. Like Hooke, Newton was not in a position to show his proofs, but unlike Hooke, he worked them out anew and presented them to Halley some months later. Halley recognized the tremendous import of the matter and with the moral support of the Royal Society, to which he reported it, promoted the publication of the *Principia,* financing it himself and overcoming Newton's temperamental reluctance because of a quarrel with Hooke over the credit which the latter claimed.

Although a distinguished biographer of Newton makes the statement that the problems of the *Principia* "were originated and solved within seventeen months," [49] it is obvious that this is true only in the sense that

[46] H. T. Pledge, *op. cit.,* 65.
[47] J. W. N. Sullivan, *Isaac Newton* (New York, 1938), 61.
[48] *Ibid.*
[49] *Ibid,* 75.

the specific mathematical procedure fell within that period. In a broader sense the question had been posed for at least a generation. Newton's contribution was to close the problem with a mathematical answer that at the time only a genius could give. In particular, Newton almost certainly arrived at many of his results by means of the differential calculus which he and Leibnitz had been inventing.[50]

For his own and succeeding generations Newton converted the world into formulas of measurement. It became a world in which the physical and the mathematical appeared as the two essential and complementary aspects of reality. The empirically observed and the mathematically deduced were given a factitious identity.[51] All the more effectively because he did it in the name of empirical observation, Newton harnessed the Faustian will of the Europeans in the limiting but useful bonds of a fundamental rationalism. As Mersenne had reduced music to a set of arithmetical relations between vibrations, so physics became a set of measures. The world of matter became a world of atoms—"solid, glassy, hard, impenetrable particles"—existing in otherwise empty immaterial space and time.

It is no longer possible as it once was to conceive the principles of Newton as absolutes and his definition of the universe as final. The technical close of the Newtonian system came dramatically and suddenly with the development of relativity. The discovery that mass varies with velocity deprived physics of the supposedly fixed coefficient in terms of which all its phenomena were to be described. The immutable laws of the Newtonian system became "formulae for the prediction of the probability of an observable occurrence."[52]

Like physics, history is thus confronted with a relativistic problem. It becomes necessary to recognize that Newtonianism closed off the paths to relativism which Nicholas of Cusa in the fifteenth century and Giordano Bruno in the sixteenth had opened up. In Galileo's assumption that "uniform velocity" has a sufficiently definite meaning, and in Newton's operationally successful development of this assumption, the points of both the general and the special Einstein theories came up for decision and were postponed in such a way that the issues remained untouched for two centuries.[53]

[50] A. Wolf, op. cit., 212.
[51] John Dewey, op. cit., 130 et passim.
[52] Ibid., 206.
[53] H. T. Pledge, op. cit., 36–37; E. A. Burtt, op. cit., 153; Susanne K. Langer, "The End of an Epoch," Atlantic Monthly, 147 (1931), 772–75.

For two centuries, then, the effort of the Europeans to master their world was caged within the limiting framework of a deterministic system. Within that framework, they achieved an unparalleled lordship of nature. It is as though the limitation had served to make the achievement more practicable.

In these decades, as the lifetime of Newton and Boyle, of Huygens and Cassini, of Leeuwenhoek and Malpighi, European man organized his intellectual forces to enter upon the lordship of nature that Descartes had foreseen. His heritage from the ancient past was no longer a thralldom but a part of his world to explore and exploit as a vast compendium of soluble mysteries. The bondage of the unbounded, all the baffling complexities of the Pandora's box he had opened up had not yet emerged. Wherever he turned, the world only awaited his new vision to be mastered. The picture that he saw with himself as lord of space and matter was the baroque.

Chapter Two

BAROQUE

I. BAROQUE IN THE HISTORY OF EUROPE

THE baroque began in the sixteenth century with Michelangelo and was to reign well through the eighteenth. The few years covered by this narrative, then, do not include the life, indeed not even the whole maturity, of the baroque, but they do include a fullness and greatness of baroque expression such as no similar period can equal.

Formerly the baroque was interpreted as a pathological degeneration of the classicism which the moderns thought they saw in the Renaissance. Since the turn of the past century, however, it has taken its place as a phenomenon of first order in the evolution of the European spirit. The "rediscovery" was largely the work of Karl Lamprecht and Alois Riegl; the fundamental redefinition was made by Heinrich Wölfflin.[1]

Baroque was revolution. Like Cartesianism, it was the assertion of man's freedom in the universe, of a new conception of the world as process, as becoming rather than being. A distinguished historian of science does not hesitate to make it the central fact of the movement of the European spirit which expressed itself in science, in politics and in the economic structure, as well as in the arts.[2]

Baroque was individualism. In the baroque apotheoses, in the royal portraits and palaces, in the dramas of Corneille and Racine, most of all in the extraordinary dance forms, the individual was invested with a hieratic importance quite irrelevant to his real qualities. Baroque individualism was one with the individualism of Descartes and Pascal, of Spener and George Fox, of the inventors and explorers.

Baroque expressed the will to the lordship and possession of nature that was the ultimate motivation of scientific investigation. The mastery of space, the regional and city planning, the huge churches and palaces, the great gardens, the large perspectives of baroque painting exhibited

---

[1] Karl Lamprecht, *Deutsche Geschichte* (12 vols. in 16, 1895–1909), especially Vol. 7 (1896); A. Riegl, *Die Entstehung der Barockkunst in Rom* (Vienna, 1923); H. Wölfflin, *Kunstgeschichtliche Grundbegriffe: Das Problem der Stilentwicklung in der neueren Kunst* (Munich, 1915; 7th ed., 1929).

[2] Sigerist, "William Harvey's Stellung in der Geistesgeschichte," *Archiv für Kulturgeschichte,* 19 (1929), 158–68.

the dynamism that was, and is, the most distinctive mark of Europe as a culture.

Baroque was clarity. In all of the forms, the baroque artist undertook the full and explicit exposition of his vision. This did not exclude, on the contrary it dictated, the most thorough exploration of his intention. The portraits and religious pictures of Rembrandt reflect an unsparing analysis along with complete communication. Racine elevated sex motivation to an almost Freudian seriousness. Schütz, Buxtehude and Lully made music speak with directness and power. Baroque art was communication at the highest and deepest levels. Time and effort have carried us beyond the basic assumptions of baroque humanity, but even the "glories" of a Pozzo and the demonic inventions of a Borromini leave us in no doubt as to what they intended.

Baroque was intellectualism. Learning became a precondition of literary success. A whole society undertook to lift itself above the groundlings. The contrast of Shakespeare and Dryden is a whole history of the baroque in literature. Poetry, music, architecture, the dance became an affair of codes, manuals, and academies. The baroque identified itself with the European passion for technique. "One day," writes Sacheverell Sitwell, "the century between 1650 and 1750 will be recognized as the period in which every detail of workmanship was more perfect than at any other time since the twelfth century."[3] The fantastic in baroque corresponded to the fantastic in the projects of the virtuosos, the explorers and the writers of imaginary travels.

The baroque was indissolubly connected with the Counter Reformation. It is not merely that the Gesù, the capital church of the Jesuits, was one of its earliest manifestations or that Catholic churches and the palaces and gardens of Catholic kings were its most typical forms. It is less in the aggressive counteraction of the Catholic Church as an organization than in the transformation of the religious problem from the theological and political issues of the sixteenth century to the intensely individual, intensely human search for God of the seventeenth century that baroque identified itself with Counter Reformation. By its identification with the state and its dissociation from art, official Protestantism was unprepared to reflect in new forms the mentality or the needs of a transformed society. It is in this larger sense of general revolt against the patterns of the sixteenth century, earlier in Catholicism than in Protestantism, that baroque and Counter Reformation are to be identified.[4]

---

[3] *German Baroque Art* (London, 1927), 25.
[4] For various modern interpretations of this relationship, see Edward I. Watkin, *Catholic*

Finally, the baroque as a whole, from architecture to the minor arts, manifested a uniform character and affirmed a taste wholly its own, absolutely original, not immune to bombast and infantilism, full of redundancies, of the amazing, the showy, but not for that less admirable for its exuberant vitality, its creative vigor, its fantasy, and that strong individuality which clearly marks off a great style from that of any other period or culture area. A paragraph of Sacheverell Sitwell effectively formulates this unity:

Extreme affectation of manner and personality went with the coloratura singing of the age of Farinelli and with that perfection of dancing which Lambrazini's book upon the subject reveals at the first opening of its pages; therefore the architecture of that age had to provide a background for these curiosities and to be suitable for them. It must never be of that plain substance against which a crowd of khaki figures or a mob of factory workers or shoppers at bargain sales would feel no embarrassment from there being no hint of sarcasm in their surroundings.[5]

In its extension in time and space, baroque meets the objective tests, cherished by the historian, of a great style. The goal of the tourist, that pious pilgrim to the holy places of European culture, is predominantly and almost wholly the baroque. It is impossible to "see Europe" without visiting the Gesù in Rome, the Salute in Venice, Versailles in France, the Zwinger in Dresden, St. Paul's in London. In architecture, art, music and literature, the forms in which European culture has found its most distinctive expression, the baroque masters after nearly three centuries still exercise an authority that shows no sign of weakening. Bernini and Borromini, Bach and Handel, Rubens, Rembrandt and El Greco, Dryden, Molière, and Racine—such names not only meet academic tests but are registered as the common heritage of a world that would seem strange to them. The dynamic of the baroque carried it to the ends of the world. Wherever Europeans prospered, they found expression in some of its patterns. Baroque was the last great folk art.

Who would know that baroque is great style let him stand at San Juan Capistrano or San Luis Rey de Francia in California and sense the spiritual integrity and artistic effectiveness with which the missionaries of Europe, out on a distant and isolated frontier, wrought in the name

Art and Culture (New York, 1940); W. Weisbach, Der Barock als Kunst der Gegenreformation (Berlin, 1921); G. Schnurrer, Katholische Kirche und Kultur in der Barockzeit (Paderborn, 1937); B. Croce, Der Begriff des Barock und die Gegenreformation (Zurich, 1925).
⁵ Op. cit., 88.

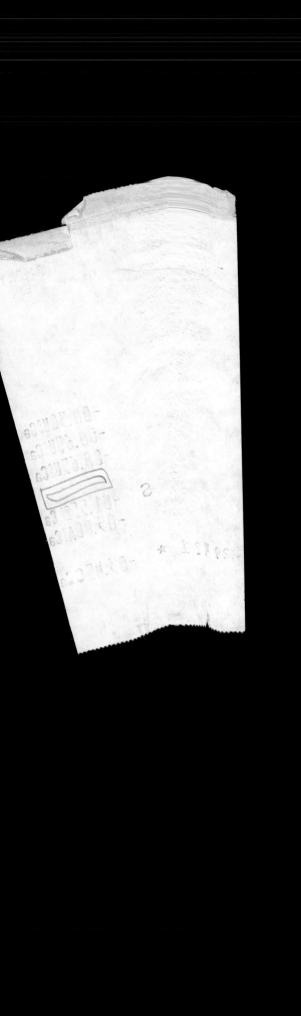

PE   NE S
BOOK &   STATIONERY
315 14   Ave., S. E.

— ■ ■.30 NSCa
— ■ ■.60 NSCa
— ■■.65 NSCa

S — ■ 1.55 ILCa
— ■ 5.00 ATCa

29 ¥ 21 ★ -03 _45 CCa

YOUR RECEIPT
THANK YOU

of their God and under the impulse of their culture. Let him examine—in pictures, since it is rare that one individual can see for himself the wide-flung materials—the dozens and scores of masterpieces scattered over South America and Central America and Mexico. Let him sense the weeks and months of travel that separated these corners of the world from the seats of power, authority and organization. Let him see these things, I say, and know that the style which informed the remotest mission as well as the Gesù in Rome, the palace of the French king at Versailles, the abbey of Melk, the Belvedere at Vienna, was a great style.

II. THE BAROQUE AS ARCHITECTURE

In architecture as in music and painting Italy was the fountainhead of the baroque. Michelangelo had announced the new style; Vignola (Giacomo Barocchio, 1507-1573), builder of the Gesù had affirmed it in terms to be repeated in hundreds of churches from China to Peru. The architectural treatises of Andrea Palladio (1518-1580) had formulated the style as a set of rules. During the early part of the seventeenth century, Bernini (1598-1680) and Borromini (1599-1667) had attained a dominant place among European architects. They were already old men in 1660, but Bernini was active for another twenty years and Borromini was putting the seal of greatness on his work by completing his great S. Agnese on the Piazza Navona.

Bernini occupied a unique position in the eyes of his contemporaries. His epitaph says, with more than common truth, that "popes, princes and peoples mourned him." As architect of St. Peter's since 1629, he had already built one of the most impressive monuments of the Christian world, the plaza with its great colonnades. As the greatest living architect, he was summoned to the court of Louis XIV to submit plans for the new Louvre. His reception was almost like that of a sovereign—but, anticlimactically, the French court preferred the design of Claude Perrault. The cosmopolitan influence of Italy was beginning to succumb to the growing national taste. Bernini's bust of Louis XIV, however, remains from this venture as a very expressive nonverbal commentary on the age, the style, the artist and the subject. Some of Bernini's most important work as architect dates from these last two decades of his life. The Scala regia in the Vatican, for instance, is a magnificent demonstration of the high technique of the time and of the simplicity of effect that is also baroque.

In comparison with Bernini, Borromini is generally less sympathetically regarded, especially by those critics who actively dislike baroque. Yet he was perhaps most completely the architect of his time. In him, architecture was at one with the inventing and discovery, the adventure and projecting that made his day great. It is in his work that the revolutionary intention of the baroque is most clearly manifest. Rejecting all the restrictions of rule and custom, he devised a whole world of new and individual forms and patterns based solely on his personal taste. His nonconformity extended to an aversion to straight lines. His church of S. Carlo alle Quattro Fontane (1640–1667) was an exploitation of an irregular plot, with all the architectural accents on the irregularities. The S. Ivo della Sapienza (1660) was even more deliberately organized with a façade concave to the court and therefore opposed to the curve of the oval element. The architects have never forgiven Borromini for this violation of a rule, but a layman may still take pleasure in S. Ivo. That Borromini was a great architect by any definition is demonstrated by his great S. Agnese in the Piazza Navona (begun 1652) in which Carlo Rainaldi (1611–1691), another good architect, also had a hand. Here the emphasis on curves was carried to such a point that even the marble bas-reliefs of the niche altars are concave. Rainaldi was the sole architect of S. Maria in Campitelli, a church of much more severity of aspect than most Roman churches. Borromini's limits of eccentricity were far surpassed by his pupil Andrea Pozzo (1642–1709), who demonstrated the extreme possibilities in his *Perspectiva pictorum et architectorum,* published in 1692.

The great cities of the Italian peninsula were still independent enough each to develop its own form of the baroque. Venice, of course, was marked by the S. Maria della Salute, with its two great domes and the great spiraled drums that, as buttresses, appear to support the domes. They are quite false, yet no one who knows Venice would wish them removed. Baldassare Longhena (1604–1682), who had completed S. Maria della Salute just before our period opens, in the last years of his life built the Palazzo Pesarro. The rustication of the lower stories, which rather harms the palace, is much more beautifully employed in the Dogana (1676–1682) built by Giuseppi Benoni. In Milan, the Theatine monk, Guarino Guarini (1624–1683), developed designs that went far beyond Borromini in eccentricity and bizarreness. They were too much for the brothers of the order, but he did get built two remarkable buildings, the very special little church of S. Gregorio at Messina (with a spiral steeple), destroyed by an earthquake in 1908, and the Palazzo Carignano (1680) in Milan, the façade of which winds in serpentine fashion. In Naples, the architectural effort and attention were almost wholly turned to the interiors of the churches and the exploitation of marbles and stucco. Stucco decoration was developed to a degree of extraordinary elaboration in Sicily. The great master was Giacomo Serpotta (1655-1732), whose maturest work lies beyond our period. Only recently noted in the literature,[6] the baroque structures at Lecce, in the heel of the peninsula, constitute a veritable museum of seventeenth-century architecture. The greatest example, perhaps, is the Church of the Holy Cross (S. Croce). It is baroque in a wholly special sense, more Spanish than Roman, and rich with color and elaborate working that is possible only with the local stone, which is soft and white as quarried, but hardens in the air and turns to a beautiful golden saffron.

In Spain, the development of the baroque was complicated by the diverse influences of that country's past, Arab, Germanic and Hispano-Roman, and of the exotic variations returned upon the peninsula from New Spain. In the sixteenth century the ascetic rigor of Philip II was reflected in the bare simplicity of the Escorial. In the seventeenth, the example and influence of Bernini were readily received and the severity of the Escorial yielded to the gentler and more human Italian standards. The government house at Toledo, designed by the son of the great painter El Greco, and the Panaderia in the Plaza Mayor of Madrid, rebuilt (1674) by José Ximenez Donoso, are convenient examples. Alonso Cano (1601–1667), the architect of the west façade of the cathedral of Granada, introduced in Spain the influence of Borromini.

The two influences were combined in the work of José Churriguerra (1650–1723), who, like Guarino Guarini, sought in extreme development the fullest realization of the ideals of the baroque. In Churriguerra's own hands the application of his principles is immediately convincing, as his government house in Salamanca demonstrates.

Two very distinctive churches belong to our time, S. Juan Bautista at Toledo, designed by the Jesuit Fray Francisco Bautista, who died some time after 1667, and the S. Cayetano of Saragossa, built between 1678 and 1683. Both illustrate admirably that rigor and seriousness which is so characteristic of Spanish baroque. In the Toledo church two grim towers thrust themselves up beside and behind the central element sweeping down on each side from an almost equal height. The S. Cayetano gets its severity from the contrast of a rather highly decorated lower wall with the bare but shapely towers above. This emphasis on verticality, which appears sometimes in the upthrusting towers, sometimes in strong pilasters or engaged pillars (as in the cathedral of Lima, Peru, or that of Murcia by Jaime Bort), sometimes in direct elevation of the central gable

[6] M. S. Briggs, *In the Heel of Italy* (1910).

of the façade with reduced or subordinated scrolls revealing and accentuating the angle rather than concealing it, suggests a persisting Gothic feeling.

Ultimately, ornamentation was more highly developed in the Spanish and Portuguese baroque, especially in the colonial churches of Mexico, Peru and Brazil, than anywhere else in the European world. Churriguerra and his contemporaries of the late seventeenth century stand midway in this development; his town hall in Salamanca illustrates the point.

The rejection of Bernini's design for the Louvre is typical of the history of baroque in France. Since the Renaissance the French had constituted themselves the particular guardians of the classical ideal, the ordered principles of which were antithetic to the fantastic and willful freedom of the baroque. Although France had remained Catholic and although Counter Reformational mysticism had distinguished and forceful representation in French Catholicism, it was not in the French spirit to undertake the expression of an irrational transcendence by means of a style essentially anarchic in its versatility and freedom.

Nevertheless, France does not constitute a difficult exception to the spread of baroque over western civilization. The baroque manifested itself in the clothes and manners of the court and its circle. It was obvious in the pomp and circumstance of courtly festivals and above all, perhaps most permanently, in the mourning and funeral customs. More effectively than elsewhere, French baroque utilized classical standards of restraint and simplicity. It is not enough to say that it was characterized by an opposition, theoretically advanced and practically demonstrated, to the principles of Bernini and Borromini. French baroque, like German, Spanish and colonial baroque, was racy with a specific quality that set it off from its sixteenth-century antecedents and from the successive rebel movements through which later generations attempted to throw off its shackles, as well as from the baroque of other national and local culture areas. If specific baroque forms of Italian or Spanish usage, like the sprung gable, the eccentric cartouches, the ornamented window openings, the multiplication of members and angles, were disapproved and barred, the baroque objectives of pomposity and "representation" were as effectively achieved in France by other means. Bernini's designs for the Louvre were rejected for Perrault's, whose pillars still extend themselves a quarter of a mile along the quai du Louvre and the rue du Louvre: they are correct and they are powerful, but their social expression is far closer to that of Bernini's arcade at St. Peter's than to Paestum or the Acropolis. J. H.

Mansart's church of the Invalides, with its severe balancing and general restraint, perhaps comes as near classical expression as anything of his time, but it is easier to find in it denial of the baroque than affirmation of the classic. The figures on the façade stand with more nearly classic self-containment than those, let us say, of S. Maria della Salute; the buttresses of the dome, severely chaste and undeveloped, are as false as those of the Salute.

The limit of this severe academic classicism in architecture is at once indicated when we turn to the interiors. Indeed it was almost a principle of the French architects (and of the society of which they were a part) that the front of a building should be differentiated from the garden side, quite in contrast with the efforts of modern architects to hold themselves and their clients to unitary wholes, consistent front and back. So the Château of Versailles, not by accident but by design, shows a rather hard face on the village side in contrast to the more intimate garden façade.

The interiors of the churches, moreover, were filled with quite definitely baroque altars and memorials, and the great virtue of baroque sculpture, its effective incorporation with structural elements, is nowhere better illustrated than in these altars and memorials, subject always to a curious displacement or misfit deliberately adopted for accent. In the interior decoration of Versailles Le Brun and his fellow workers loaded their walls and celings with an unending series of pictures, each in its turn loaded with a complex of garlands, cherubs, allegorical figures and decorations attempting to be eccentric and conformist at the same time.

The surrender to the baroque became complete in the gardens. Those of Versailles, with their *allées* and fountains, their garden statuary, their sculptured trees and shrubs, their carefully organized rusticity, identify themselves with the gardens of Italy and Germany. Coysevox's tomb monument for Mazarin and Girardon's for Richelieu are admittedly more restrained than Bernini's, but none the less baroque in their pathos and movement. The furniture which Boulle created during and after our period bulges and sweeps in undeniable baroque.

In Germany, the sixteenth-century late gothic seemed to anticipate the baroque. The seventeenth- and eighteenth-century critics with some validity used "gothic" and "baroque" as epithets for closely related styles. Late German gothic style, like the baroque, was primarily a style of movement and invention, including all the arts and all the surfaces in a single composition deeply and even violently religious in feeling. The influence of the Renaissance limited the development of the late gothic in its own forms, although the effective appropriation of the classical and effective identification with the southern form-feeling was not achieved in Germany in the seventeenth century.

In spite of premonitory native manifestations, the baroque of the seventeenth century was imported into Germany by Italian architects. Nevertheless, the productions of these architects, perhaps as a result of the intervention of their patrons (these epigones were not usually as authoritative as Michelangelo) or of the native craftsmen, were plainly distinct from the Italian fashion and seem racily German, indeed, in some cases, specifically Bavarian, Viennese, Bohemian.

The Thirty Years' War itself and, less completely, the poverty of the postwar period, put a stop to German monumental building. Nevertheless, our quarter-century saw some important construction. The Theatine Church in Munich, one of the chief examples of a basilica with a transept and a dome over the crossing, was designed by one Italian, Barelli, and executed by another, Lucalli, between 1661 and 1675. The façade and the interior alike are marked by a pleasing restraint which subordinated and sobered even the ornate pillars of the altar. The immense Czernin Palace at Prague, with its thirty huge pillars reaching only part way to the roof, was completed in 1682 by Francesco Caratti. The fountains in the Residenz Platz of Salzburg by Antonio Dorio (1664–1680) were lovely creations. Just at the end of the period, the Pilgrimage Church in Vilgertshofen in Upper Bavaria begins to show that characteristic emphasis on lightness of coloring, a kind of specific German gaiety, that appears over and over again in the churches of the next century. The pomp and vigor of the baroque were expressed not only in great buildings but also in the spatial organization of whole districts and towns, such as Karlsruhe, Mannheim, Saarbrücken, Erlangen and Potsdam. Even old towns like Vienna, Dresden, Bayreuth and Würzburg were replanned.

The great baroque architects of Austria were still young during our period. J. B. Fischer von Erlach (1650–1723) with his son Josef Emanuel (1695–1742) created a grave and seemly form of the baroque that fitted well with the imperial temper of the Austrians. The emperors, the great nobles like the Clam-Gallas and the Liechtenstein, the great generals like Eugene of Savoy, built lordly homes in lordly gardens for themselves and for the world. The strong Catholic and Jesuit influences manifested themselves in the Karlskirche of Vienna and the Abbey of Melk, thoroughly baroque in its magnificent stateliness and its appropriateness to the bold headland above the Danube on which it is set. Almost all this development, however, though integral with the activity of our period, fell beyond it.

Everywhere on the continent the baroque found expression in noble buildings. In Belgium, Luc Fayherbe (1617–1697), a pupil of Rubens, built several important churches, the most notable of which were the Sts. Peter and Paul at Malines and the Jesuit St. Michael's at Louvain. In eastern Holland—"the other Holland"—the country houses of the Dutch nobles, such as Ruykendaal near Utrecht, reflect the expanding French influence. The Dutch example was influential, too, in neighboring Germany. In Sweden the great palaces built with the war-created wealth of the nobility show both French and Italian influence. Simeon de la Vallée, who built the House of Peers between 1641 and 1674, was French. Nicodemus Tessin, who built the royal palaces of Stockholm and Drotningholm, had studied with Bernini. In Prague, the Wallenstein Palace and the Church of the Holy Cross (1678–1688) magnificently illustrate the penetration of the baroque. Italian architects carried the style into Poland, where the Church of the Holy Cross in Warsaw, and Wilamov, the royal palace of Sobieski, were built between 1682 and 1696 by Belotto. The Ukraine (Kiev in particular) has much baroque, and from Kiev the style was transmitted along with other western influences to Russia, to be reinforced later by the baroque artists and architects imported by Peter the Great.[7]

In spite of St. Paul's and its great architect, Sir Christopher Wren, and of Blenheim and Sir John Vanbrugh, baroque did not win domicile in England or its rising colonies. No more did it do so in bourgeois Holland. The bourgeois did not require the grandiose setting appropriate to the pretensions of the courts. Nevertheless, the magnificent city planning (the *Grachten*) in Amsterdam and Rotterdam connected the Dutch with the European baroque.

Nowhere did the style win a more complete naturalization or receive a more characteristic development than in the Spanish and Portuguese colonies in America. The solidity of the Conquest, the prosperity of the colonies and the rich store of technical ability among Quechua, Mayan, and Aztec artisans permitted a fusion that not only produced extraordinary examples of the ultimate in baroque, but especially of its capacity to syncretize foreign elements of remote cultural origin.[8]

[7] Paul Miliukov, *Russian Culture*, Part III, *Architecture, Painting and Music* (1943), 16–17.

[8] P. Kelemen, *Baroque and Rococo in Latin America* (Philadelphia, 1951); R. C. Smith, *The Colonial Art of Latin America* (Washington, 1945).

III. THE BAROQUE AS MUSIC

As a major form of the European culture, music was the product of the baroque period and of the baroque spirit.[9] Monteverdi and Cesti, Schütz and Buxtehude, Lully and Purcell gave it new intention and function as a mode of expression. When, in defiance of the prejudices of half a millennium, the great Mantuan Monteverdi composed music with the "dominant seventh," the stone that the builders had rejected became the head of the corner. Modulation, made possible by the fact that the dominant of one key coincided with the tonic chord of another, permitted flexibility and range of expression hitherto unknown. Chromatic harmony had been discovered.[10]

It was a revolution that opened up a vast new world of function to music. In a culture confronted with a Cartesian universe full of unknowns transcending the limitations of verbalism, music that undertook the expression of the ineffable was an understandable necessity. This function chromatic harmony enabled music to assume. The music of Palestrina is as verbal as the Nicene Creed. Like the sculpture of a medieval cathedral, say the Last Judgment at Bourges, its function was symbolic. In the operas and the oratorios, on the other hand, the combination of solo voices with richly developed accompaniment made it possible to express depths of passion, of devotion, of agony and delight, of which the old polyphony could only speak objectively. The explicit word ceased to hold its primacy as musical medium. The organ and the violin were refined and developed. The orchestra with its multiple instruments capable of a wealth of color was practically invented. The professional virtuoso began to cast his blight on the simple social forms of music.

The revolution in music manifested itself in three general forms, the development of the opera and the oratorio, the development of Catholic and Protestant church music, and the development of instrumental music.

Like the architecture of the baroque, the opera originated in Italy. Monteverdi (1567–1643) and his successors, Francesco Cavalli (1600–1673), Marc Antonio Cesti (1620–1699) and Giacomo Carissimi (1604–1674), made Venice, Rome, Bologna and Naples capitals of opera as they were of painting. In 1637 the first opera house was built in Venice. Be-

---

[9] Manfred F. Bukofzer, *Music in the Baroque Era* (New York, 1947); Hugo Leichentritt, *Music, History and Ideas* (Cambridge, Mass., 1938); L. de La Laurencie, *Les créateurs de l'opéra français* (Paris, 1921).

[10] Erich Schenck, "Uber Bëgriff und Wesen des musikalischen Barocks," *Zeitschrift für Musikwissenschaft,* 17 (1935), 377–92; Andrea della Corte, "Il barocco e la musica," in *Mélanges de musicologie offerts à M. Lionel de La Laurencie* (Paris, 1933).

tween that date and 1700, no less than seven hundred operas were produced in Italy. Their export from Italy was favored by the existence in various countries of less developed musical forms that united music and dramatic action, such as the popular Spanish zarzuela and German Singspiel, the more courtly English masque and the French court ballet.

In France, in Germany, in England, in Spain, in Sweden, and even in Poland and Russia, Italian opera, either in its original form or modified by native influences, attained that peculiar primacy it has continued to hold. "Without opera," wrote Romain Roland, "we should scarcely be acquainted with half of the artistic mind of the seventeenth century, for we should see only the intellectual side of it. Through opera, we best reach the depths of the sensuality of that time—its voluptuous imagination, its sentimental materialism, in short, the quaking foundations on which the reason, the will and the serious business of the French society of the great seventeenth century rested." [11]

Opera was not immediately popular in France. Luigi Rossi produced his *Orfeo* in Paris in 1647 and in 1660 Cavalli was brought from Italy to produce his *Serse* (with much ballet added by Lully to suit French taste, as later in the case of *Tannhäuser,* in 1861). It was unpopular, nevertheless, and the *Ercole amante,* which Cavalli designed especially for the Paris stage, had only slightly better success two years later. The literary men with few exceptions were hostile or indifferent to music as an adjunct to poetry. Boileau pontificated to the effect that opera was limited because music could not narrate and could not match poetic passages of true sublimity. Molière was perhaps the writer of the day who best understood music. He was intimately associated with Lully and it was upon his advice that Lully turned at last to opera.[12] The French musicians were also generally hostile. Perrin, who did as much as anyone to introduce opera, charged the Italian operas with bad librettos, extravagances and "detonations." [13] In spite of this hostile climate, Pierre Perrin, a mediocre poet, and Robert Cambert, a moderately capable composer, in 1659 under Mazarin's patronage produced the first French opera. In 1669, Perrin was granted a privilege for an academy of music and the monopoly of opera. In 1671, he and Cambert achieved a great triumph with the latter's *Pomone.*[14]

Native opera promptly conquered the French public. Its popularity is attested by the numerous parodies. Comic twists of pompous phrases and

[11] *Some Musicians of Former Days,* 19.
[12] Th. Gerold, *L'art du chant en France* (Strassburg, 1921), 132–33, 167.
[13] L. de La Laurencie, *op. cit.,* 177.
[14] *Ibid.,* 144–46, 180–81.

allusions delicately conveyed by some familiar air became the common stock of the comedians. Whole plays, *The Country Opera, The Village Opera, The Union of the Two Operas,* were made out of one joke and were played for years.[15]

When it appeared that Perrin and Cambert might add popular success to the privilege that had been granted them, they were displaced by a master of intrigue as well as of music, who proceeded to win a monopoly in the field that lasted till long after his death. This was Jean-Baptiste Lully (1633-1687), who from a very low station in life had risen to become the leader of *les petits violons* (1658) and the king's favored composer of court ballets. He had shared the general aversion to Italian opera, but had been influenced by the form. His tragedy-ballet *Psyche,* performed January 17, 1671, was in effect opera without recitative.[16] In 1672 the monopoly of opera production was transferred to him and from that date to his death in 1687, he wrote an opera every year.[17]

Lully achieved an extraordinarily dominant influence not only in France but in the rest of Europe. The French public was his. The letters of Madame de Sévigny contain many allusions to his operas and expressions of warm admiration. Some of his airs have passed into folk song, notably the familiar *"Au clair de la lune."* [18] In some respects, however, his legally supported monopoly was less than fortunate. Musicians fully his equal, such as Charpentier,[19] organist at Saint-Eustache, were restricted to church music and instrumental music not covered by the monopoly. Lully's influence affected also these forms, church music less than fortunately, instrumental music more happily. He practically gave the orchestra its modern form as a balanced and disciplined group of choirs.

Lully's operas were promptly exported. Brussels had his *Persée* seven months after its first presentation.[20] Huygens testifies that he was known and admired in Holland. Foreign musicians like Pelham Humphrey from England, George Muffat from Scotland and Thomas Kusser from Hamburg came to study with him.[21]

[15] D. J. Grant, "Seventeenth Century Parodies of French Opera," *Musical Quarterly,* 27 (1941), 211–19, 514–26.

[16] L. de La Laurencie, *op. cit.,* 201.

[17] H. Prunières, "Lully and the Académie de Musique et de Danse," *Musical Quarterly,* 11 (1925), 528.

[18] R. Rolland, *op. cit.,* 245.

[19] A. Gastone, "Notes sur les manuscrits et sur quelques oeuvres de M. A. Charpentier," in *Mélanges de musicologie offerts à M. Lionel de la Laurencie* (Paris, 1933), 154–60.

[20] E. van der Straeten, *La musique aux Pays-Bas avant le XIXe siècle* (8 vols., Brussels, 1867–1888), II, 165.

[21] R. Rolland, *op. cit.,* 247.

Vienna became a great capital of Italian opera. Ferdinand III and Leopold I were both enthusiastic amateurs and patrons of music. Cavalli was brought from Venice several times to produce his operas and when Cesti put on his *Il pomo d'oro* for the marriage of Leopold I in 1666, he was retained for some years as second choirmaster in the imperial chapel. Italian opera and Italian musicians were imported into all parts of Germany, but German opera as such was produced on a broad scale and given substantial foundations. Johann Kasper Kerll produced four German operas at Munich. The great center of German opera, however, was Hamburg, where the first German opera house was opened in 1678.[22] There, despite Pietist opposition, no less than thirty-one new operas, some of them definitely calculated to appease the Pietists, were composed and presented between 1678 and 1690 by composers now generally forgotten except by the musicologists. Hamburg attained a peculiar pre-eminence under Kousser and Keiser, who were active there from 1693 through the first decades of the next century. Dresden was still dominated by the tradition of Heinrich Schütz (died 1672), who had dabbled in opera in his youth but who in his old age had returned to polyphony. But G. A. Bontempi and Carlo Pallavicino found employment there, as Steffani, who wandered over most of Germany, did in Hanover. In general, through these decades, the Italian influence grew stronger and the purely German elements, the Singspiel in particular, declined in significance.

In England the development of French and Italian influence in music was largely an affair of the Restoration. Charles II was fond of French music and sent Pelham Humphrey to France to learn the secrets of Lully. Hortense Mancini, duchess of Mazarin, in the 1670's helped to establish French and Italian opera in London, where the fame of Rossi had been carried by that distinguished literary exile and missionary of French taste, Saint-Évremond. The masque, which had received such a high literary stamp from Jonson, Milton and Dryden, and was, so to speak, institutionalized as a part of the public exercises of schools and even of the universities, influenced the opera in England even more effectively than the ballet in France or the Singspiel in Germany. The *Psyche* of Shadwell and Locke (1675) reflected the deep-set English fervor for drama. It was essentially a play in which the music was used to heighten the dramatic action: the principal actors did not sing. Even the great genius of Henry Purcell (1658–1695) was employed through most of his all-too-brief career in the musical setting of plays. Nevertheless, Purcell's operatic music for Dryden's *King Arthur* (1691) and his *Dido and*

[22] Daniel G. Mason, ed., *The Art of Music* (9 vols., New York, 1936–1937), IX, 30.

Aeneas (1688–1690) was not equaled in dramatic power and directness until Gluck. The great achievement of Purcell was the terminus of operatic creation in England. The powerful influence of Handel changed the style, and from that day almost to this England remained colonial in the field of opera. English music of the last quarter of the seventeenth century remains an interesting monument of unfulfilled promise.

The Italian opera and Italian ballet penetrated even the remote corners of Europe. Great schemes to establish an Italian opera in Stockholm were disrupted when Christina abdicated.[23] Some form of Italian opera had reached Poland as early as the third decade of the century. A Muscovite ambassador to Tuscany astounded the Russians by tales of what he had seen of the ballet in Florence.[24] The equestrian ballet originated in Italy whence it was carried to Vienna in 1631, and later to the court of Louis XIV, to Dresden, Durlach, Munich and other German courts.[25] It died out in the eighteenth century, but until recently it could still be seen, a perfect baroque performance in its proper baroque setting, in the carrousel at Saumur.

In the field of church music it is difficult to see this period in its proper perspective because the titanic figures of Bach and Handel obscure the scene behind them. It is to be remembered that both these masters were proud to learn from Buxtehude in his old age.

The oratorio was the development in religious form of the *dramma per musica*. Overtheatrical at the beginning, it was refined by Giacomo Carissimi (d. 1674) to the restrained form it still preserves. The Jesuits appropriated this new form of music, and until Handel's time it was known as the "Jesuit style." Like the opera with which it vied, the oratorio became a vast framework for the new forms of solo, choral and orchestral music. At the hands of Heinrich Schütz (d. 1672), the greatest composer of church music before Johann Sebastian Bach, who served as head of the famous Saxon court chapel for sixty years, the oratorio received a prodigious development. His surviving works fill sixteen great volumes, most of it religious music of the first order.[26] Although, interestingly enough, he returned to polyphony in his old age, the main body of his work was baroque and served as a principal channel for the introduction of baroque music into Germany.

[23] Carl-Allen Moberg, "Essais d'opéra en Suède sous Charles XII," in *Mélanges de musicologie offerts à M. Lionel de La Laurencie*, 124.

[24] Cyril Beaumont, *The Ballet in Russia* (London, 1930), 3.

[25] Paul Nettl, "Equestrian Ballets of the Baroque Period," *Musical Quarterly*, 19 (1933), 74–83.

[26] Edited by P. Spitta, Munich, 1885–1894.

Schütz was religiously eclectic, but for his successors a cleavage in form and spirit coincided with the cleavage in religion. In the south and the Catholic states generally, the Italians dominated and preserved the Italian forms. In the Protestant communities, under Pietist influences, folk music was the starting point for the development of the chorale. Michael Praetorius, Johann Hermann Schein, the numerous musical members of the Bach family, Andreas Hammersmidt and Melchior Franck, to mention only a few, constituted a galaxy of minor stars that nevertheless is a glory to German music.[27] In Holland and Switzerland, too, the repressive attitudes of Calvinism were giving way to the popular demand for music in the churches.

The ultimate expression of the baroque in music was the development of instrumental—"absolute"—music. It was not an accident that the elaboration of the organ into a complicated and flexible instrument, the evolution of the crude and limited viols into the refined and expressive violin, were contemporaneous with the Gesù, the Salute and the Belvedere. Obviously baroque in their physical form, the organ and the violin were the specific instruments by which the voice and the word were supplanted as the highest form of music.

The organ had long been known, but the sixteenth and especially the seventeenth century saw a vast improvement in many of the organs in various parts of the European world. The technicians who achieved these advances remain unknown. It may be assumed that their efforts were the result of pressing demands from musicians who had something more to say than could be said by means of the crude and clumsy machines that had to be struck with the fist. Judging by his compositions, Frescobaldi had an excellent instrument while he was organist of St. Peter's, but the first known organ of really noble proportions was that developed under Buxtehude at St. Mary's, Lübeck.

In contrast to the organ, the violin was developed by craftsmen who won great fame. It did not differ in principle from the viols but embodied important advances in refinement and technical capacity. The important step was taken by one of the well-known Amati family, whose most famous member, Nicolò (1558–1684), transmitted his technique to the even greater Guarneri and Stradivari. During the last half of the seventeenth and especially during the first third of the eighteenth century violins were produced that have not since been equaled.[28]

[27] P. Landormy, *A History of Music*, 71.

[28] G. R. Hayes, *Musical Instruments and Their Music, 1500–1750* (Oxford, 1930), II, 191.

Like the opera, organ music in this period manifested the revolutionary influence of Italy. Frescobaldi not only commanded an immense public as organist at St. Peter's, but also wielded commanding influence over organists all over Europe. He introduced the modern tonality and laid the foundations of the tonal fugue. A great pupil of his, Johann Jakob Froberger, continued his influence at Vienna, and Johann Kaspar Kerll (1627–1693), although not his pupil, followed Italian models. Somewhat less directly Italian, the influence of Jan Sweelinck, a pupil of Gabrieli in Venice, was spread wide from the Netherlands over all northern Germany. The greatest of this school was Dietrich Buxtehude (1637–1707), from 1668 organist of the Marienkirche at Lübeck, likewise a great virtuoso, whose influence was so significant in the development of Johann Sebastian Bach. The Bach family itself, with its numerous distinguished organists and their neighbors in Thuringia and Saxony, was affected by influences from both the north and the south. Johann Pachelbel (1653–1706), whose professional life carried him from Vienna to Eisenach, Erfurt, Stuttgart, Gotha and Nürnberg, was perhaps the most representative of this eclectic group. These men and their followers were pioneers in the development of the chorale–prelude, which they had raised to an admirable standard before Bach began his lifework. If they fell short of his achievement, no one else has equaled theirs.[29]

The music of the violin was still rather incompletely defined. Louis XIV had his twenty-four *violons du roi* and Charles II a similar group in frank imitation of the French king. It was, however, the pressure of orchestral needs that seems first to have elevated the violin to its primal position. From about 1650 the writing of pieces for a small group including the violin or accompanying it as a solo instrument became self-conscious enough to claim a name, the "sonata." The name and concept reflect the assertion of a function independent of vocal forms, corresponding to the capabilities of the instrument. The concerto, the concerto grosso and the suite were being developed by Arcangelo Corelli, Giuseppe Torelli and Giovanni Battista Vitali.[30]

Regardless of the subjective considerations that must always enter into the formulation of the history of an art, one clearly objective fact emerges as an important aspect of the history of music in our period: it involved the activity of an extraordinarily large proportion of the population. It was a major concern of the courts of Paris, Vienna, London, Moscow, Stockholm and a dozen minor capitals. The Emperor Leopold I and

[29] C. H. H. Parry, *The Music of the Seventeenth Century*, 99–121.
[30] P. Landormy, *op. cit.*, 80; G. R. Hayes, *op. cit.*, II, 196.

King John IV of Portugal were themselves industrious and reputable composers. Music commanded the serious attention of men of affairs and savants like Christopher Huygens, Samuel Pepys and Francis North, Lord Guilford, Keeper of the Seals and author of *A Philosophical Treatise on Music* (1677). At Oxford that cloistered pedant, Antony Wood, parted painfully but regularly with his weekly sixpence for the "musicall meeting." Wood tells of the two thousand people crowded in to hear the "musick reading" and the "musick lecture" in 1680.[31] Servants were hired for their skill with the viol or the lute and taken to the taverns with their masters to make "consorts" with gentlemen and other servants. In the bourgeois homes which the Dutch genre painters studied with such care, musical activity was a prominent feature.

In Italy, in Belgium and the Dutch Netherlands, in Vienna and in Switzerland, amateur musical societies—"colleges," "academies"—were a prominent feature of social life. In 1660 there were three musical societies in Antwerp.[32] In Switzerland, musical "colleges" or clubs flourished at Winterthur, Zürich, Saint-Gall, Schaffhausen, Coire and Basle.[33] At Neuchâtel, music and music-teaching concerned the whole community.[34] In London, gentlemen hired rooms in taverns for their "consorts." [35] In Paris, certain cabarets such as Bon-Paris and Bel-Air were well known in a similar way as centers for singing "Bacchic airs." [36]

Like architecture and poetry, music was being reduced to theory. The *Harmonie universelle* (1637) of Marin Mersenne started a long line of books and manuals. The great Descartes himself undertook to include music in his system and, characteristically, reduced it to a matter of intellectual relations.[37] Like the languages, music was being harnessed to a rigorous grammar.

The musical gilds were wholly unable to adjust to the new demands. Their organic, nonintellectual system of education could only transmit the traditional forms. Like the industrial gilds, they failed to survive not because of price competition but because they could not satisfy the new requirements. They gave way to the academies and the more highly

[31] *The Life and Times of Antony Wood* (edited by A. Clark, Oxford, 1891), s. d., July 10, 1680.
[32] E. van der Straeten, *op. cit.*, III, 78.
[33] George Becker, *La musique en Suisse* (Geneva, 1874), ch. 14.
[34] E. M. Fallet, *La vie musicale au pays de Neuchâtel du XIIIe à la fin du XVIIIe siècle* (Strassburg, 1936), 72–120.
[35] Roger North, *Memoirs of Musick* (London, 1846), 112.
[36] Th. Gerold, *op. cit.*, 158.
[37] A. W. Locke, "Descartes and Seventeenth Century Music," *Musical Quarterly*, 21 (1935), 423–31; cf. André Pirro, *Descartes et la musique* (Paris, 1907).

trained musicians of the kings, the princes and the impresarios. In Brussels the four-hundred-year-old Société de Saint-Job could not meet the polite request of the Prince of Thurn and Taxis that they name a Kapellmeister who was expert in musical composition: their privileges rapidly disappeared.[38] In Paris, the establishment of Perrin's academy in 1669 similarly overrode the privileges of a Parisian gild.

The popularity of music in all classes of society, its increasing technicalization, and the emergence of the virtuoso produced a very natural result, a kind of professionalization of music that put a blight upon the hitherto unashamed amateur. The opera in Italy was from the beginning a professional enterprise dependent on mass support. After the Restoration and certainly not later than 1672, John Bannister had begun the first series of public concerts in London.[39] About the same time, Buxtehude initiated his famous *Abentmusiken* (vespers) in Lübeck (1673) and the *Tonkünstlersocietät* was organized in Vienna (1672). With the help of Constantin Huygens, Charles Hacquart started a similar venture at The Hague.[40] In London, "the violent inclination to follow musick" grew to such an extent that "a fabrick was reared in York Buildings on purpose for publick musick."[41] The advent of the professional musician abashed the amateur. In Spain popular and courtly music went separate ways.[42] Pepys notes the diffidence of the servants whom he brought to perform when there were professionals present. As Lully increasingly used the services of his professionals, the general participaton in the court ballets was reduced to a formal and minor practice. Even in the Grand Ballet, where Louis XIV represented himself as the sun, Lully was his mentor.

Music had been transformed by the development of new modalities, of new forms, of new standards of technical achievement in composition and performance. It had become a major form of the culture—secularized, socialized and professionalized. The new music had spread over all Europe. In music, as in painting and architecture, the baroque was destined to evolve through numerous revolts, revolutions and rebellions. Nevertheless, its patterns and problems had been set in forms common to the whole culture and abiding in time.

[38] E. van der Straeten, *op. cit.,* I, 176; II, 73.

[39] Hugh Arthur Scott, "London's Earliest Public Concerts," *Musical Quarterly,* 22 (1936), 446–57; cf. Roger North, *op. cit.,* 105–12.

[40] *Correspondence et œuvres musicales de Constantin Huygens* (edited by W. J. A. Jonkblaet and J. P. N. Land, Leyden, 1882), ccxxii.

[41] Roger North, *op. cit.,* 113, 116.

[42] Eduardo Chavarri, *Musica popular española* (Barcelona, 1927), 92.

IV. THE BAROQUE AS PAINTING AND SCULPTURE [43]

Like the musicians of the baroque, the painters and sculptors of the seventeenth century turned from commentary on life to the direct expression of life itself. Like the writers, they achieved their ends by a new and deeper analysis. As Poussin expressed what he had learned from Domenichino, they sought "to enter into the passion of their subject." Rembrandt was the supreme example. Many of his pictures, like the Storm at Sea in the Gardner Museum in Boston and The Mill in the National Gallery in Washington, display the external features of baroque, exaggeration and overintensity, that led the inhibited epigones to cover with an epithet a greater style than their own. He was not less baroque when in some of his portraits which are devoid of decoration he focused all his genius upon the inner life. The Christ at Emmaus and the portrait of his young son Titus not only illustrate the spiritual power of his unique genius, but exemplify the high possibilities of baroque perception and expression, not to be approached again until the art revolution of the late nineteenth century set the moderns free from the prim conventionalities of the schools. The art of the baroque was pictorial art, but in its higher forms its objectives wholly transcended delineation. As modern art has detached itself from the obligations of literalism, the whole achievement of the baroque has been revalued, as well as the achievement of individual artists.

No fact is more obvious than that the seventeenth-century painters and sculptors were generally bound by the demands of kings, nobles, ecclesiastical princes and rich bourgeois. Nevertheless, through the whole movement from Caravaggio to Hogarth, Houdon and Goya runs a strain of the picaresque, of the concern with the homely and simple, even with the ugly and brutal. The rape of Lucretia, Susanna and the Elders, Saint Sebastian and other painful martyrdoms were popular subjects. In Italy, in Spain, in France and in Holland, on the other hand, the greatest painters turned from mythology, court life and rich patrons to portray peasants, workers, tavern loungers, vagabonds and gamins of the street. Among the French and Dutch painters especially, the self-portraits, the

---

[43] A. Springer and C. Ricci, *Manuale di storia dell'arte* (6 vols., reprint of 4th ed., edited by B. Molajoli, Bergamo, 1947); Werner Weisbach, *Die Kunst des Barocks in Italien, Frankreich, Deutschland und Spanien* (*Propyläen Kunstgeschichte*, Berlin, 1924); M. J. Friedländer, *Die Niederländischen Maler des 17. Jahrhunderts* (*Propyläen Kunstgeschichte*, Berlin, 1923); René Schneider, *L'art français: dix-septième siècle* (Paris, 1925); André Michel, ed., *Histoire de l'art*, Tome VI, *L'art en Europe au XVIIe siècle* (2 vols., Paris, 1921–1922).

family portraits and the portraits of fellow painters manifest a directness and sincerity often missing in their commissions for their patrons. In Holland, during the last half of the century, painting went almost wholly domestic in subject and purpose.

Although the lines of influence were considerably complicated by the essential cosmopolitanism of the painting fraternity, the capital and homeland of the painters was Italy. At Rome an international society of artists had come into being, subdivided into national groups which recognized common standards and exercised upon each other a considerable reciprocal influence. The Flemish-German group was known as the Schilderbent. The French immigrants, among whom Poussin in his later years exercised a genial deanship, formed a school equally independent of the official French school and of the true Roman tradition. Poussin and Lorrain, whom the cataloguers on political grounds claim for France, lived out their entire careers in Rome. In 1666 the French Academy paid the supreme tribute to Rome by establishing its school there.

The Italian influence flowed in two broadly distinct lines: that of Caravaggio (1568–1609), whose chiaroscuro, synthetic organization of space, simplicity and picaresque subjects are reflected in Spanish and Dutch painting down to the end of the century; and that of Correggio as developed by the Carracci, Domenichino and Albani, less penetrating, more decorative and "scenic" (and more popular), which was at the basis of most French painting of the time of Louis XIV. It was the Carracci and their followers who populated the walls, the ceilings, the domes of so many churches and palaces with floating and gesticulating figures decorated with ideal landscapes, clouds, flying draperies. The Carracci school had all the faults of the baroque, but however much their quality may be questioned, the sheer distribution and persistence of their pictures makes it necessary to accord them some validity for a society that was not only pompous and pretentious, but also grandly creative in science, in music, in literature and in religion. Their canvases fill the museums from Leningrad to San Francisco and their imitators persisted even in the late nineteenth century, as shown by the older building of the Library of Congress. However valuable revulsion and rebellion may be to artists and their professional critics, social history cannot condemn such a style on the ground of supposed superior standards.

The purely Italian painting of the last part of the century was without great significance. It was wholly decorative in purpose. Its most characteristic products were the extraordinary ceilings and domes such as Luca Giordano's vault of the Treasure Chapel in the Certosa at Naples, the ceiling of the Barberini Palace at Rome by Pietro da Cortona (1596–1669) and the vault of the Gesù by G. B. Gaulli (1639–1709). Lacking as they are in spiritual significance, they reflect the new cosmos of the Galileos, the Descartes's and the Newtons. Floating figures with flying draperies, cleverly foreshortened and deceptively lighted, inhabited the unbounded space opened up to the Europeans by the new science.

Two painters whom the banal patriotism of the cataloguers has re-annexed to France in themselves constituted a distinctive Italian school without immediate influence, but are significant here because by contrast with the current movements, they emphasized the essentially nonclassical character of the Carracci school. Nicolas Poussin (1594–1665), after making his reputation in Rome, went to France for two years and returned in disgust to Rome, where he lived out his life. He was a devoted classicist, whose paintings suggest the cool balance of a Greek bas-relief and connect with the baroque only through the significant organization of the space relations. Claude Gelée (1600–1682), called Lorrain, was always regarded as part of the German colony in Rome. He was much influenced by Poussin and, even more than Poussin, dissociated himself from the prevalent realism. Unconcerned about the data of people, trees and rocks, his purpose was concentrated on the problem of space, sky and, above all, light. Turner was proud to claim his influence.

The Carracci influence was firmly established in France by Charles Le Brun (1619–1690). After a relatively brief Italian experience, he returned to France and established himself with Fouquet as his patron. When Fouquet fell, Louis XIV, recognizing Le Brun as a painter after his own heart, put him in charge of reorganizing and developing the Academy, which, from its inception in 1648, had gradually succumbed to various oppositions. A second-rate painter, Le Brun effectively organized some scores of painters and sculptors to carry out the immense enterprise of decoration for the king's buildings, especially Versailles. As permanent chancellor of the Academy, he set up provincial academies, one of which, that of Lyons, developed some life and significance. In 1666 he effected the establishment of the Academy's School of Rome. In 1667 he started the annual salons. As director of the Gobelin tapestry works, he organized schools of design, generally regarded as his most important achievement.

Le Brun was essentially commonplace in his taste, but as a decorator was without a peer in his time. The *salle de Venus,* the *salle des gardes de la reine,* the Hall of Mirrors at Versailles, to mention only a few of his achievements as painter and director of painters, show that he knew perfectly how to set the pomp and pretence of the court of a Louis XIV. As

Lully did in music, he pushed equally worthy competitors into the background. Pierre Mignard (1612–1695) managed to survive Le Brun and after Colbert's death in 1683, with Louvois's support, more or less displaced him. Mathieu Le Nain (1600–1677) continued to paint touchingly realistic scenes of country life and city streets. Philippe de Champaigne, the painter of Port Royal, paralleled the profound religiosity of Zurbarán.

It was a moment of decline for the Caravaggio influence. Velásquez died in 1660 and Francesco Zurbarán (1598–1662), devout painter of devotion, had only two more years to live. In Holland, Rembrandt and Frans Hals in Amsterdam, and Jakob van Ruysdael in Haarlem were ending their days in poverty and neglect. Some shift of the social pattern was displacing the cultured patriciate, which had known how to honor them, with a clientele of less aristocratic taste, more disposed to little pictures, less penetrating and more domestic.

The misery and poverty of Rembrandt's last years did not prevent the development of the last and greatest phase of his art. The numerous self-portraits, those of his young son Titus, the Staalmeesters of 1661 (Amsterdam), the Jewish Bride of the last year of his life, mark the complete freedom of the artist and the complete mastery of his material and his method. It was then that the Caravaggian chiaroscuro reached, at his hands, its ideal fulfillment. Frans Hals accepted his submergence in a Haarlem almshouse more casually. His Young Man in a Slouch Hat (1660), painted with the old power, has none of the festive gaiety and self-confidence of the Laughing Cavalier. The group portraits of the directors and directresses of the two Haarlem almshouses reflect the age of the subjects and of the painter. Ruysdael, poet and Spinozan, struggled vainly against the more obvious virtues of the Everdingens and Vermeers and after twenty years returned to Haarlem also to die a pauper (1683).

Painting in Holland became an industry. It was the heyday of the art dealers and the craftsmen. The craftsmanship of a Vermeer, of a Ter Borch, of a Dou, is not to be lightly contemned; it has remained significant for a whole world for whom Rembrandt, Ruysdael, even Hals are only museum names. In our day, the egregious Mr. Van Meegeren exposed the essential difference between art and craftsmanship: the great and supremely valued Vermeer himself could be forged so successfully that the imitation could not be distinguished from the original, even by the experts. The artists of the new generation set themselves to make a vision of the world in the prosaic terms of the new bourgeois, without royalty and without religion, even without more philosophy than a comfortable bourgeois acceptance of solidity and luxury. That they succeeded within their limits is borne out by their prosperity in their own day and their persistent popularity down to our own.

Jan Vermeer of Delft (1628–1691) was only the most distinguished and most successful of a score of painters of Dutch domesticity, indoors and out, who are still remembered. Without absurdity, he brought to his quiet and luxurious Dutch interiors the Caravaggian organization of light and space that Rembrandt was carrying to such heights. In his placid Dutch figures it is possible to recognize something of the Rembrandtian "interior," but only at a commonplace level. In his landscapes, such as his View of Delft (The Hague), the same unperturbed realism contrasts with the cosmic implications of Ruysdael's idealistic landscapes. Meyndert Hobbema (1638–1709), a pupil of Ruysdael, combined his idealism with a very attractive but literal realism, as in his famous and much loved Road to Middelharnis. Still life became an outlet for the virtuosity so plentiful among the Dutch.

In Spain, El Greco (Domenico Theotocopoulis, c. 1548–1614), like Caravaggio profoundly influenced by Tintoretto, had brought the new seriousness and intensity into Spanish painting which marks Velásquez and Zurbarán, both of whom gave his mastery generous recognition. Velásquez kept four of his canvases in his studio and called his work the Bible of painting.[44] The influence of Caravaggio was reinforced by the considerable prestige of José Ribera (1588–1652). After 1660 Bartolomé Esteban Murillo (1618–1682) marks a descent like that of Rembrandt's successors from the tragic intensity of Velásquez (with whom he briefly studied) and from the religious intensity of Zurbarán. Essentially a simple man of the people, Murillo carried over the picaresque realism and sentimentality of his Beggar Boy (Louvre), Dice Players and Melon Eaters (both at Munich) into his numerous Annunciations and Immaculate Conceptions. He was immensely popular and correspondingly industrious. His work was even exported to the colonies. For two centuries Murillo was regarded as one of the very greatest of painters while El Greco was disregarded or contemned. Since 1900, critical opinion has completely reversed their relative positions. The reversal is an index of the change that has produced the new appreciation of the baroque.

The ascendency of Bernini as sculptor was as unchallenged as his leadership in architecture and, indeed, was scarcely to be distinguished from it. Much of the last twenty years of his long life (1598–1680) was devoted to the artistic organization of the treasure house of classical and

[44] S. Reinach, *Apollo* (Paris, 1903), 245.

Renaissance art that Rome had become. The Plaza of St. Peter's is the climactic center of a whole series of plazas with fountains developed into highly elaborated forms in which the individual statue is only a part of an architectonic conception. His followers filled the plazas, the churches, the courts and the gardens of Europe with statuary in a multitude of forms. The ideal for which he strove in Rome was carried to Versailles, to Paris, to Salzburg and to Potsdam.

Of his own sculpture the great masterpieces, The Convulsions of Saint Teresa (Rome, S. Maria della Vittoria) and the tomb of Urban VIII in St. Peter's, antedate 1660, but his bust of Louis XIV, the equestrian statue of Constantine in St. Peter's, the Four Rivers fountain of the Piazza Navona and the tomb of Alexander VII justify the leadership he continued to exercise till his death.

The baroque sculptors made free with their material. Some odd *tours de force* of technique with stone were produced, such as marble worked into veiling, fishnets, or the ragged garb of shepherds. Pierre Puget (1622–1694), a French pupil of Bernini, who worked in northern Italy and southern France, made vivid pictures in stone of dramatic action, such as his Saint Sebastian at Genoa and his Milo of Croton and Alexander and Diogenes, now in the Louvre. In Spain, a large enterprise of sculpture in wood derived from a very great artist, Juan Martinez Montañez (d. 1649) and, especially in the south and southwest, was highly developed. In Mexico wood sculpture received an important development at the hands of native artists, who also devised a light, easily workable but durable plastic made of sugar cane pith.[45]

The world which the artists of this generation strove to capture in paint and stone corresponded to the world which the cosmologists and the scientists, the religionists and the politicians were seeking to realize. All the aspects of reality which the scientists were exploring were material also for the artist, to be envisaged with his equal and differentiating vision. The unconventional freedom with which he chose as his subjects street urchins, peasants, landscapes, domestic interiors, animals, was revolutionary in the same way as the breach of the scientists with the conventionalities of scholasticism. The "glories" of the churches and ceilings of the palaces portray a world of unlimited spaces, of disrupted barriers. In the chiaroscuro of a Rembrandt and the Spinozan landscapes of a Ruysdael, the world of phenomena emerges from the dim background of the unknown, of essential facts below the level of vision, of problems to be solved only by penetration and analysis. In the apotheoses and the glories,

---

[45] Elizabeth W. Weismann, *Mexico in Sculpture, 1521–1821* (Cambridge, 1950), 167 ff.

man took upon himself the attributes of the hero and transcended the miseries and deficiencies of the humble human form. In the Dominican at Prayer of a Zurbarán and the Saint Teresa of Bernini, the experience of God was no routine of ritual or pose, but an agony of the spirit. The individuals of the great portraits stand to their destiny alone, face to face, in the phrase of Pascal, with a universe that might crush them but could not equal them.

V. THE BAROQUE AS LITERATURE

Baroque is not naturalized as a working concept among the historians of literature. It is nevertheless an obviously convenient term to express the profound identity between the plastic arts and music on the one hand and the verbal arts on the other. The dilemma of freedom and conformity, the intense practicality, the deep sensuousness, the accent on human individuality, the elevation of technique which characterize the other baroque forms of expression are manifest as well in the internal structure of late seventeenth-century literature. It is necessary to recognize the interdependence and the integrality of the forms and modes of expression of which Dryden and Schütz, Racine and Bernini, Boileau and Wren so nobly represent varied aspects and to give it a name that corresponds to its historic individuality. In this construction, the literature of the late seventeenth century was baroque.

Two voices from the past were still vocal. Milton and Vondel represented a tradition that, even before they had ceased to write, seemed to come from another age. The *Paradise Lost* of Milton recounted the rebellion of the angels and the fall of man and expressed his passionate devotion to liberty. The *Paradise Regained,* an epic poem on the temptation in the wilderness, and the *Samson Agonistes,* a tragedy in the Greek form, are even more personal in their expression. In spite of his political unpopularity, and in spite of the profound shift in taste, Milton's great masterpieces were promptly acclaimed by the critics and took their place among the classics of England's, indeed of the world's, literature. Joost van den Vondel (1587–1679), less famous, but hardly below Milton in the grandeur and religious intensity of his poetry, like Milton recounted the fall of man in his *Lucifer.* Calderón (1600–1681) was continuing the tradition of Lope de Vega and putting the period to a vast achievement of his own and to a brilliant movement in Spanish writing.

It was the age of Louis XIV in literature as in no other phase of the culture. Supremacy passed from Italy to France. The quarter-century with which we are concerned saw a complete reversal of the old relations between these two countries. While French writers freed themselves from the influence of Italian models and became critical of the old traditions still dominant in Italian poetry, French influence manifested itself powerfully in Italy. Books, plays, customs and clothes began to follow French models. In England, the transition can be even more exactly dated. Milton, formed in an earlier generation, had turned to Italy; Dryden, the man of the new generation, turned to France.

French literary influence spread everywhere. In Germany it ran athwart a germanizing movement stemming from the *Aristarchus, sive de contemptu linguae teutonicae* of Martin Opitz (1617), which had been carried on by various language societies in several centers. The language movement in Germany had broadly paralleled the French development stemming from Malherbe. The German language and literature, like the French, was systematized and ordered. Then the disruptions and disasters of the Thirty Years' War, coupled with the triumph of French power, handicapped the indigenous movement and opened the way to an undue development of French influences. Even Opitz had urged attention to French models. French became the language of the upper classes and even of the upper bourgeois. The courts, the customs, the clothes became French. In 1687 the learned Thomasius produced a "Discourse on the Form in Which One Should Imitate the French." [46]

Nevertheless, some characteristic German production saw the light in our period. In 1682 the impulse which had begun with Opitz was summed up in the *Manual of German Speech and Poetry* of Georg Morhof,[47] in which, characteristically, much space was given to French, English, Spanish and Italian literature. In 1691 appeared the first German dictionary. Although the influence of Rabelais and Cervantes is plainly visible, Grimmelshausen's *Simplicissimus* (1669) [48] was almost wholly German in spirit. A large literature close to the people and free from foreign influence but none the less baroque was produced by the Pietists and some of it, such as Paul Gerhardt's great contribution to German hymnology, rose to high standards.

In literature as in architecture, the response of the English to the baroque and in particular to French influence was partial and limited. The limitation is clearly reflected in Dryden's comment that neither English faults nor French virtues were "considerable enough to place them above us."

---

[46] *Diskurs, Welcher Gestalt man deren Franzosen in gemeinen Leben und Wandel nachahmen solle.*

[47] *Unterricht der deutschen Sprache und Poesie.*

[48] *Die abenteuerliche Simplizius Simplicissimus.*

The English were too conscious of the high standards of the past to
follow the French in a revolution that made a Year 1 of the arrival of
Malherbe, the "doctor in the vulgar tongue." With all the qualifications
that Dryden brought to his estimate of Shakespeare, still, to him, "Shakespeare's power is sacred as a King's." [49] Whatever Dryden and the other
adapters did to Shakespeare's plays, his was "the heap of jewels" [50] from
which they snatched their treasures. It was part of a historical sensitivity
which had no counterpart in France. Peter Heylyn in his *France Painted
to the Life* (1657) remarked of the French, "So little did I perceive them
to be inclining to be antiquaries, that both neglects considered, I dare
confidently averre that one Cotton for the Treasury and one Selden
(now Mr. Camden is dead) are worth all the French." The same sensitivity to the past was reflected in Heylyn's appreciation of Amiens cathedral: "One of the most glorious piles of building under the Heavens."

In France, the baroque as literature was codified in the *Art poétique*
(1674) of Nicholas Boileau-Despréaux (1636–1711). It was the product of
a movement that began in the early years of the century with François de
Malherbe (1555–1628), who had undertaken to "purify" the French language. The impulse toward correctness, of which Malherbe was the
prime representative, was continued and developed in the salons where
the *précieuses* learned, practiced and taught manners in deportment and
nicety in speech. The passion for exactness of diction and grammar penetrated even the discipline of the governmental bureaus.[51]

The spreading victory of Cartesianism elevated the reason as the general
criterion of human expression in the form of "clear and distinct ideas."
In its essence, Cartesianism seemed to exclude the works of the imagination, but Cartesian principles were compromised by the solidly established tradition of Rome and Greece. Thus "poetic art" as Boileau described it was at once classical and Cartesian.

As Cartesian, Boileau harbored no doubt that the principles of good
poetry could be formulated as "clear and distinct ideas." As classicist, he
was equally certain that they were the principles of Aristotle as practiced
by the great ones of Rome and Greece. Let the would-be poet follow them
in adhering to the unities of time, place and action; let him follow their
versification with exactness and confine himself to their subjects. The gods
and goddesses of ancient Greece were proper subjects, but not the Christian religion. As Saintsbury points out, Boileau failed even to recognize

---

[49] Prologue to Dryden's *The Tempest.*

[50] Nahum Tate, *Lear,* Prologue.

[51] W. King, *Science and Rationalism in the Government of Louis XIV* (Baltimore, 1949),
245.

how greatly his friends Molière and Racine, to say nothing of Milton and Bunyan, whom he did not know, had departed from his classical rules both as to organization and substance. Boileau remained for centuries a power in the French system of educating literary taste. Some five hundred editions of his *Art poétique* were to be counted in Saintsbury's day.[52] Although French literature even in his own time and increasingly since has gone far beyond his pattern, Boileau's *Art poétique* remains a monument marking the divergence of French poetry in its own path, as the divergence of English poetry is marked by the critical principles of John Dryden (1631–1700).

Dryden was a better critic than Boileau, perhaps principally because he knew better the literature of his time and place and of other times and places. He was fully conscious of the importance of the movements in French literature but equally convinced that neither English faults nor French virtues were "considerable enough to place them above us." He claimed for his age, as compared to the age of Shakespeare, a superior cultivation but was acute enough to recognize that something was lacking:

> Our builders were with want of genius curst;
> The second temple was not like the first.[53]

Without a Malherbe, a Boileau or an Academy, the English language too was being forced into the bonds of elegance and grammar, "so refined," to quote Dryden again, "so much refined since Shakespeare's time that many of his Words and more of his Phrases are scarce intelligible." [54]

The prose of Dryden reflected another baroque character that appeared also in his poetry, as in that of Racine and in the lyrical poetry and comedies of the period—a clarity that contrasts with the reckless involutions and complicated patterns of a Milton or a Thomas Browne. Ciceronian periods gave way to clipped sentences, juxtaposed rather than linked and essentially conversational in structure. The form in which Spinoza cast his *Ethics,* although peculiar, illustrates the geometric intention. "The intellect became the arbiter of form, the dictator of artistic practice as of philosophic inquiry." [55]

Analysis became one of the functions of literature. The instrument of

[52] *History of Criticism* (1902; 4th ed., 1922), II, 580, note.
[53] *Epistle to Congreve,* quoted by H. Spencer, *Shakespeare Improved* (1927), 45.
[54] "Preface Containing the Grounds of Criticism in Tragedy," *Troilus and Cressida.*
[55] M. W. Croll, "The Baroque Style in Prose," in *Studies in English Philology: A Miscellany in Honor of Frederick Klaeber,* edited by Kemp Malone and Martin B. Lund (Minneapolis, 1929), 455–56.

the writer became the scalpel rather than the mirror. Falstaff was a great comic character, but we shall never understand him as we do M. Jourdain, Molière's bourgeois who wished to be a gentleman. This same passion for analysis, for the understanding of interior motivation, attained classic expression in the jewel-cut *Maximes* (1665–1678) of La Bruyère. These epigrammatic formulas undertook to bring out the real forces within the men and women who strutted the little stages of salon, court and town. Scrupulously free of romantic, dramatic or poetic invention, they approached as closely as possible the severe simplicity of scientific language. Thus the Royal Society rejected all forms of poetic utterance as undesirable "ornaments of speech" and adopted "a close, naked, natural way of speaking." [56] Thus Dryden, who to the end of his life held the heroic poem "the greatest work which the soul of man is capable to perform," subordinated its poetic form to a higher purpose: "The design of it is to form the mind to heroic virtue by example; 'tis conveyed in verse, that it may delight, while it instructs." [57]

The comprehensive genius of Molière (Jean Baptiste Poquelin, 1622–1673) expressed itself almost wholly in analysis. Like Hobbes and Spinoza, Molière reflected the fundamental stoicism of the late seventeenth-century outlook by recognizing society as the essential frame of man's existence. Society, the generalized man, was his subject. With the art of the clown and the cartoonist he surveyed the whole of the French scene and exhibited an encyclopedic survey of its follies and sins, of pretense and of brutality, of hypocrisy and of stupidity, of quackery and of pedantry. At all of them he laughed, and, more important, led his world and all of us since to laugh. Like all great comic spirits, he came close to bitterness, but he never laughed to avoid weeping; he approached the sardonic rather than the pathetic. His purpose, to correct the morality of his time, was wholly unconventional. He was neither Christian nor stoic in ethical purpose. His standard was common sense, elevated to the level of eternal verity. Like Hobbes and Spinoza, he shocked his contemporaries. The elite that he mocked for its pretensions formed active coteries against him. He held only the support of the public, of Boileau and of Louis XIV. Without any intention to revolutionize literary method, he upset all the rules by his simple avowal that "the great rule of all is to please." [58] At the same point he identifies himself with the intellectual revolution: "The same good sense which formerly made observations still makes them every

---

[56] Thomas Sprat, *History of the Royal Society* (1667), 83, 111.
[57] "Dedication of *Aeneis,*" in *Essays of John Dryden* (edited by W. P. Ker), II, 154; (reference from Basil Willey, *The Seventeenth Century Background,* 221, note).
[58] *La critique de l'école des femmes,* Scene 6.

day without the aid of Horace or Aristotle." Molière's observation was akin to that of the Boyles and the Huygens'. He took his types, peasants and nobles, townsmen and officials, from people as he saw them and made them speak as he had heard them.

Substantially all of this encyclopedic canvas of the society of his time and place was achieved within fifteen years of a busy life as producer and actor. After dreary beginnings as a wandering showman in the provinces, at the age of thirty-seven he brought his troupe and his talents to Paris. There at the rate of two a year he poured out a series of masterpieces that rank in the world's heritage with those of Shakespeare and Aristophanes. In *Les précieuses ridicules* (1659) he undermined the coteries of the salons. *L'école des femmes* (1662) gave rise to a critical battle in which he replied with *La critique de l'école des femmes* (1663) and *L'impromptu de Versailles* (1664). In *Tartuffe* (1663) he exposed the hypocrisy to which the devoutness of the partisan type was liable. *Don Juan* (1664) eliminated the glamour from the seducer; *Le medicin malgré lui* (1666) and *Le malade imaginaire* (1673) mocked the quackery of the doctors. *Amphitryon* (1667) utilized the famous *Lysistrata* of Aristophanes. The *Bourgeois gentilhomme* (1670) exploited the snobbery of the half-educated.

The exploration of the human soul confronted the analysts with the *libido*. Sex was not exactly discovered in the seventeenth century, but a perspective of the literary production does bring out a distinctively large concern with sex as motive. It would be possible to argue that what the Victorians knew as "the coarseness" of the Restoration stage was the beginning—crude and clumsy, but a beginning—of analyzing sex motivations. The ground is more secure when the adaptations of Shakespeare are examined. Of *The Tempest,* the serene farewell to his world of a great artist, Davenant and Dryden made a licentious farce. Cressida and Cleopatra, instead of Shakespeare's great and gracious women confronted with the tragic implications of high destiny, at the hands of Dryden became merely women in love. Jean Racine (1639–1699) elevated the analysis of passion, and particularly the passion of love in women, to the highest levels of tragedy. In contrast to Corneille's theater, Racine's was feminine. His great plays, *Andromache, Bérénice, Iphigénie, Phèdre,* carry the names of women. From Racine dates the empire of women in literature. He was the product of the Jansenist schools of Port Royal and in the strange Bohemian world of the Parisian theater developed Port Royal's Augustinianism.[59] Unlike Corneille's Promethean protagonists of will,

[59] F. A. Waterhouse, "Racine Janseniste malgré lui," *Sewanee Review,* 30 (1928), 141–55.

Racine's heroines, mythological and royal though they were, were helpless victims swept along by the inexorable destiny imposed by their involvement in unfortunate passions. When Corneille's Medea is asked, "After so many disasters, what remains?" she replies, "I remain—and that is enough." At the corresponding climax, Racine's Phèdre has the despairing cry, *"J'aime."* The grand Arnauld, representative of all the rigor of Jansenism, with a perfect logic that surprises us now, could accept *Phèdre,* the incestuous mother, as "a Christian who has not received grace." After Racine had returned to Port Royal, in his Jansenist phase, he wrote *Esther* (1689) and *Athalie* (1691) for Madame de Maintenon's schoolgirls at Saint-Cyr. While Esther and Athalie retained much of the varnish of civilization which his other characters shook off, they too were moved by passion, and the action was directed by the all-powerful God of Port Royal.

For Racine, "love was the surest road to the heart,"[60] but sexual love was not all. Mother love, father love, even political passion were within his range. His characters were complex, torn between what they would and what they must do. His analytical problem brought him curiously close in method to the realistic Molière. In the same general situation, Racine found tragedy, Molière comedy.[61]

As Molière analyzed the mores of French society and Racine the power of love, Dryden analyzed the intellectual results of the philosophical and scientific revolution. He was open to all the currents of thought and opinion. He was a friend of Hobbes, a member of the Royal Society, an associate of the "wits," a serious Christian who evolved through the Erastian Christianity of the *Religio laici* (1682) to the curiously skeptical Catholicism of *The Hind and the Panther* (1687). Somewhere he claimed for the poet a certain superiority over the theologian, the philosopher and the virtuoso in the solution of the new problem of man in the universe. In his production, this mission emerged at every point. He undertook to put the whole new world into a workable system of language. He was aware of Cartesianism, but he moved toward the skepticism of Gassendi and Montaigne. He understood that Richard Simon's biblical criticism reduced the Christian to an act of faith. He was not uninfluenced by Hobbesianism but he held to the social values of religious sanction in politics. He was himself a principal agent in the refinement of speech but he knew the greatness of Shakespeare. Much of his best writing was occasional and racy with reference to the milieu in which he wrote. He

---

[60] Quoted by G. Lanson, *Histoire de la littérature française,* 547.

[61] G. Reynier, "La 'Science des dames' au temps de Molière," *Revue des deux mondes,* 99 (1929), 436–64.

put his contemporary world of science and religion, of philosophy and taste, of politics and erudition together in the framework of a language modernized to contain it.

Dryden in himself exemplified almost the whole range of literary production in England. He was not only one of the most learned and perceptive of critics, but also dramatist, satirist, annalist, lyricist, translator and adapter. Better than almost any one else in the whole range of European literature, he represented what may conveniently be called the Cartesian element in the baroque, the passion for clarity and exactness. Whole pages of his poetry as well as of his prose carry the reader through difficult and complex patterns without raising a single obstacle and without registering a single phrase as a treasure to be retained in the memory. Dryden once remarked that he had chosen a particular form of verse because "it was best fitted for discourse and nearest prose." It would be difficult to find an expression that more effectively differentiates Dryden from Shakespeare, Donne and Milton on the one hand and from Wordsworth, Shelley and Keats on the other. His poetry was a poetry that could readily be translated into prose. That this prosaic quality was of the essence became manifest in the sequel. It was not Racine nor Molière who was destined to give direction to literary development, but Dryden.

Between 1678 and 1684 one of the classics of the English tongue crept as it were unawares upon the literary stage. John Bunyan, tinker by trade and uneducated preacher of the little provincial town of Bedford, launched his *Pilgrim's Progress*. For centuries it persisted like folklore, transmitted by the humble and unlearned. We have no reason to believe that among the sins that Bunyan catalogues so thoroughly in *Grace Abounding to the Chief of Sinners,* the sin of reading worldly books was either purposely or accidentally omitted. Yet the work of this untutored tradesman was one with the literary expression of his learned contemporaries in the clarity and simplicity of its structure and in its rationalized fantasy. Its allegorical form does not conceal its place in the evolution of the novel. Even in the autobiographical *Grace Abounding* we may suspect Bunyan of an edifying reconstruction of his own character. In the *Pilgrim's Progress* he made characters of the abstractions of Christian experiences, just as Aphra Behn and Madame de Lafayette were making characters with rather less success of more worldly experience. The *Pilgrim's Progress* was an "extraordinary voyage," like those that Fénelon in his *Télémaque* and Montesquieu in his *Lettres persanes* were to use with such effect, and like some long-forgotten efforts of an inferior sort in Bunyan's own day.

Chapter Three

LEVIATHAN: THE ORGANIZATION OF POWER I

I. ABSOLUTISM IN EUROPEAN HISTORY

IN THE latter decades of the seventeenth century, European society was turning from the atomistic and nominalist concepts of feudal right and divine right to a realist concept of society and of the state as its power form. Jean Bodin in the sixteenth century and Hugo Grotius in the earlier decades of the seventeenth had adumbrated the new pattern of thought, but it remained for the political philosophers of the later decades to make the definitions by which Europe still lives its political life.

In 1651 Thomas Hobbes of Malmesbury (1588–1679) launched upon the confused world his terrible definition of the state: *Leviathan, or The Matter, Form and Power of a Commonwealth, Ecclesiastical and Civil.*[1]

It was the third of three parts of a complete system of philosophy, monistic and materialistic, with which Hobbes hoped to displace Cartesian dualism. His achievement fell far short of his ambition, and in the history of Europe he stands as the author of the *Leviathan,* the prophet of the absolute state. The *Leviathan* was and remains repugnant to Europeans because it violated their localistic and feudalistic traditions of freedom. Nevertheless, as successive developments and revolutions involved the recasting of the patterns of power, the Hobbesian analysis was justified by history.

Hobbes discovered society. Instead of atomistic individuals in various relations determined by accidents of history or by the Divine Will, he saw man embodied in the social group. On the other hand, instead of generalized stoic humanity, he saw the social group as determined by local choice. Man was both the "matter" and the "artificer" of this entity. This aggregated man created the state.

---

[1] The *Leviathan* exists in many forms, down to and including an edition in Everyman's Library with an introduction by A. D. Lindsay (London, 1914). The best interpretations of Hobbes as a phenomenon of political and social thought are F. Tönnies, *Thomas Hobbes, Leben und Lehre* (3rd ed., Stuttgart, 1925) and G. E. C. Catlin, *Thomas Hobbes as Philosopher, Publicist and Man of Letters* (Oxford, 1922). Valuable accounts of his political thought are also to be found in the histories of political thought, such as C. E. Vaughan, *Studies in the History of Political Philosophy before and after Rousseau* (2 vols., Manchester, 1925), Vol. I, ch. ii, as well as in the more general histories of philosophy.

Sweeping to one side the theological arguments of the schools, Hobbes found in the origin of the state in human need and action. Before the state came into being, the life of man was "solitary, nasty, brutish, poor and short." By a process which Hobbes was not concerned to substantiate historically, man arrived at a solution: a quasi-contract between himself and his fellows by which they collectively instituted a commonwealth, "that great *Leviathan,* or rather (to speak more reverently) that *Mortall God,* to which we owe under the *Immortal God,* our peace and defence." As Hobbes succeeded in saying best in the famous frontispiece of his work, the essence of the commonwealth is "one person, of whose acts a great multitude . . . have made themselves every one the author." The embodiment of this sovereignty—"he that carryeth this person"—may be either a single person, a group or the whole group, but in any case, whether monarchy, aristocracy or democracy, the sovereignty thus established is limited neither by religion, nor by usage. No other power exists in the commonwealth to check or counterbalance it. It is the source of morality, of property and of perquisites. In other words, it combines total responsibility with total power. On the other hand, according to Hobbes, it has no sanction outside itself. If it fails to provide protection, justice and welfare, by that fact rather than by any procedure, the sovereignty is dissolved and a new commonwealth and a new sovereignty replace it.

In a word, Hobbes furnished definition for the new political concept, the state, which Europe had created for itself. Unlike the feudal organization, it concentrated power and responsibility in the sovereign. Unlike the Catholic Christendom of the Middle Ages, it was geographically limited. It was a revolutionary creation, the historical function of which was the elimination of all the sanctions of localism and universalism. In the course of its earlier development, its sanction had been sought in Roman law—"The king in his kingdom is emperor" (*"rex est in regno sui imperator"*)—and in the "divine right" of the theologians. It was the achievement of Hobbes that he recognized, defined and established a sanction that was at once solid and adaptable, "the Convenience, or Aptitude to Produce the Peace, and Security of the People." It was a dictum that was echoed, among many other instances, most clearly in the American Constitution of 1789: "We, the people of the United States, in order to form a more perfect Union, establish Justice, insure domestic Tranquility, provide for the common Defence, promote the general Welfare, and secure the Blessings of Liberty to ourselves and our Posterity, do ordain and establish this CONSTITUTION for the United States of America."

The Leviathan represented the libertarianism of the time. The bonds that restricted thought and action were the historic claims of localism and the church, which Hobbes subordinated to his commonwealth. In the eighteenth-century revolutions, John Locke's *Essays on Government* were obviously more influential or, at any rate, furnished more of the terminology. Locke's doctrine, however, was basically feudal. The problem as he saw it was the limited right of the governor and the irreducible "natural" right of the subject. For Hobbes, on the other hand, the feudal concept of right disappears and only responsibility (coupled with power) remains. Frederick William I of Prussia was speaking as a pure Hobbesian when he declared, "I am the first servant of the state."

Spinoza, just as absolutist as Hobbes, was much more concerned with the liberty of the individual.[2] In his *Tractatus theologico-politicus,* published in defense of his friend, John de Witt, in 1670, and in his *Ethics,* published after his death, he struck at the roots of divine right by criticizing the basic biblical texts on which it was based. Like Hobbes, he based political society upon a hypothetical contract and upon considerations of social utility. Like Hobbes, again, he conceived the function of the state as unlimited. But unlike Hobbes, who thought of the state as a curb on men's natural and evil propensities, Spinoza conceived it as a necessary instrument of man's self-fulfillment.

Both Hobbes and Spinoza recognized a reality antecedent to the state, namely, society, which created it. The ineffectualness of Robert Filmer, whose *Patriarcha* (1680) was a favorite "straw man" for Locke and his followers to beat, was just in his failure to recognize the social origins of power. Bossuet, in his *Discours sur l'histoire universelle* (*Discourse on Universal History* 1681) and his *Politique tirée des propres paroles de l'écriture saint* (*Politics Taken from the Very Words of Holy Scripture,* 1709), as a good Cartesian modernized divine right by doubling the theological argument with arguments from social utility.

Two logical omissions of Hobbes were supplied by James Harrington, his contemporary and opponent.[3] In his *Oceana* (1656) Harrington recognized the importance of the economic basis of power and attributed the disorders of his time to the change of the balance of power resulting from the redistribution of landed property under the Tudors. Secondly, he

---

[2] Harry A. Wolfson, *The Philosophy of Spinoza* (2 vols. in one, Cambridge, 1948), II, 240–50.

[3] *The Oceana . . . and Other Works,* edited by John Toland and Thomas Birch (Dublin, 1737); H. F. Russell Smith, *Harrington and his Oceana* (Cambridge, 1914); A. E. Levett, "James Harrington," in *Social and Political Ideas of the Sixteenth and Seventeenth Centuries,* edited by F. J. C. Hearnshaw (London, 1926).

made a place for the imperial function: "To ask whether it be lawful for a Commonwealth to aspire to the empire of the world, is to ask whether it be lawful for it to do its duty, or to put the world in better condition than it was before." Neither Hobbes nor Harrington was a democrat, but modern democracy has not departed from their principles.

In varying ways and with varying degrees of success, the several states of Europe were, during our period, evolving toward Hobbesian absolutism. That evolution was the function of the monarchs. It had been demonstrated that neither the epigones of the feudality nor the rising bourgeois, separately or in combination, could manifest "the Convenience, or Aptitude to Produce the Peace, and Security of the People." In France and in England great civil wars had been fought in the name of liberty to challenge the latest stages in the historical process. In both countries the rebels had won all the victories and lost the wars. In England, after they had reduced the state to an ersatz monarchy, rebels and loyalists were glad to return to the ancient form of king, lords and commons. In France the feudal-noble and bourgeois-noble *Frondeurs* proved unable to present even a token resistance to the assertion of absolutism by the sixteen-year-old Louis XIV. In Sweden and Denmark the apparent submergence of the monarchy by the magnates was undone by the sudden emergence of strong rulers. In the Hohenzollern lands the multiplex limitations faced by the Great Elector could neither dampen his ardor nor defeat his efforts to make a state. In the Hapsburg lands every success and every disaster seemed to favor the enlargement of the integrating function of the ruler. In Spain the presence of a weakling on the throne and incompetents in the places of power produced no disposition to undo the work of Charles V and Philip II or even to find another symbol to represent that unity. Even in distant Russia, only beginning to feel the impulses of the European *Geist,* the hardly sanctioned Romanovs could not be withstood by the boyars or by the church. Only in Poland, Holland, Switzerland and in the Holy Roman Empire did Leviathan fail to cohere.

II. MERCANTILISM AS A PHASE OF ABSOLUTISM [4]

The control of economic life in the interest of the state, to which Adam Smith gave the name "mercantilism," was the form in which absolutism attained most nearly ideal expression.

At its apogee medieval Europe had been a great catholic commercial system. At the fairs a common law and common tribunals governed mer-

[4] The basic book for the reorientation of modern thought about mercantilism is Gustav Schmoller, *The Mercantile System and Its Historical Significance* (translated by W. J.

chants from all over Christendom. As the *regnum dei* was displaced by the *regnum hominis*—as the secular forms of power pushed aside the religiously sanctioned church and Empire—the kings were quick to recognize in some degree that the economic life could serve their purpose. Their economic ideas and impulses were naïve. The power and glory of Spain in the century of the discoveries confirmed their already established idea that money was a source of power. Experience and the critical analysis of thinkers like Bodin had undermined the simple economics of this response. Bullionism was ideologically dead in the latter part of the seventeenth century, although it was still part of the vulgar mentality of kings and politicians. By the seventeenth century the concern of the intellectuals and some statesmen had turned to the broader pattern. Money (and, to a limited extent, credit) had become in their minds secondary and instrumental to the problem of production. In Holland, in Sweden, in France, in Brandenburg-Prussia, in England and in many smaller units, the enlargement of production—material production in the sense of things and economic production in the sense of income—had become the aim of the rising states. As their competition for power broadened out in the sixteenth and seventeenth centuries to unprecedented range, the need to broaden the economic basis of power became a commonplace of statesmanship. The converse was also obvious: the problem of relative power might be solved by reducing the economic basis of rival states. The story of mercantilism therefore belongs in part with what has elsewhere been called "the anarchy." [5]

Economic thought as well as economic policy was segmented in the pattern of the states. "One loves his country and serves it," was the opening sentence of Thomas Mun's treatise, *England's Treasure by Trade,* a famous monument of mercantilist thought (1621, published 1664). The ethical problem of righteousness between men, which characterized most of the thought even of the sixteenth century, was left to the priests and the preachers, who struggled with the problem of adjusting the Christian ideals of poverty and charity to the hard secularism of the mercantilist world. [6]

Ashley, New York, 1896). The recent work of E. P. Heckscher, *Mercantilism* (translated by M. Shapiro, 2 vols., London, 1935), is the most nearly encyclopedic study available. Of more specialized studies, Louise Sommer, *Die österreichischen Kameralisten in dogmengeschichtlicher Darstellung* (2 vols., 1920–1925), and J. Morini-Comby, *Mercantilisme et protectionnisme: essai sur les doctrines interventionnistes en politique commercial du XVᵉ au XIXᵉ siècles* (Paris, 1930), most clearly formulate mercantilism as a phase of absolutism.

[5] Chapter Five below.

[6] Max Weber, *The Protestant Ethic and the Spirit of Capitalism* (translated by Talcott

Something of the older concern for justice and the protection of the consumer was carried over in the regulation of industry by the state. It is apparent that control by the buyer of goods had broken down as the producer and consumer grew more remote from each other. Even the more formal controls of the craft gilds had disappeared as those organizations declined. The Thirty Years' War, the civil wars in England, the disorders and confusion of the Fronde in France, all had created situations in which the standards of production were lowered to the point of damaging the markets of hitherto reliable centers of production. It is from this point of view that the redevelopment of industries, such as the important woolens trade, on a new basis of regulation by governmental agencies must be viewed. Colbert, for whom the kingdom was the prime consideration, thought it obvious that the weaver who wove bad cloth and thereby damaged the reputation of French woolens in the Levant was contributing perhaps to his own immediate prosperity but certainly to the injury of the trade as a whole and thus of the kingdom. The authors of the many pamphlets attacking the inferior quality of English woolens were probably not disinterested observers, but it is difficult to reject their universal testimony that the depersonalization of the market had lowered quality with resulting damage to the market as a whole. From the seventeenth century down to the twentieth, the European production system had to put its highest premiums on quantity rather than quality to keep up with the increasing demands upon it. In the historical process, mercantilist regulation was swept aside as anachronistic and the successful debasers won the approval of the economists and the historians. We are not yet free of the materialism of that season of the European climate, but the disparagement of mercantilist regulation is no longer to be accepted without question.

Enough has been said to indicate that any attempt to define mercantilism as an economic system encounters the irreducible fact that every thought and act of the so-called mercantilists was colored by political motivation. In the original intention the kings used the businessmen (whom they may be said to have created), but the original intention was very quickly matched by the development of vested interests and a very positive use of the kings by the businessmen to promote those interests. In their search for rationality, historians of mercantilism fail to take into account the reverse of the medal: if mercantilism was the pursuit of power by means of productivity, it was equally and perhaps more im-

Parsons, New York, 1930); R. H. Tawney, *Religion and the Rise of Capitalism* (London, 1925); H. M. Robertson, *Aspects of the Rise of Economic Individualism* (1933).

portantly the pursuit of profit by means of power. If these two aspects are kept in mind it may be possible to sketch a history of mercantilism as a social phenomenon that avoids some of the incoherence into which the nature of the subject leads able scholars, viewing it primarily as a problem of intellectual history.

Shaftesbury, who understood better than most what went on around him, knew very well how this new form of international friction had started. It was imitation of the Swedes and the Dutch, who had made business the affair of their governments. Gustavus Vasa had elevated Sweden to the level of a great power by organizing it as a great mining and lumber-producing system. The superior administrative system of Sweden had made it possible effectively to co-ordinate the economic life on a national scale.[7] Similarly, the dominant oligarchies of the northern Dutch towns had made of rebellion against Spanish tyranny a profit for merchants and of the political structure of the United Netherlands a tool of conquest and exploitation in both halves of the world. In France, Colbert resolved not only to emulate them, but to take what he could from the Dutch and destroy the rest. The English, enraged first by Dutch prosperity and then by that of France, struck at both.

Colbert, the eponymous hero of mercantilism, led France in a highly idealistic program of economic totalitarianism. With only a dim sense of what free French energies had accomplished, regardless of successive defeats and failures and of complete lack of confidence on the part of the business community, he labored to organize all of foreign business in the form of companies which he could dominate to the advantage of the king. All of them failed to attract adequate capital and all of them collapsed. The Company of the North served to establish some continuing connection with the Baltic area; the Company of the East Indies was wholly unsuccessful in the business sense; the Company of the Levant and the Company of the West Indies were only impediments to the development of the trade of Marseilles with the eastern Mediterranean and to the exploitation of the West Indies islands until they were given up.[8]

Within France, where Colbert was able to apply compulsion without encountering the test of competition, his program of economic totalitarianism was more successful and more creditable. "He led the plebs by the nose and ears to the sources of profit." Old forms of industry, particularly the gilds, were nationalized. New forms of industry, especially

---

[7] Eli P. Heckscher, "The Place of Sweden in Modern Economic History," *Economic History Review*, 4 (1932), 6.

[8] See below, pp. 89 and 218.

the *marchands-manufacturiers* (putters-out), who had established the textile industry in the countryside about Rouen, Lyons, Nîmes, Tours and other centers, outside the range of gild restrictions, were given a free hand. Standards of quality, not very intelligently conceived, were maintained by inspectors of manufactures. New industries, such as glass and silk from Italy, fine cloths from Holland, tapestry work at Paris and Beauvais, were established with capital from the king's revenue and with extensive privileges for the entrepreneurs. Under Colbert's impulsion, roads, rivers and canals were considerably improved and the Canal of the South, connecting the Mediterranean and the Bay of Biscay, was brought to completion. The freighting service was nationalized and extended. Colbert cherished the hope of wiping out the bizarre complex of internal barriers to trade, but all he achieved was the establishment of the northern third of the kingdom as a customs unit (the Five Great Farms) without eliminating the local tolls and other dues in the hands of privileged individuals. The infant industries were protected by a moderate tariff in 1664, and in 1667 Colbert, hoping to ruin the Dutch by cutting off the French market, made it prohibitive by doubling and tripling the duties. By the Code Savary (1673) he laid the foundations of a common law for commerce.

English mercantilism [9] was less idealistic, more complex, than Colbert's program. The unwritten, not to say unspoken, bargain at the return of Charles II from exile left economic affairs to parliament. Unhampered by a program, the parliament men showed themselves flexible and opportunistic in the pursuit of advantage to themselves at the expense of the Dutchmen, Frenchmen, English colonists and Englishmen at home who did not share in the advantages of parliamentary representation. As has been pointed out,[10] the dominating group in English society and politics was composed of landlords actively investing in business and of businessmen equally eager to invest in land. The complex origin of decisions made it possible to operate without regard to doctrine or principle, as opportunity seemed to offer advantage. Thus the cherished restriction on the export of bullion was relaxed in 1663 to facilitate the business of the East India Company, while a few years later the merchants trading with Massachusetts induced the Board of Trade to prohibit the export of coin to the American colonies in order to restrict the enterprise of their Boston cus-

[9] Much of Heckscher's picture of mercantilism is taken from English thought and action and his *Mercantilism* (2 vols., London, 1935) is valuable in this connection. The most encyclopedic coverage is provided by E. Lipson, *The Age of Mercantilism,* Volume II of his *Economic History of England.*

[10] G. N. Clark, *The Later Stuarts* (Oxford, 1934), 35–36.

tomers and competitors.[11] Since parliament was dominated by landlords, not unnaturally parliamentary mercantilism extended to agricultural interests. The export of grain was subtantially freed in 1663; on the other hand, the importation of beef from Ireland was severely restricted. The confinement of the underpaid worker to his own parish for poor relief and the new prison-like workhouses reveal as autocratic a disposition to use the mass of the population for the benefit of the ruling minority as anything in Holland or France.

The negative aspect, the will to destroy or cripple rivals, was as strong in England as in France. The pamphlet literature justifying the Second Dutch War reiterates the importance of reducing the commercial ascendency of the Dutch. The French advance aroused even more hostility. When Charles II was negotiating the Treaty of Dover with his sister,[12] he wrote her that the attempt in France to build up trade and sea power was such an occasion of jealousy in England that nothing solid could be done "until the greatest of [English] interests, namely commerce, had been guaranteed."[13] The jealousy did not decline and, as England veered away from France and toward Holland, culminated in total prohibition of French imports (1678). Savary recognized that the hostility to France was deep-set.[14] Englishmen, he claimed, were better treated than anyone else in France, while Frenchmen were treated worse than anyone else in England.

The same ruthless repression was applied to the supposedly helpless Englishmen in the colonies. English protectionists, reluctant to see an adequate money supply operate to promote competition with themselves, prevented the relaxation in favor of the colonies of the laws against the export of coin. The sixty to seventy exporters to New England were directly instrumental in securing the annulment of the Massachusetts charter in 1684 and inducing the Lords of Trade to subject all the colonies to the direct control of the crown.[15]

The prime expression of English mercantilism was, however, the Navigation Act, first enacted in 1651 and promptly re-enacted and strengthened by the Convention Parliament in 1660. Motivated chiefly by the

[11] Curtis Nettels, "British Policy and Colonial Money Supply," *Economic History Review,* 3 (1931), 219–45.

[12] See below, p. 99.

[13] Quoted by J. Morini-Comby, *op. cit.,* 65; see also, J. J. Jusserand, ed., *Instructions données aux ambassadeurs et ministres de France, XXV Angleterre,* II, 30.

[14] *Le parfait négociant* (1675), quoted by H. Hauser, *Les débuts du capitalisme,* 283–284.

[15] C. Nettels, *Money Supply in the American Colonies* (Madison, 1934), 157; C. M. Andrews, *The Colonial Background of the Revolution* (New Haven, 1931), 12–13.

desire to cut down Dutch ascendency in maritime commerce, it struck equally at the free development of the English colonies and at the prosperity of Scotland and Ireland. As it developed in succeeding years, it became a strait jacket for all trade that could be reached. By act of parliament foreign ships were barred from the colonies and from bringing goods from other countries to England. Export from the colonies was rigorously channeled through English markets. A faint trace of imperial thinking was to be detected in the definition of English ships, which included ships built in the colonies and manned by their citizens. Fortunately the administrative capacity of the English government did not equal the egoism of its commercial interests. An extensive system of evasion at home and abroad qualified the intended effects. The portentous authority of Adam Smith, who was really a mercantilist at heart, sanctioned a long-held view that the Navigation Act was justified by the great development of English shipping and maritime commerce in the century after its passage. His was a partial view, which overlooked the corresponding development in areas not affected by the act and even in areas, such as the colonial settlements, where its operation could only have been negative.

In the problem of construction and reconstruction faced by the Great Elector of Brandenburg-Prussia, mercantilism was hardly distinguishable from the welfare policy of modern states. His rationalization of the tax system, integration of his widespread territories by the improvement of transport and communication, encouragement of immigration, employment of experts, establishment of commerce colleges, promotion of industries new and old, toleration of religious variations—all conceived in the specifically mercantilist spirit of statism and absolutism—corresponded so completely to the needs of his depressed and disrupted society that, from a human point of view, it is impossible to withhold admiration.

The Great Elector followed the mercantilist fashions. His ventures in the West Indies and in Africa[16] were mainly motivated by imitation of the Dutch and the French and by a desire to share in the exploitation of the rest of the world. After his time, when the reconstruction problem had been solved, his system, like mercantilism elsewhere, became a bulwark of privilege and a pattern of conflict.

As a rationalist, Hobbes not unnaturally assumed that his Leviathan was operated from the head. With a more complex psychology and physiology we inevitably turn his figure of speech to conform to the patterns imposed by Freud, Watson and Pavlov. Leviathan responded to impulses from his whole organism. Among them, to labor the figure,

16 See below, p. 118.

those from the grasping hands were persistent and predominant. A Colbert might live in the dream of a national society of toilers laboring for the glory of the king. A Frederick William might labor all his days to remedy the economic deficiencies of his people. As in England, to change the figure to Aesop, the grasping hands soon learned to demand that they should be satisfied first. When Colbert and Frederick William were gone, mercantilism became a system of special privilege for particular groups.[17]

III. ABSOLUTISM AS FAÇADE: FRANCE [18]

Louis XIV professed absolutism but he did not achieve it. In fact, he froze the situation at a point of institutional lag. It was a century before the work he began was completed by the Revolution. The structure that he reared was more imposing than the absolutisms of Denmark, Sweden, Brandenburg or England, but behind the façade it was less nearly complete.

On March 8, 1661, Louis XIV took upon himself the whole responsibility of government. Cardinal Mazarin had died the day before, thus ending the succession of great ministers to whom the function of government had been enfeoffed. "To whom shall we address ourselves?" asked the archbishop of Paris. "To me," replied the young king, with an aplomb that was never to desert him, but which at the time covered an intense excitement. "It was the moment for which I had waited and which I had dreaded," he wrote in his *Mémoires*. It was the announcement that the king had undertaken the function of sovereign in the Hobbesian sense.

It was a function to which the nation had long summoned its kings. "The French nation was not subjected to the absolute monarchy, the nation created it." [19] The classical expression had been given by the estates-general of 1614: "No other power on earth, spiritual or temporal, has any authority in his [Louis XIII's] kingdom." However the absolutism might be condemned in the name of historic right or later in the name of natural right, it was not founded in force or fraud, but in general consent.

---

[17] See especially, C. W. Cole, *French Mercantilism, 1683–1700* (New York, 1943), and H. Rachel, *Der Merkantilismus in Brandenburg-Preussen* (*Forschungen zur brandenburgischen und preussishen Geschichte,* 40 Bd. 2. hälfte, Munich and Berlin, 1927), 221–66.

[18] The synthesis presented by E. Lavisse in Vol. VII, Parts 1 and 2 of the encyclopedic *Histoire de France,* which he also edited, is still basic both for a comprehensive organization of the data and for the valuable bibliographies, including accounts of the principal sources. For the particular subject here treated, James E. King, *Science and Rationalism in the Government of Louis XIV, 1661–1683* (Baltimore, 1949), is also of primary importance.

[19] Augustin Thierry, *Éssai sur le tiers état* (Paris, 1850), ch. IX.

In the monarchy rested the hope of Frenchmen to escape the multiplied tyrannies of anachronistic localisms.

Between 1661 and 1685 this hope was to a degree fulfilled and, to a degree, frustrated. For government by feudal nobles who claimed their offices as heritage, Louis XIV and his ministers substituted government by trained bureaucrats. The military forces, which had been autonomous bands of *condottieri,* they converted into obedient instruments of the king and his ministers. The jurisdiction of the *parlements,* whose members claimed their places as vested interest, hereditary or purchased, was subjected to the higher jurisdiction of the king's council. When the *parlements* claimed the right to question the propriety of the king's decrees, they were humiliated, silenced and ignored. The remaining provincial estates were eliminated as obstacles to the royal will by a combination of bullying and bribery. The towns, ruined by corrupt oligarchies, were subjected to complete controls.

Louis XIV immediately repudiated all claims to place in his government based on birth, rank or custom. He assembled "all those whom he customarily called—and dismissed them most civilly with the statement that, when he had need of their good advice, he would call them." [20] As a political order, the nobility had ceased to function. The nobles retained their social prestige and their perquisites of lordship, but by investment in bourgeois enterprises, by marriage into bourgeois families and by the competition of ennobled bourgeois they were becoming merely a privileged caste. Many of them received the perquisites of offices which had been reduced to merely formal functions. The governors of provinces were nobles, but they were subject to orders transmitted by the intendants. Nobles were expected to serve in the army, but even there were put to school by Louvois before they were commissioned, and as higher officers were sharply controlled by him. In the navy they had to compete with men to whom the sea was a profession, such as Duquesne and Jean Bart. Many of them were domesticated to courtly functions of a parasitical type. Louis XIV kept them fed, amused and hopeful of royal favors.

At the beginning of the reign a part of the nobility were not yet domesticated, but lived wild lives in the country as robber knights. The *Grands Jours* of Auvergne,[21] a special court set up in 1665 to repress "the murders, abductions, rapes, robberies and extortions" perpetrated by the

---

[20] Minutes of the session of the Council of Three, March 9, 1661, in J. de Boislisle, *Conseil de 1661* (Paris, 1905), I, 1.

[21] E. Fléchier, *Mémoires sur les grands jours d'Auvergne* (edited by P. A. Chéruel, Paris, 1856); Baudoin, *Journal sur les grands jours en Languedoc, 1666–1667* (edited by Le Blanc, Paris, 1889).

gentlemen of Auvergne and the neighboring provinces, convicted and sentenced many noblemen, most of them fugitives. Some castles were destroyed and some lords lost their rights of justice. The powerful in Auvergne and in the other parts of the kingdom like Languedoc, Guienne and Bordeaux, where *Grands Jours* were also held, learned that there was royal justice that might reach them.

The provincial estates, of which twelve remained in 1661 and three more were added by the reunion of Cambrai, Walloon Flanders and Franche-Comté, were mere remnants of the feudal oligarchy. By a combination of bullying and bribery, they were reduced to subservience to the intendant.[22] In his *Mémoires* the king wrote, "The estates commenced to use their liberty only to make their submission more pleasing to me."

The ancient *parlements,* almost coeval with the kingship, continued to administer justice. Among the nine courts (increased to twelve by 1685), the *parlement* of Paris had achieved a certain ascendency as the high court of the kingdom. The position of the *parlements* in general and of the *parlement* of Paris in particular as courts of last resort was reduced by the development of the practice of "evoking" to the king's council cases of particular interest because of the issues or persons involved.

The political ambitions of the *parlements* had been dashed in the Fronde, but they attempted to retain their privilege to restrain the legislative action of the king. The ultimate legalization of a decree was its registration by the *parlement,* which, in the weaker days of the kingship, had acquired the right to decide whether to accept it. Even in his minority, Louis XIV had met the issue by declaring to the *parlement* of Paris that it had no function of deliberating about his decrees. In 1665 the *parlement* was silenced in humiliating fashion. Lamoignon, the premier president, ambitious for favor, undertook to prevent the *parlement* from meeting to discuss edicts already registered. The king, learning of the matter, ordered the chambers convoked because he wished "to make a striking example either of the entire submission of that company or of my just severity in punishing it." The chambers of the *parlement* assembled, the premier president communicated the instructions of the king, and in complete silence the members filed out. The practice of registration, and even the right of remonstrance, if the king did not expressly forbid it, were maintained, but in 1673 new letters-patent directed immediate registration of all edicts, after which, within a limited time, remonstrances might be made. Unless the king chose to make some amendment, no

[22] A. Rébillon, "Les états de Bretagne et les progrès de l'autonomie provinciale au XVIIIe siècle," *Revue historique,* 159 (1928), 261–90.

further discussion was to be carried on. The king had obtained "the entire submission" of the *parlement*. Colbert wrote to the intendant of Grenoble, "It is of no use to write about speeches made in *parlement*. As you know, the noises of *parlement* are no longer in season."

The towns retained much of their medieval character as corporations. Most of them had been ruined by the ruthless and greedy oligarchies that governed them. Their financial difficulties enabled the crown to subvert their autonomy. The government took them over. Their finances were reformed by a radical repudiation of the existing debt and their future activity was subjected to the control of the crown. The old offices were retained for their ceremonial and traditional value, but new ones were created and sold, often repurchased by the town. The gilds were in effect nationalized and incorporated into Colbert's industrial system.

Thus, from top to bottom, the whole traditional system was preserved in form and vitiated in fact. The rights to perquisites and prestige were generally maintained; the right to govern was taken away from every element that could claim sanction as against the king.

Within the very definite limits of a negative formulation, the work of Louis XIV was complete. No one but the king could claim or exercise power on a national scale or limit by traditional right the power of the king to act. On the other hand, the remaining century of the *ancien régime* was to show that Louis XIV fell far short of the possibilities and of the requirements for effectively co-ordinating the positive forces of French society. Although he defeudalized his kingdom, he remained himself feudal. He believed it was enough for a government to be strong. The habitual resort of his government to military violence—to suppress rebellious peasants, to enlist reluctant recruits, to collect taxes, to put down Protestantism—not only offends our susceptibilities but marks the degree of his failure as creator of the absolute state.

Louis XIV governed France with an essentially new machine that was expressive of his absolutist and monarchical intention. Nominally, his primary agencies were a series of councils. The high council (*conseil d'en haut, conseil des trois*), composed of his closest advisers, in practice outranked all the others and decided all major questions. The council of parties was a somewhat larger group which discussed the same kinds of question. Both these councils were able to "evoke" cases from the established courts at any stage in the procedure. The council of finance and the council of war were somewhat more specialized. The council of conscience—the king and his confessor—handled appointments to bishoprics and abbacies and other questions of church politics.

The membership of these councils was indeterminate, wholly dependent upon the king's will. The practice of establishing ministers as officers of state by letters-patent was discontinued. If a man was summoned by the king, he was a minister; if he was not summoned, he ceased to be a minister. The ministers henceforth were merely the king's servants. "Never as long as you live," wrote Colbert to his son, who was to succeed him, "send out anything in the king's name without his express approval."

Louis XIV did not intend to give his whole confidence to any one person. He gave his partial confidence to only a few, never more than five at one time, and only to seventeen advisers in the course of his entire reign. He began with three, Le Tellier for military affairs, Fouquet for finance, and Hugues de Lionne for diplomacy. Colbert promptly displaced Fouquet; Le Tellier retired in 1668 to the honorific position of chancellor and was succeeded by his son, the marquis of Louvois; Lionne after the disappointments of the treaties of Nimwegen gave way in more routine fashion to Pomponne. Colbert and Louvois attained an ascendency in their respective fields that reduced their fellow councillors to the status of assistants and even at times compelled the king against his personal judgment.

Both Colbert and Louvois, like the king, were hard workers and exacted hard work from their subordinates. Colbert's chosen instruments were the intendants, who became the essential agents of such unity as France achieved under the monarchy. They were not a deliberate invention. Colbert began his ministry with a comprehensive inquiry into the state of every part of the kingdom (1664), carried out by the *maîtres de requêtes* (masters in chancery). After several years in their "generalities," they became indispensable. In every part of the kingdom the governors, the military, the corporations, the clergy, the financial officers, were confronted with a disciplined agent of the king who could do and did do almost everything. Nicholas Foucault,[23] who left memoirs of his life as intendant at Montauban, Pau and Poitiers, hunted down vagabonds, inspected militia, reformed courts, surveyed rivers, converted Protestants, collected historical material, inspected the tobacco farm, presided at tribunals. The letters of Nicholas Arnoul, intendant at Marseilles from 1665 to 1674, show how intendants overcame local and personal resistance to even the most beneficial projects.[24] The letters of Colbert to his son,

[23] *Mémoires de Nicholas-Joseph Foucault* (edited by F. Baudry, *Collection des documents inédits sur l'histoire de France, première série: histoire politique*, Paris, 1839).
[24] G. Rambert, *Nicholas Arnoul, intendant des galères à Marseille, 1665–1674* (Marseilles, 1931).

who succeeded him, show how responsibility was imposed on an incompetent.[25]

IV. THE CONTROL OF THE ARMY AND THE NAVY [26]

The political revolution of which the monarchy was the expression was nowhere more clearly manifest than in the changed relations of the fighting forces. Army and navy, in the sense of the totality of national forces organized and directed through an official hierarchy culminating in a single command, became for the first time valid expressions in French politics. "The army has become a republic," wrote Le Tellier in 1643 to Mazarin, "with as many cantons or provinces as there are lieutenant generals." The Condé and the Turenne of the Spanish wars and of the Fronde were champions who disposed of themselves. The Condé and the Turenne of the Devolution War were instruments of the war department.

Under Michel Le Tellier and Louvois the army was enlarged to a level thitherto unknown in Europe—about 400,000 effectives—and administratively reorganized with full responsibility from bottom to top. The enlistment system remained crude and ineffective, but its deficiencies were made up by a large employment of foreign troops. Both Le Tellier and Louvois made great advances in the system of army supply. The individual soldier was made more effective by the introduction of an elaborate discipline, beginning with the manual of arms.[27]

The officer personnel was equally subjected to the crown. Cadets were put to school. The colonelcies and captaincies remained "venal," but the actual direction of troops was in the hands of more professional lieutenant colonels and lieutenants. To reduce the proprietary airs of the colonels, the regiments were gradually given territorial names.

Even the generals were subjected to orders. Turenne defied the repeated orders of Louvois and crossed the Rhine in order to keep the bishop of Münster in the French alliance,[28] but Dufay, the successful defender of Philippsburg, was threatened with cashiering and imprisonment for hav-

---

25 J. E. King, *op. cit.*, 112–14.

26 For the reorganization of the army, see Louis André, *Michel Le Tellier et l'organisation de l'armée monarchique* (Paris, 1906); Camille Rousset, *Histoire de Louvois et de son administration politique et militaire* (4 vols., Paris, 1861–1863); R. G. Picavet, *Les dernières armées de Turenne, 1660–1675* (Paris, 1914); P. Lazard, *Vauban* (Paris, 1934); for the reorganization of the navy, the almost classical work of Ch. de la Roncière, *Histoire de la marine française*, Tome V: *Colbert* (Paris, 1920).

27 See plate No. 32.

28 Mary C. Trevelyan, *William III and the Defense of Holland* (London, 1930), 226.

ing a soldier shot without trial.[29] To Madame de Sévigné it seemed that the armies were moved about solely at the will of the minister.

The concentration of command was justified by the organization of a staff of high technical capacity. Vauban, who elevated fortification to a science, Du Metz, who did for artillery what Vauban did for engineering, Martinet, whose name has become the symbol for strict military discipline, Chamlay, who, according to his admirers, knew every creek and pond in the kingdom, constituted a galaxy almost unmatched in the history of armies. "M. de Chamlay can camp without me, but I cannot camp without M. de Chamlay," wrote Turenne. The technical effectiveness of the Le Tellier machine made subordination to it as inevitable as it was advantageous. The army became a system.

Relatively powerful and efficient though it was, in the external areas for which it was primarily designed, the army of Louis XIV was destined to frustration.[30] As an instrument for maintaining the structure of power within the kingdom, it successfully met every test. Nothing could be improvised to meet the elaborate machine of Louvois on equal terms. Every year of the reign was troubled with risings in one or several parts of the kingdom. Except for the resistance of the Protestants in the Cévennes after the Revocation, the reasons of the revolts were always some aggravation of the burden of taxation. Sometimes they extended geographically over a whole province, as in Guienne in 1674, in Brittany in 1675. At no time did a rising unite the whole society of a province or a region. The alignment was almost uniform—the "canaille" against the nobility, the magistrates and the bourgeois. Sometimes the insurrections seemed threatening enough to evoke the attention of Europe. In 1670, when the Vivarais was in revolt, the Venetian ambassador wrote that "important changes can be expected in the affairs of Europe if the rebels keep on gaining." In 1675, when Brittany was aflame, "great hopes" were entertained at Cologne.

The risings, however, were always deficient in leadership and organization. When the troops released by the end of a campaign were directed against a rebellious region, the rebels fled and the innocent were left to pay for the guilty. Systematic hanging and quartering was the milder aspect of the king's vengeance. In Brittany the soldiery devastated an area four leagues wide, pillaging every house and committing atrocities that surpass the standards of modern wartime propaganda. The brutalities of the dragonnades in the "conversion" of Protestants were only less hor-

[29] A. de Saint-Léger and P. Sagnac, *La préponderance française* (Paris, 1935), 201.
[30] See below, Chapter Five.

rible. The persistent loyalty of the rebels to the king constituted a phenomenon that political science has not yet encompassed. The rebellion was always against the local grandee, the intendant, the tax collector; "if the king only knew" their oppressions, he would surely do his people justice.

At the hands of Colbert, the navy underwent much the same process of construction and discipline as did the army under Louvois. At the beginning of the personal reign it showed the consequences of long neglect. In 1665 Colbert took over the administration and began the foundation of a true navy. To meet the immediate deficiencies he bought ships in Holland, Denmark and Sweden. At the same time he organized the timber supply, the naval stores industry of the Landes, the cannon foundries in Nivernais, in Burgundy, at Lyons, in Périgord, and the sailmaking industry in Brittany. Brest became the principal shipbuilding center for the navy. By 1667 the results were already visible: France had a navy that England and Holland feared as a rival. Brest and Rochefort on the Atlantic, Toulon on the Mediterranean, were improved as ports and fortified as bases. Dunkerque, after its purchase from England, was made into a base for the famous corsairs of Jean Bart.

The recruitment of crews was a serious problem. The Mediterranean galleys were at first manned by slaves, mostly Turks, but as the requirements grew larger, increasing use was made of convicts. The Huguenots furnished a considerable contingent. In 1687 six hundred were serving in the galleys of Marseilles. On the Atlantic side, the old system of impressment at the outbreak of war of all sailors to be found in the ports was replaced in 1673 by a "sailor's roster" (*inscription maritime*). All sailors were enrolled and required to serve one year in three in the navy, six months on duty and the rest of the year on half-pay. The "sailor's roster" caused much protest among the sailors and especially among the shipowners interested in the fisheries. Colbert persisted and by a combination of diplomacy and force imposed his will. The officers also were brought under discipline by the establishment of the intendants of the navy, who took over from the commanders the administration of justice, police and finance. This double system led to friction, but Colbert's energetic support of his intendants brought order into the service without stifling the military initiative of the commanders.

Like the civil administration, the army and navy became the responsive instruments of the royal will. As a result of the work of Louvois and Colbert, the military strength of France on land and sea attained a level hitherto unknown.

All that was lacking was the wisdom to abstain from its use.

V. THE WORK OF COLBERT: ECONOMIC AND LEGAL UNIFICATION [31]

Colbert, son of a draper and man of business, undertook to contribute to the glory of his king by making him rich. Within the limits of his time he was an economic determinist. He recognized that the rise and fall of Venice, the rise of Holland, the momentary ascendency of Spain, were all connected with their prosperity or impoverishment. With this simple logic he undertook to convert the king and the nation to the ideal of money-making. He required an industrious, economical king, who would live within his budget, render justice to his people in person and organize his army for effectiveness rather than parade. The people were to work, the rich by investing in commerce and industry rather than bonds or offices, the poor at the old trades or new ones that Colbert would import from other lands along with the craftsmen whom he would induce to immigrate. The nonproductive elements in society were to be put to work. In the revolutionary atmosphere of his first years as minister, Colbert dared even to contemplate the suppression of the monasteries and of the legal profession.

The burdens of taxation were to be equalized and reduced and the barriers of customs lines and administrative variations within the kingdom were to be eliminated, so the industrious would have an unrestricted national market for their productions.

Thus, France with its twenty million people and its great resources would produce its own goods and be free of the tribute it paid to the Dutch, the Hamburgers and the English. France with a few hundred vessels was dependent upon the Dutch with their fifteen thousand ships and the English who were expanding their small share. France would have its own merchant ships to carry on its own trade. The rivals of the king would be humbled and ruined and France would easily become supreme in Europe.

Colbert was frustrated in almost every phase of his grandiose dream.

He purposed to create a free national market, but all he was able to accomplish was to clear the northern third of the kingdom, the region of the Five Great Farms, of the numerous local customs barriers, so that

[31] Basic to all later work on Colbert is P. Clément's edition of the *Lettres, instructions et mémoires de Colbert* (10 vols., Paris, 1861–1882) and his *Histoire de Colbert et de son administration* (2 vols., 1874; 3rd ed., Paris, 1892). In the *Histoire de France* (VII, Parts 1 and 2), E. Lavisse provides a synthesis of the work of Colbert that has hardly been equaled (and here has been generally followed).

all duties were collected at the frontier. The Farm-General (which was a consolidation of the Five) felt obliged to extend its activities far within this frontier, and, as evidenced by Colbert's complaints at the end of his life, the last state was not better than the first. Two other general divisions of the kingdom (each with wide local diversities) remained unchanged in any essential, "the provinces reputed foreign," that is, all the older provinces not in the Five Great Farms, and "the provinces actually foreign," those recently acquired. Over all these parts of the kingdom a complex of tolls (*peages*), many of which had fallen into the hands of privileged persons or towns, continued to burden intercourse without any performance of the road repair, bridge repair, or other obligations still nominally associated with them.

Colbert accepted the bad organization of the finances and hoped to raise the productivity of the country to the point where it could endure even greater burdens. To that end he spared neither himself nor such of his king's subjects as he could enlist in old or new forms of economic activity.

He was a townsman and lacked a genuine feeling for the country and for the undistinguished mass of tillers of the soil. Nevertheless, he had his ideas. He hated the vineyards, which took up good land that might better be used for grain. One of his most substantial achievements was the establishment of silk culture. He cherished the forests and if he did not succeed very well in his attempt to recover those lost to the royal domain, by his Ordinance of the Forests (1669) he did much to stop the deforestation that Ronsard and Palissy had recognized even in their time. He established horse-breeding as a substantial industry in Normandy, Poitou and Berry.

The supply of grain was handicapped by primitive farming methods and still more by the absence of a free market. Colbert was unable to break down the fear of famine and the narrow restrictions by which each local market sought to protect itself. In the latter years of the century, the pressure of urban demand broke down the old restrictions in the region of Paris and illustrated what free trade could do to stimulate production. In most of the kingdom the old localistic restrictions remained and as a consequence famine continued to be a familiar phenomenon. When the harvest was good, Colbert permitted export, but always with a kind of fearful caution.

It was not from agriculture but from industry that Colbert expected the profitable expansion that would serve his end. In spite of his survey of 1663, he supposed everything remained to be done. The people were to be cajoled and impressed to labor. They were to produce large families to supply the hands necessary for the huge tasks he planned. Foreigners who had techniques unknown in France were attracted by handsome rewards. Emigration of Frenchmen, on the other hand, was a breach of loyalty. Beggars were to be put to work in mass industries such as soap-making and coarse hosiery. Colbert tried to divert the charity practiced by the monasteries to supplying the poor with industrial materials. The rich were to be disgusted with bonds so that they would invest in enterprise.

The control of industry passed to the crown. The old institutions, gilds, regulation, privileges, remained, but were co-ordinated in a national system. Some industries, such as the Gobelin tapestry works, were reconstituted as departments of the government. Others, such as the Van Robais fine-cloth industry at Arras, the Beauvais tapestry works and the Venetian glass industry, were operated by entrepreneurs subsidized by the king. Colbert intended to favor private enterprise. "Everything that restrains the liberty and the number of merchants is worthless," he wrote. Nevertheless, he did not hesitate to command the Norman merchants to establish a linen industry in Burgundy or the hosiery merchants to set up establishments in Auvergne. He helped his entrepreneurs when he could, but often he was compelled to put them off. He pressed the provincial estates to do their part, with some success in Burgundy and Languedoc. He attempted with very little success to make over the municipalities into instruments for the promotion of industry.

Over all these activities Colbert tried to rule like a pedagogue, only to find himself baffled by corresponding resistance. The buildings and the wars of the king reduced his budget for promotion from over half a million *livres* in 1669 to eight thousand *livres* for each of the years 1676, 1677 and 1678. He totally failed to interest the investing public in his industrial enterprises. His system of control was vitiated by conflicts of jurisdiction and by the complete lack of sympathy with his purposes in nearly all the local oligarchies. None of the workers would work as he wished.

Nevertheless, with all his disappointments, he could record a considerable list of new industrial establishments that he claimed for his efforts. Sugar refineries, iron works, glass works, textile industries of various sorts, did get established, whether because of the impulsions of Colbert or because of the general stimulus that business was feeling in all parts of the European world, is impossible to say. He was proud to believe that he had succeeded in ruining the lace industry of Genoa and Venice, and in cutting seriously into the glass industry of the latter. He put the king's ambassadors to bribing foreign craftsmen to bring their skills to France. The luxury lines to which he devoted his most earnest efforts all entered into the prosperity of France in the eighteenth century.

Increased production was the necessary condition of Colbert's program, but the point of realization from his point of view was international trade. It was the means, he held, of increasing "the power and the glory of His Majesty and lowering that of his enemies and rivals." When he began, the commerce of France was not inconsiderable, but it passed through intermediaries, Dutch and English. Though the much quoted figures of six hundred vessels for France and fifteen thousand for Holland may be regarded with some skepticism, it remains certain that French participation in external trade was anomalously low. The cost of shipbuilding in France and the cost of operating French ships was double that for Holland. The French were well established in the Levant and had substantial footholds in the West Indies and in Canada. The colonial trade, however, was almost wholly in the hands of the Dutch and the English. The market for Canadian furs was concentrated at London and Amsterdam. Dutch merchants supplied slaves to the French islands and sold the products of the colonists in Europe.

Colbert's concepts of business and economic life were quite naïve. He apparently believed that the application of his all-powerful master's authority would solve all problems, external as well as internal. Like most of his contemporaries, he believed in tariffs. When the Dutch retaliated for his tariffs of 1664 and 1667, he became as bellicose as Louvois. When the war ensued in 1673, he supposed the expected victory would resolve his problem. He proposed that not only the Dutch colonies, but also Dutch commercial and financial institutions be redistributed among the French. Should annexation be impossible, he urged that Dutch wealth be used to end poverty in France and thus make possible the collection of more revenue. Although the Treaty of Nimwegen put an end to his cherished tariff policy and committed France to a policy of reciprocal free trade, he continued to advocate the re-establishment of the tariff of 1667.

Colbert projected a national system of companies to exploit the commerce of the whole world. The prosperity of the India Companies of Holland and England led him to suppose that he could emulate them by means of organizations which he would create and control. The East Indies Company (1664), the West Indies Company (1664), the Company of the North (1669) and the Levant Company (1670) were to be so many bureaucratic instruments in his hand, of which he was to direct the capital investment, the materials of trade, the reception by the consumers and the returns to France. The capital of the East Indies Company was extorted from nobles of the court who hoped for the king's favor and from officers of finance and justice who were enjoying it. The bourgeois evaded the promotion efforts of Colbert's agents. The capital collected remained insufficient. Colbert expected the Levant Company to carry on its trade with textiles from Carcassonne rather than with silver from Spain. When he discovered that the French textiles were not acceptable in the Levantine markets, he could only rage at the manufacturers. The French colonists in the West Indies were called upon to accept the expensive Negroes brought in by the West Indies Company and to seek no further for their supply, although it remained deficient. The sugar, coffee and indigo which they produced were to be brought back to France in spite of the overwhelming demand of the English colonies on the near-by continent. The capital to supply the ships for the Baltic trade was simply not available to the Company of the North.

In short, Colbert, in spite of his training as a businessman and in spite of a comprehensive vision that Lavisse does not hesitate to call "Cartesian," "philosophic," seems never to have correlated his ends with the means available or to have recognized that his presence in a proposed organization aroused distrust and hostility. He apparently believed sincerely the myth that the king and himself as the king's minister had only to command. By a contradiction that is not easy to explain in a minister who had created the efficient system of intendants at home, he allowed the control of affairs abroad to fall into the hands of unsympathetic incompetents. He neither succeeded in closing France to foreign trade nor in appropriating the commerce of the world. None of his companies prospered and all of them had to be eliminated before French commerce could prosper.

His success at home contrasted strongly with his failures abroad. Even at home he was defeated in his laudable aim to equalize and lower the burden of taxation. Nevertheless, he did succeed in establishing new industries, expanding old ones, building a merchant marine of respectable dimensions, preserving the natural resources, improving the routes of communication and the organization of services, co-ordinating the law of commerce and raising the social level of the businessman.

His mistakes and his successes were on an imperial scale. In every part of the network of French economic activity, he effected (at what cost!) a co-ordination to the national purpose, which he would have called "the grandeur of the king." Over a diversity of economic localisms as various as the elements of Hellas he imposed patterns of community. He grooved the ways for the creation of a national economic policy.

Legal unification [32] was one of the great objectives which Colbert held before the eyes of his royal master as "a design worthy of his greatness, of his spirit and of his age." It was perhaps impossible on any terms and at any rate was quite impossible to Louis XIV with his repugnance to revolutionary methods. The diversity of law in detail and in spirit was so deep-set that it seemed hopeless to achieve anything approaching Roman or English unity. What remained was a process of codifying certain limited elements of law.

Procedure, already in the hands of the royal courts, was reduced to a common basis by the Civil Ordinance of 1667 and by the Criminal Ordinance of 1670. In 1665 a council of justice, with not a single member of the *parlement* in its membership, but frequently presided over by the king himself, began its five-year task. The civil procedure was simplified and facilitated, while the criminal procedure was rendered very severe. The right of counsel, the right to abstain from self-incrimination, the right of confrontation, were denied the accused and torture was retained, even though the council thought it "indecent" to prescribe the forms in an ordinance.

The Ordinance of Commerce, the Ordinance of the Marine, and the Colonial Code, from the nature of the subjects to which they applied, offered a less obstructed field for royal legislation. The Ordinance of 1673 was a deliberate synthesis of current practice among the merchants of the nation. It set up a system of special "jurisdictions" for commerce, which has proved useful in France down to our own day. Indeed, the whole code, restudied in the 1780's and under Napoleon, has had a continuous life. The Marine Ordinance of 1681 performed a similar service for admiralty law. The *Code Noir*, as the colonial code was almost always called, was published in March, 1685, "to maintain in the islands the discipline of the Catholic church," especially as against Jews and Protestants, and "to regulate the status of slaves." The Roman definition of slavery was adopted: the slave was a chattel. Nevertheless, the code provided colonial intendants a legal basis for protecting the slaves against their owners. The power of life and death was taken away from the owner; the obligation to supply food was established.

Despite the revolutionary impulse of Colbert and Pussort to sweep away the whole complex of ancient structures and build in good baroque

---

[32] Paul Viollet, *Histoire du droit civil français* (Paris, 1893); the legislative work of Louis XIV is summarized in A. de Saint-Léger and Philippe Sagnac, *La prépondérance française*, 176–80.

and Cartesian, a single new structure of law for the whole of France was not achieved. Nevertheless, the legislative work of Louis XIV during Colbert's ministry was considerable and constituted a very necessary preliminary to the work of Maupeou, of the later Lamoignon and of Napoleon.

VI. THE CO-ORDINATION OF RELIGION

The co-ordination of religious life with the other aspects of the all-inclusive state was difficult. The papacy, the Jansenists [33] and the Protestants constituted oppositions that any politician might have feared. It is evidence of the solidity of the monarchy that it was able to achieve a substantial victory over each of the three.

When in the face of a hostile papacy the French clergy had welcomed Henry IV at the foot of the altar of Notre-Dame, the secular alliance between the clergy and the monarchy had received its final seal. The clergy, nevertheless, still constituted a political order which the monarchy was unable to reduce. The assembly of the clergy, which met every five years to grant the king a "free gift," was the only body in France with which Louis XIV condescended to discuss his intentions and his needs. Colbert wished to abolish it, but Louis XIV, less revolutionary, chose to manage it by less direct means.

He commanded the spontaneous support of the national clergy in his conflict with the pope over the issue of "Gallicanism." "Gallicanism" was, in effect, the assertion of the existence of a French church, with a discipline and a tradition independent of Rome. The Gallicanism of the bishops, who desired autonomy in their dioceses, differed from the Gallicanism of the civilians, who wished to subject the church to the king. With the support of the ministers, especially Colbert, of the *parlements* and of the Sorbonne, the minority (about one-third) of the bishops who were Gallican in the civilian sense dominated the assembly.[34]

The issue was fought out over the question of the *régale*. This was the right, which the king exercised in all of the kingdom but the south, of taking over the revenues of a vacant bishopric. In 1673 a royal edict extended it to the whole kingdom. Clement X, who had been elected by

[33] For Jansenism, see Chapter Six, "The Search for God," below.

[34] V. Martin, *Le gallicanisme politique et le clergé de France* (Paris, 1930); H. Brémond, "La Sorbonne, le roi et le pape," *Le Corréspondant*, 101 (1929), 641–63; Paul Dudon, "Gallicanisme politique et théologie gallicane," *Récherches de sciences religieuses*, 19 (1929), 513–29.

French influence, was complaisant, but when Innocent XI became pope in 1678, he violently condemned this encroachment upon the rights of the church in France. The French church did not welcome his intrusion. In 1680 the assembly of the clergy in a letter to the king expressed "its extreme displeasure at the pontifical letter." Incited by Colbert, the Gallicans grew more violent and, on his side, Innocent XI more intransigent, until it seemed, as the English ambassador put it, "soon both countries [England and France] would be of the same religion." Fifty-two bishops, permitted to assemble "spontaneously," proposed a national council or, at least, a special assembly of the clergy to settle the question. Louis XIV drew back. Catholic by inheritance, by education and by policy, he did not choose to be head of the church. He called in Bossuet, bishop of Meaux, former tutor of the Dauphin and powerful antagonist of Jansenism and of Protestantism, to dampen the revolutionary temper incited by Colbert.[35]

The special assembly was held, but the king had reason to be "very content" with Bossuet's effort. The quarrel of Louis XIV with Innocent XI was sustained by the passage by the assembly of the Four Articles of 1682. On one point the Articles were quite clear: the king was not subject in any way to the head of the church. The other articles were more ambiguous suggestions of possible consequences. The superiority of the general council was mentioned; the liberties of the Gallican church, without being defined, were maintained; and the infallibility of the pope was alleged to be dependent on the consent of the church. In spite of fulminations from Rome, the Four Articles were published and included in the curricula of the seminaries. The assembly then began to discuss the establishment of a patriarchate of France. At this point the king recognized the evil consequences of the assembly and dissolved it. Innocent XI still would not compromise. He refused to invest bishops who adhered to the Four Articles. Before he died in 1689, thirty-five vacancies existed because of what Louis XIV called Innocent XI's stubbornness.

Innocent XII was more pliable but not less pertinacious, and the issue was not settled until 1693. The king got the *régale,* but at the price of abandoning the whole program of 1682 and the Gallican bishops.

France remained Roman Catholic; the king escaped the problem of dealing with the corporate church, while his effective power over it was undiminished.

[35] Alfred Barry, "Bossuet and the Gallican Declaration of 1682," *Catholic Historical Review,* 15 (1929), 143–53.

VII. THE REVOCATION OF THE EDICT OF NANTES [36]

Among the various divisions that complicated the problem of government, Louis XIV found himself king of two nations on the same soil, each ready to fly at the other's throat. Expedient though it had been in 1597, the Edict of Nantes had operated to freeze the differentiation between the two religious communities, which had separate institutions of government and of education as well as of worship. The Catholics and the Protestants hated each other and in the south, the west, in Picardy and in Alsace often came into open conflict. The long-standing antipathy between the two communities had been further intensified by the religious revival in the Catholic church and especially by the development of lay societies devoted to the promotion of piety and morality, such as the Company of the Holy Sacrament.[37] The Protestants were only a small minority, probably something more than a million and certainly not much more than a million and a half, but they remained clearly separate, marked by a certain superiority in industry, commerce and finance. Explicitly and implicitly, they challenged the beliefs of the overwhelming majority.

When Louis XIV began his personal reign, he was disposed to continue the policy of Richelieu and Mazarin and to permit the Protestants to live in their own way. As had been officially recognized in 1652, they had demonstrated a peculiar loyalty during the Fronde.[38] Their loyalty was not enough to save them. Richelieu and Mazarin had found it easy to protect them from the enemies of their government. Louis XIV could not escape his friends. The assembly of the clergy promptly renewed and persistently maintained their attack on the Edict of Nantes. In 1665 the assembly proposed a whole program. With some hesitation, the king yielded. The general plan was to construe with literal strictness the provisions of the

[36] E. Lavisse, *op. cit.,* VII, Part 2, 39–81; A. de Saint-Léger and P. Sagnac, *op. cit.,* 71–76, 187–200, 242–46; F. Puaux and A. Sabatier, *Études sur la révocation de l'édit de Nantes* (Paris, 1886); H. M. Baird, *The Huguenots and the Revocation of the Edict of Nantes* (2 vols., London, 1895).

[37] The religious revival is the subject of the great work of Henri Brémond, *Histoire littéraire du sentiment religieux en France, depuis la fin des guerres de religion jusqu'à nos jours* (6 vols., Paris, 1916–1922; Eng. tr., 3 vols., London, 1928–1936); a briefer summation in Louis Prunel, *La rénaissance catholique en France au XVIIᵉ siècle* (Paris, 1921); for the Company of the Holy Sacrament, Prunel, *op. cit.;* R. Allier, *La cabale des dévots, 1627–1666* (Paris, 1902); A. Rébelliau, "Un épisode de l'histoire religieuse du XVIIᵉ siècle," *Revue des deux mondes,* July 1, August 1, September 1, 1903; August 15, 1908; October 15, November 1, 1909.

[38] A. Galland, "Les pasteurs français . . . et la royauté de droit divin, de l'édit d'Alais à la révocation (1629–1685)," *Bulletin de la société de l'histoire du protestantisme français,* 77 (1928), 225–41, 413–22.

Edict. Since national synods had not been explicitly permitted, they were forbidden; provincial synods, which had been provided for, continued to meet, but were forbidden to communicate with each other. The Edict permitted chapels where they had existed in 1597; those built since were to be destroyed.

Two methods were available to convert the Huguenots—persuasion and authority. Persuasion was seriously attempted. According to the distinguished historian of the Huguenots,[39] the Reformed church under the Edict had lost much of its original spiritual vigor. Many conspicuous Huguenots, chief among whom was the great Marshal Turenne, returned to the Catholic church. The spiritual impulsion of Bérulle, Olier, St. Vincent de Paul and others had operated powerfully at the centers, but it had not yet been generalized throughout the country. Thus, persuasion was ineffective against the educated clergy and the close confessional discipline of the Huguenots. The government tried to reinforce verbal persuasion with money. In 1676 a converted Huguenot, Pellisson of the Academy, invented the "Conversion Fund." At the expense of the king and the church a sum, averaging about six *livres,* was to be provided for each convert. The total result of all these measures was disappointing.

The resort to force lacked sanction. The European position of France involved the important Treaty of Nimwegen with the United Provinces, and treaties of alliance with Sweden and Brandenburg, all warmly Protestant countries. The popes, well aware that force might also be used against Catholic minorities, while they approved the negative pressures applied against Protestantism since 1661, formally disapproved conversion by bargain or by force.[40] The king himself needed to be converted from his life of open sin. Ably assisted by the king's confessor, Père La Chaise, the ex-Huguenot, Madame de Maintenon, who ultimately brought the royal sinner to the more sober joys of bourgeois marriage, convinced him that his own reformation was necessary and that the conversion of a king should be marked by a royal service to the church.

As Louis's new piety progressed, the ecclesiastics seized the occasion to renew their demand for the suppression of heresy. The king ordered the intendants to do everything to co-operate with the bishops. The government men recognized their cue. Louvois threw himself into the campaign in order to remain "the indispensable man" even when there was no war. Colbert hesitated, hoping to save his Huguenot businessmen, financiers

[39] E. G. Leonard, "Les protestants français du XVIII⁰ siècle," *Annales d'histoire sociale,* II (1940), 5–20.

[40] Louis O'Brien, "The Huguenot Policy of Louis XIV and Pope Innocent XI," *Catholic Historical Review* (1931), 29–42.

and industrialists. When he learned that he was suspected by Madame de Maintenon, he saw the light. In 1680 he instructed his intendants to drop everything else and devote themselves to the campaign. As the king showed himself more and more pleased with the reports of conversions, the politicians recklessly outbid each other.

From 1679 to 1683 a whole series of edicts, *arrêts* and acts of *parlements* shut the Protestants out of one career after another and progressively reduced the protections of the Edict of Nantes that even Richelieu had preserved. The king himself was outraged at the "dragonnades," the quartering of rough soldiery on Huguenot families who refused to abjure, with no instructions except to make their stay uncomfortable. Marillac, the intendant of Poitou, who had invented this device, was recalled in disgrace—and given a promotion. Huguenot families were exposed to the loss of their children, who were allowed to declare themselves Catholic at the age of seven, then to be brought up as wards of the king. The Huguenot secondary schools at Sedan and Saumur were closed. Even the poor and ill were obliged to turn to Catholic hospitals and the dying were required to receive an official whose duty it was to determine whether they wished to die in the Huguenot religion. The pastors were forbidden to remain more than three years in one charge. For a seditious sermon, evidence for which was provided by Catholic observers, or for the appearance of a relapsed convert to Catholicism or of a new convert to Protestantism, the penalty was the closing of the temple.

The Protestants made surprisingly little protest. The seventeenth-century coreligionists of the great rebels of the sixteenth became famous for patience. In 1665 they were still able to protest against the program which the assembly had induced the king to accept. In 1678 the famous pastor Claude had presented the cause of Protestantism in a great disputation with Bossuet. It was the last time Protestantism appeared to the French public as a legitimacy. In January, 1685, the Protestants submitted their last petition. They recalled their rights under the Edict, their long record of loyalty to the house of Bourbon, the brutalities that had been used against them in violation of "the rights of nature and of civil society." The petition was received in order to say that it had been received, but not the least consideration was given to it. It was apparent to everyone, including the petitioners, that the revocation was imminent.

The Edict of Revocation, which Louis XIV signed on October 18, 1685, declared that his grandfather, father and he himself had granted and re-granted tolerance to the Huguenots only for the purpose of withdrawing it. The edict ordered the demolition of the chapels and the cessation of all public exercise of the cult as well as the closing of all Protestant schools. Children born of Huguenots were to be baptized and brought up in the Catholic religion under the wardship of the local judges. Emigration was permitted to the pastors if they did not wish to become Catholics, but was forbidden under penalty of the galleys to the laymen. A last clause seemed to grant the unconverted Huguenots—until it pleased God to enlighten them—to live untroubled by the attentions of the missionaries.

In spite of the nominal guarantee of liberty of conscience, Louvois and the intendants continued the brutal methods of repression with which they had begun.[41] Although thousands conformed, some 200,000 made their way to foreign lands. These were, in the main, the bourgeois leadership. The Church in the Desert, refined and democratized, persisted in spite of all governmental efforts. French influence was carried to Berlin, to Amsterdam, to London, to Boston, Charlestown and Cape Town.[42]

Louis XIV had accomplished his aim. France was wholly of his religion. Like the other states of Europe, his kingdom had only one church. If the Protestant world outside France condemned him for the misfortunes of their coreligionists, none of his contemporary sovereigns except the Great Elector could throw the first stone, and Frederick William was hardly representative of the hard sectarianism of each part of his scattered domains. In the world of which he was the sun, Louis XIV's act was hailed, not only by hard-handed *policiers* such as Louvois and Foucault, but by skeptics like La Bruyère, humorists like Madame de Sévigné, wits like La Fontaine. Vauban and Saint-Simon disapproved, but very quietly.

Absolutism had been achieved in France as a façade. It had been sacrificed to the monarchy. The forces in French society that could make it a reality had not been more than partially integrated with the function of power. Outworn institutions incapable of adaptation were preserved like casts to inhibit normal development. Privilege continued to combine power with irresponsibility. Economic life was oriented to uneconomic ends and distorted by the unresolved complex of thousands of localisms. Justice was co-ordinated in form but left in confusion as to substance.

[41] Louis Bastide, "La révocation de l'édit de Nantes à Rennes," *Bulletin de la société de l'histoire du protestantisme français,* 77 (1928), 242–57.

[42] G. Chinard, *Les refugiés huguenots en Amérique* (Paris, 1925); Charles Chasse, "La Belgique terre d'éxil," *La grande revue,* 125 (1928), 569–85; B. Favre, "La colonie française de Berlin," *Revue d'Allemagne,* 5 (1931), 193–208; C. G. Botha, "The Huguenots in South Africa," *Proceedings of the Huguenot Society of London,* 13 (1929), 579–90; A. H. Hirsch, "French Influence on American Agriculture," *Agricultural History,* 4 (1930), 1–9.

France was brought to one religion: it was never less Catholic than in the eighteenth century. Too many historic rights continued to be recognized; too many current wrongs continued to be ignored. The failure of Louis XIV as absolutist was registered a century later in the famous declaration of Calonne to Louis XVI: "Sire, in its present state, France is impossible to govern."

VIII. KING OR PARLIAMENT: ABSOLUTISM IN ENGLAND [43]

The return of Charles II to the throne of England after a long exile initiated a long and intense struggle for power between the king and parliament. The failure of the Protectorate to show any viability after the death of Cromwell had left a vacuum into which the defeated parties of the Civil War stepped without the involvements that a more difficult victory would have brought. They had not been compelled to define their terms. Charles had indicated the general character of his program in the Declaration of Breda—amnesty, toleration, property settlement according to the will of parliament and discharge with pay of General Monk's soldiers. The Convention Parliament had been equally brief and non-committal. They had resolved that "the government is and ought to be by king, lords and commons." The event was to show that the ancient phrase had not by any means acquired the solidity that would obviate severe conflict over the relative weight of the several parts.

Charles was monarchist and Catholic. His experience as an exile had brought him into contact with the miseries and incoherencies of the Fronde and with the arrogant domination of their High Mightinesses the states of Holland over the rest of the United Provinces. The failure of the Protectorate, from his point of view, was a demonstration of the necessity of the kingship, if not as divinely ordained, at least as the sole available solution of the problem of government for the nation.

Charles was Catholic. His personal adherence to the Church of Rome was probably not intense, but it is impossible to deny a certain sincerity to his recognition (when in 1669 he announced to the French ambassador his intention to "go over") of spiritual advantage to himself as well as of political advantage to the kingship. At any rate, he was a political Catholic. On the same occasion he declared his conversion "was the only

[43] D. L. Keir, *The Constitutional History of Modern Britain* (London, 1946); G. N. Clark, *The Later Stuarts* (Oxford, 1934); David Ogg, *England in the Reign of Charles II* (2 vols., London, 1934); Arthur Bryant, *King Charles II* (London, 1931); Keith Feiling, *A History of the Tory Party, 1640–1714* (Oxford, 1924); J. Pollock, "The Policy of Charles II and James II," in the *Cambridge Modern History*, Vol. V, 198–235.

way of re-establishing the monarchy." A corresponding expression, with a directly opposite intention, was used by the earl of Bristol, when he was supporting the Test Act of 1673; he declared himself "a Catholic of the Church of Rome, not a Catholic of the Court of Rome."

The policy of tolerating religious difference which Charles had enunciated in the Declaration of Breda as a cardinal point of his program suffered an untoward fate at the hands of his parliaments. In effect, parliamentary supremacy was substituted for royal supremacy over the church. As in his proposal of amnesty he put aside his family feud with the enemies of his father, so in his proposal of toleration, Charles sought to obviate the religious quarrels which had so radically divided the nation. In the Convention Parliament, with the support of a public declaration from him, an attempt was made to eliminate the most important of these quarrels by combining Episcopacy with Presbyterianism. The proposal was voted down by the Presbyterian majority. Another attempt in the same direction was made by getting the bishops and some prominent Presbyterians together in the Savoy conference. Proposals were made from one side and the other but the months of discussion only made it apparent that the Presbyterians did not wish to tolerate Catholics or sectaries and that the bishops did not wish to accommodate the Presbyterians.

By the time the Savoy conference came to its fruitless end, Charles II's first regularly elected parliament had been summoned. The Cavalier parliament was almost solidly Anglican. In temper it resembled the French *chambre introuvable* of 1815, but, for good or ill, it was to have an active life longer than even the interrupted span of the Long Parliament of Charles I. It was uncompromising in its will to undo all the revolutionary developments since 1640, and even was brought, somewhat unwillingly, to repeal the Triennial Act,[44] which had provided for the assembling of parliament independently of the king's will if he attempted to govern without it. The act excluding the bishops was repealed and they reappeared in the house of lords in November, 1661.

To perpetuate the Anglican ascendancy, the Cavalier parliament proceeded to reverse the policy of toleration laid down in the Declaration of Breda. A Corporation Act of December, 1662, purged the governments of corporate towns by imposing an oath that the Covenant and the bearing of arms against the king on any pretext were unlawful. The zealous commons undertook the amendment of the Prayer Book, but the king handed

[44] The Triennial Act of 1664 maintained the principle but did not provide any mode of enforcement.

the task over to convocation, where it was completed in December, 1661, with changes calculated to make it less rather than more acceptable to the Puritans. In the following spring the revised Prayer Book was approved by parliament, which proceeded to make it the basis of a new Act of Uniformity (May 19, 1662). All clergy, all fellows and university officials, all tutors and schoolmasters were required to make declaration of their unfeigned assent and consent to all the Prayer Book contained as well as to take the nonresistance oath and renounce the Covenant as required in the Corporation Act. Some twelve hundred refused the oath and had to surrender their livings. This was followed by two other measures, the Conventicle Act, which imposed penalties for attendance at worship not in Anglican forms, and the Five-Mile Act (1665) which forbade any non-conformist minister to live or visit within five miles of any corporate town where he had acted as minister. These acts together are known as the Clarendon Code, although Clarendon was probably opposed to a policy of persecution.[45]

Both before and after the Act of Uniformity, Charles II made serious attempts to achieve the fulfillment of his program of toleration. His effort to induce the Savoy conference to establish the principle of comprehension has already been mentioned. When the Act of Uniformity was under discussion, Clarendon introduced on the king's behalf a proviso allowing him to exempt from deprivation ministers who objected only to the surplice and the use of the cross in baptism. Although the proviso passed the lords, it was rejected by commons. When the act was passed, the king promised the Nonconformists to suspend it for three months, but this promise was frustrated by the opposition of Clarendon and Archbishop Sheldon. The acceptance of the act was accompanied by a proclamation releasing imprisoned Quakers. Finally, late in 1662, under the influence of Bennet and the earl of Bristol, Charles II issued a declaration announcing his intention to exempt from the penalties of the act peaceable persons whose conscientious scruples prevented them from conforming. Parliament was invited to pass an act which would enable him to exercise "with a more universal satisfaction" his inherent dispensing power. An act to that effect was introduced into the house of lords where it was bitterly opposed by Clarendon. Nevertheless, limited to Protestants, it passed the lords, but commons rejected it, and both houses joined in a petition for the enforcement of the laws against the Catholics.

By repudiating Charles II's program of toleration and putting under

[45] Keith Feiling, "Clarendon and the Acts of Uniformity," *English Historical Review,* 44 (1929), 289–91.

penalties and disabilities the Catholics and the Presbyterians to whom he owed so much, the Cavalier parliament divided England and made the Anglican church politically as well as religiously sectarian. It is from this point of view that the "political Catholicism" of Charles II must be defined. Like parliamentarism, Protestantism had proved to be a way, not of uniting, but of dividing England. Parliament had no intention to include the nation in the church. Anglicanism became merely the badge of political privilege and monopoly. The alternative to a Catholic monarchy, tolerant and comprehensive, was an oligarchy, eccentrically based and fanatically bent upon excluding the rest of the nation from participation in political life. Charles was "infinitely troubled" by his defeat and, not unnaturally, angry at Clarendon. A badly managed attack upon Clarendon by the earl of Bristol was apparently all that saved him from dismissal as early as 1663.

The will of parliament to act like "Commonwealth men" was also manifest in the treatment of Scotland and Ireland. The Navigation Act, repassed in 1660 to satisfy the still relatively minor commercial interest, excluded Scotland from the colonial trade, although Ireland was still included. A tariff of 1663 imposed a heavy tax on the importation of Scottish cattle and sheep, corn and salt. In the same year, Irish ships were excluded from the colonial trade and in 1666 the importation of Irish cattle of any kind, living or dead, was totally prohibited. The latter act was the object of a lively struggle. Clarendon sacrificed the last shreds of his popularity with the country party in attempting to preserve some basis for Irish prosperity and some right of the king and the lords against the encroachments of the commons. The lower house refused to yield. The interest of the kingdoms as a whole was subordinated to the interest of the English landowners. "The house of commons," commented Clarendon, "seemed much more morose and obstinate than it had formerly appeared to be, and solicitous to grasp as much power and authority as any of their predecessors had done."

Parliament was hardly less aggressive in exercising its influence upon the relations of England with the rest of Europe.[46] There was no conflict with the generally anti-Spanish, pro-Portuguese policy which the king followed upon his return and which was promptly sealed by his marriage to the Infanta Catherine of Portugal with the substantial dowry of Tangier, Bombay and two million *crusados*. The alliance with Portugal was popular because it brought port and gold and opened vistas of empire from Tangier and Bombay. Jamaica and Dunkerque, acquired under the

---

[46] See below, Chapter Five.

Protectorate, were not returned to Spain, and commons passed a bill annexing them in perpetuity to the crown of England. The Protectorate's close connection with France was maintained. The Princess Henrietta was married to Louis XIV's brother, the duke of Orleans, and became soon the channel for the diplomatic dealings between Charles and Louis in furtherance of a very different foreign policy from that with which Charles began. The Portuguese marriage and the sale of Dunkerque, too expensive for the badly organized English treasury to maintain, constituted other links in an Anglo-French union, almost as substantial as that between Cromwell and Mazarin.

If the Portuguese alliance was popular, it was the quarrels with the Dutch that brought out the will of parliament to determine high policy. England was increasingly in competition and conflict with the Dutch in that semipiratical and wholly anarchic activity "beyond the line" that was then known as commerce. The Protectorate's Navigation Act, which had already brought one war with the Dutch, was renewed in 1660. As will be shown more particularly in another connection, the rivalry between these two would-be heirs to the world empire of the Iberian powers inflamed every question, even those of minor importance. For our present concern, the essential thing is that Charles was pushed into the Second Dutch War by his people and especially by the City and by parliament. "I never saw so great an appetite to war as is in both this town and country, especially in the parliament men," he wrote to his sister on June 2, 1664. "I find myself almost the only man in my kingdom who doth not desire war," he added a little later.

Parliament imposed on the king the responsibility of the war without providing him with the power to wage it successfully or, in the long run, even creditably. Inadequate efforts, defective alike in imagination and good-will, were made to supply money. Only at the end of the war did the actual revenue equal what the Long Parliament had raised during the First Dutch War, although it was a bigger war and both countries were wealthier. Nor was parliament any more prudent in the matter of assuring the quiet of the country. Scotland's last market was cut off by the war and the completion of the Clarendon Code aroused rumors of conspiracies for the restoration of the republic. An anonymous letter to Charles himself declared, "The nation are ready with every puff of wind to rise up in arms because of the oppression that is laid upon them." Two devastating catastrophes, the Plague of 1665, which in London swept away nearly seventy thousand persons out of a population of rather less than half a million, and the Great Fire of 1666, which destroyed two-thirds of the capital, reduced English morale to almost zero.

The war was badly managed. Parliament, irritated and suspicious because of the inadequacy of its own financial measures, gladly adopted the Dutch device introduced by Sir George Downing of making specific appropriations, and in the middle of the war initiated a committee of inquiry which not unnaturally found many examples of incompetence and malversation. By 1667 the financial difficulties were so great that the great ships of the navy were laid up and the unpaid sailors who had been rioting in the streets of London were permitted to seek employment on merchant ships. Negotiations for peace were begun at Breda, and when the English showed themselves disposed to haggle, de Witt sent de Ruyter up the Thames to burn several of the decommissioned ships and to tow away the greatest of them, the *Royal Charles.* In the circumstances peace was promptly signed on the terms which the Dutch had originally offered.

Public feeling in England demanded some satisfaction for what was felt to be a national disgrace. Parliament, of course, did not feel its own responsibility and put the blame on Clarendon, along with Sir George Carteret and Sir William Coventry, who were responsible for the administration of the navy. There was a general feeling that parliament must take the whole management of affairs into its own hands. But for the sudden prorogation of parliament, an address in favor of alliance with the house of Hapsburg and a war with France would have been presented to the king. Clarendon was thus an obstacle to peace at home. On August 30, 1667, by the king's order, he gave up the great seal, and presently, also by the king's order, withdrew to France where he died seven years later.

In dismissing Clarendon, Charles had satisfied parliament, but in a real sense it was a victory for him. Clarendon, as the great Royalist leader during the days of exile, had held his office by a title independent of the king's will. He had a policy that was not exactly the king's policy. For all his stiffness in defense of the prerogative, he was equally stiff in defense of the Anglican supremacy. His firm faith in the antebellum government by council and his determined effort to restore it made him a bad manager of parliament. The privy council, by the development of party cleavages, by the abolition of the various conciliar jurisdictions and by the sheer growth of the problems of government, had become anachronistic. An attempt had been made to strengthen it by referring special problems to committees. Even before Clarendon fell, the important questions were passing to the heads of the departments and especially to the rising secretaries of state who were the king's servants, not his tutors.[47]

Charles' new ministers were his own choice and in his heart he must have agreed with the courtier who told him that he was now king, which he had never been before. A few months after the formation of the new ministry, he wrote to his sister, the duchess of Orleans, "One thing I desire you to take as much as you can out of the King of France's head, that my ministers are anything but what I will have them. . . . Whatsoever opinion my ministers had been of, I would and do always follow my own judgment, and, if they take any other measures than that, they will see themselves mistaken in the end."

The new government was a ministry of all the talents, the famous cabal, consisting of Sir Thomas Clifford, Lord Arlington, the duke of Buckingham, Lord Ashley, and the earl of Lauderdale. The cabal contained several of the cleverest and most capable men in England, but not a sincere Anglican among them. Clifford and Arlington were Catholics, Buckingham was an Independent (by marriage) and Ashley and Lauderdale were Presbyterians. All of them from very different motives desired to relax if not to abrogate the penal laws. The cabal, considered as a whole, might have been expected to succeed where Clarendon had failed, in the management of parliament. Unfortunately, they neither possessed political coherence among themselves, nor was there party organization or discipline in parliament to correspond to such coherence had it existed.

The first problem of the cabal was one which they solved reasonably well and the solution of which in a more ordered situation should have served them well as political capital. They were immediately confronted by the War of Devolution, Louis XIV's brash assertion of his intention to disregard his former abnegations of the Spanish heritage. With this new development, Sir William Temple's plan for a defensive alliance with the Dutch was favorably received by the cabal as well as by John de Witt. By December, 1667, the basic treaties of the alliance were signed and a few months later Sweden adhered to make it the Triple Alliance. Louis XIV thereupon made peace with Spain. Although Charles, no more broken to the discipline of ministerial responsibility than his ministers or his parliament, betrayed the secret articles of the alliance to Louis XIV and offered him a close alliance against Holland and Spain, the king and the cabal had the appearance of successfully stopping the advance of the French.

[47] D. L. Keir, *The Constitutional History of Modern Britain* (New York, 3rd ed., 1946), 246–47.

The Triple Alliance was as popular as anything that had been done by the crown since the Restoration.

When parliament met on February 10, 1668, it therefore seemed opportune to introduce a measure to achieve "a better union and composure . . . in matters of religion." Careful preparation had been made. The cabal, for once, was thoroughly in agreement. Presbyterians and Anglicans had been consulted. The measure was prepared by the Lord Chief Justice Hale. It was skillfully put forward in the king's speech in close connection with the expressions about the Triple Alliance. Yet neither the success of the government abroad nor the hope of better order at home reduced one whit the inflamed Anglicanism of the commons. They responded with a bill to renew the Conventicle Act, which expired in 1668, and when the bill was rejected by the lords, insisted upon an even more stringent measure in 1670.

In 1669 Charles II announced to the duke of York, Clifford, Arlington and Arundel his intention to reconcile himself to the Catholic faith and to turn England Catholic with him. The rejection of the Comprehension Bill made it plain to Charles that time was bearing him not toward but away from the ideal with which he had begun his reign of a national church essentially Catholic, but broad enough to include a majority of Protestants and tolerant of all dissent. He had thought to be free to move in the direction of toleration when he was rid of Clarendon, but commons had shown that they were not going to surrender the Anglican monopoly.

The Catholicism Charles had in mind was not Tridentine. When he began negotiations with the pope in 1662, his proposal included communion in both kinds and a national independence at least equivalent to the Gallican liberties. Mysterious negotiations with his Jesuit son, offspring of his earliest liaison, and with the Brussels Internuncio only reflected by their lack of outcome the fact that Charles was not a good Catholic in the ultramontane sense. It was to the Gallican-oriented king of France, as political and as little personal in his Catholicism as Charles, that he turned for the aid necessary to achieve a "Catholic" revolution in England.

Neither Louis XIV nor Charles II was actuated by simple piety. For a moment in their parallel careers as sovereigns of neighboring and rival nations, their interests seemed to coincide. England could be a valuable ally for Louis XIV against the Dutch and Louis XIV could furnish the funds that would make Charles independent of parliament. If Charles could be committed to a Catholic policy, in the existing state of English opinion he might be the more permanently attached to the purse strings of the French king. With no notion on either side of making any sacrifice beyond what was necessary for their respective purposes, the two kings negotiated a public Treaty of Dover, which provided for common action against the Dutch, and a secret treaty, which provided for French aid in the suppression of parliament and the establishment of Catholicism on the part of Charles.

By the terms of the secret treaty Charles was to declare himself a Catholic and Louis was to furnish money and troops to carry out the plan, if it should be resisted. Charles was to aid Louis in an attack on the Dutch Republic and when war broke out was to receive £225,000 a year. He was to have first claim on the islands controlling the mouth of the Scheldt. As will be shown elsewhere, this treaty meant little in actual practice except that France and England supported each other in attempting to put down the Dutch Republic and Charles during the ensuing years received considerable sums of money. If it was ever sincerely intended, the moment for the religious change never came. The overthrow of the Dutch Republic and the accession to power of William of Orange soon rendered England's part in the war meaningless from the standpoint of Charles, and by 1674 England and Holland made a separate peace. The threat of rapprochement with Holland was used from time to time to extort new payments from Louis XIV. Charles did not hesitate to marry off his niece Mary, the daughter of the duke of York and heiress presumptive after her father, to William of Orange in 1678. In short, if we disregard the words of the treaty, it amounted to a means of cooperating with Louis XIV to satisfy the dynastic and commercial jealousy of the Dutch which Charles shared with his parliament and ministers, and to furnish Charles with some of the revenue which parliament was reluctant to supply. The measures that were associated with its beginning and the ill success of the war in the face of the heroic resistance William of Orange was able to evoke from his people made the war unpopular with parliament. The easy victories of the French army expected by the English were made impossible by the opening of the dikes. The battle of the Texel on August 21, 1673, precluded an English invasion of Holland from the sea or even the blockade of the Dutch ports.

It had been hoped that a new Dutch war would serve to unite the nation under the crown, but that hope had been deceived by the violent protest aroused by two acts at the beginning of the war. Public finance, as has already been noted, was very imperfectly developed in England, but Sir Thomas Clifford had learned to pawn prospective revenues with the goldsmiths, who had other people's money to lend, somewhat after the fashion of giro banks. When the penury of the government led to delay in payments, the goldsmiths refused to make any further advances. Thereupon Clifford, to secure the funds necessary to put the fleet into action, on January 2, 1672, formally suspended all payments to the bankers for a year with provision for interest at 6 per cent. The goldsmiths attempted to pass on the moratorium to their clients, but the king intervened and their payments were resumed in a few days. A commercial panic was thus narrowly averted. None of the goldsmiths failed and normality was soon restored. The credit of the crown was nevertheless damaged.[48]

The Declaration of Indulgence of 1672 was in a sense an attempt to repeat with more profit to the king the situation of 1668. On March 15, Charles, basing himself on his "supreme power in ecclesiastical matters," suspended all penal laws against "whatsoever sort of nonconformists and recusants," that is against Catholics as well as Protestants.[49]

This effort, however, produced an even more hostile reaction than that of 1668. With all the secrecy that had been successfully maintained, the Treaty of Dover had become the focus of general suspicion. "The public articles are ill enough, what are the private articles?" was openly asked in the house of commons. The profound popular hostility to "popery," to France and to arbitrary power, which was to be for so long a prime character of the English mind, was being solidified. Catholicism in high places added to the distrust with which every move of the king was regarded.

When parliament was at last summoned in 1673, it responded with a still more drastic assertion of the exclusive right of the Anglican element to govern. The king was denied any appropriation for the war until he had canceled the Declaration of Indulgence. Parliament thereupon passed the Test Act (1673), which required the holder of every office, civil or military, to take the sacrament of the Lord's Supper according to the usage of the church of England, to take the oaths of supremacy and allegiance, and to sign a declaration that they believed "that there is not any transubstantiation in the sacrament of the Lord's Supper."

The Test Act brought about the collapse of the cabal. Clifford was excluded and also the duke of York, in spite of the victory he won over the Dutch at Southwold Bay. Ashley, who had been made earl of Shaftesbury and lord chancellor, and had earnestly striven to make the war popular, was apparently becoming aware that he was being deceived. In

[48] D. L. Keir, op. cit., 254; Arthur Bryant, King Charles II (London, 1931), 221–22; R. D. Richards, "The Stop of the Exchecquer," History, 2 (1930), 45–62.
[49] Frank Bate, The Declaration of Indulgence of 1672 (London, 1908).

spite of his really deep commitment to a policy of toleration, he voted for the Test Act. In November he was dismissed. "It is only laying down my robe," he said, "and buckling on the sword." The Catholic policy, if such it may be called, passed out of the plans of Charles after a tenuous and shadowy existence of less than five years.

Under the able direction of Sir Thomas Osborne, the persistent king undertook a new plan to get control of the situation. Osborne was in effect Charles' Colbert and without too much economy was able to make Charles' revenue so effective that when he left office in 1679 the treasury had a balance instead of the deficit that had been chronic. More important for our present purpose, he anticipated Walpole and Newcastle in developing government by corruption. He applied to pensions and places, which had formerly been distributed in the spirit of largesse, the same economy he applied to the money revenue and by this means built up for the government a compact body of votes in parliament. Failure to support the government meant exclusion from office as definitely as failure to deny transubstantiation.

By 1675 Osborne's machine appeared strong enough to enable him to put through a "nonresisting test." This was a measure to exact from all officials, including the justices of the peace and members of parliament, a declaration that to take up arms against the king "on any pretence whatsoever" was unlawful and an oath never to attempt any alteration in government or religion. The king, who five years before had signed the secret Treaty of Dover, was offering the Anglican church an apparently perpetual tenure of power, and the nation an anti-French policy as long as Osborne was in charge of affairs. The price, of course, was the subjection of parliament to the crown. Osborne's machine was effective. The measure passed the lords and seemed about to pass the commons also. In the opposition, however, was an equally clever politician. Shaftesbury used an issue of jurisdiction between the two houses with such success that Charles had to prorogue parliament from June to October, before the nonresisting test could be discussed in commons.

The moment had been missed. When parliament met again, Shaftesbury managed to revive the dispute between the two houses, and began to press for dissolution. To the discomfiture of Shaftesbury and his supporters, Charles retorted by proroguing parliament for the unusually long period of fifteen months. The nonresisting test was dead but Osborne was made earl of Danby.

Thus party, the political device that was destined after much refinement to reconcile the existence of a strong parliament and a strong govern-

ment, was being invented. Danby and Shaftesbury, by methods and instruments none too delicate on either side, contended for a majority in
parliament. Danby with his crude methods of bribery seems less significant than Shaftesbury with his appeal to public opinion. Shaftesbury's
Green Ribbon Club and its extensive system of agents, agitators and
pamphleteers was the first step, necessarily incomplete until the opposing
party was organized on corresponding lines, to organize the active elements of the nation for or against a given line of policy and to make possible shifts of policy according to the national interest without the disruptions involved in change by the king in his own person. In the light
of the development of party in later years, the shifts of Charles II were
not mere vagaries, but responsibility that fell upon him in the absence of
a device such as Shaftesbury, with complete unconsciousness, was inventing.

As long as the Tory party was not invented and indeed until kings
learned that they had a place above the political struggle, party presented
the aspect of faction. Charles, switching from Clarendon to the cabal and
from the cabal to Danby, was trying to find a way to get the country
governed, just as William III was in the latter years of his reign when
he switched from Whigs to Tories and back again. From Charles' point
of view, Shaftesbury was trying to create a situation in which freedom
to shift would be lost to the king and to remove from him in the interest
of a faction the powers which his responsibility as ruler of the whole
nation entailed.

The systematization of the "opposition" by Shaftesbury increased the
range of action of Louis XIV and, indeed, of his opponents. By the use of
sums of money that seemed considerable then, they were able to influence
on the side of the opposition as well as on the side of the king the decisions which might be of concern to their national interests. The issue of
non-resistance had already brought a flood of foreign gold into the struggle on one side and the other, French gold for votes against the measure
in order to weaken Danby, who was anti-French, and to keep Charles
dependent on French subsidies, and Dutch and Spanish gold for votes in
support of it in order to make possible the developing Dutch alliance,
which had been marked by the marriage of the Princess Mary to William
of Orange. It was till necessary, however, for Louis XIV to pay large
sums to keep Charles neutral. Charles got a million from parliament for
a war with France early in 1678, but the last successes of the French in the
war with the Dutch made him recoil. Louis XIV was able to keep England neutral by giving Charles II a large subsidy to dissolve parliament

and disband his army, while Barillon negotiated with similar arguments to the same ends with Shaftesbury and his followers.[50]

The Treaty of Nimwegen (August 10, September 17, 1678), which ended the war between France and the United Provinces, left Charles and Danby in a very strong position. In addition to the generous supply of parliament and the generous subsidy of Louis XIV, Charles had a formidable army released from foreign service. Louis XIV was still ready to support the opposition, but the forces against the Whigs seemed so overwhelming that retirement from the field seemed the only course open to them.

They were momentarily saved from political extinction by the Popish Plot. The preceding decade had sensitized Englishmen of all classes to rumors and allegations of plots and counterplots aimed to restore England to the Roman obedience. The violence and arbitrariness of their own regime of religion led them to expect an equal degree of ruthlessness and violence from a Catholic reaction. Politics, in the absence of even an elementary morality, presented itself to the public mind and to the active participants as a matter of intrigue. The ordinary instruments of the Anglican squires against dissenters, of the cabal against the majority in parliament, of Danby against the Tories and the Tories against Danby, had been informers and spies drawn from the lowest elements of society. Thus, when Titus Oates, a perjurer and renegade, deposed before Sir Edmund Berry Godfrey and before the privy council that a plot existed under the direction of the pope and the Jesuits to conquer the country, to assassinate the king (and the duke of York unless he assented), with the names of over a hundred conspirators, neither the low character of Oates nor the obvious discrepancies of his story interfered with the devout belief of an alarmed populace in his allegations. When it was discovered that the secretary of the duchess of York was actually engaged in treasonable correspondence and when on October 12 Godfrey was found murdered, the doubters were silenced, if not convinced. The shameful reign of terror that followed took the lives of many innocent men, but gave new life to Shaftesbury and the Whigs.

When parliament resumed its sitting in the fall of 1678, both houses flung themselves into the agitation. Under Shaftesbury's leadership, a joint resolution solemnly declared that "there hath been and still is a damnable and hellish plot . . . for assassinating and murdering the King and rooting out and destroying the Protestant religion." The central feature of the

[50] C. L. Grose, "Louis XIV's Financial Relations with Charles II and the English Parliament," *Journal of Modern History,* I (1929), 177–204.

Whig program became the exclusion of James as a Catholic from the succession to the throne. With the support of Barillon, the ambassador of Louis XIV, the Whigs launched their attack from all quarters. Ralph Montagu, the English ambassador at Paris, was paid fifty thousand crowns by the French government to publish his instructions of March, 1678, to demand six million *livres* from Louis XIV as the price for the dissolution of parliament. The fact that the Whigs were at the moment more fully in Barillon's pay escaped notice. The demand for Danby's dismissal grew loud, and to protect his minister Charles was forced to the step that he would have been wise to take in 1668: he dissolved the Cavalier parliament. Danby was dismissed and committed to the Tower by the house of lords. He had done more than any other man to consolidate the royal power.

Charles was left alone to face the renewed fury of the Whigs. Three experiments in regulating the relation between the supremacy of the crown in administration and policy and the supremacy of parliament in legislation and finance had been tried and failed—the revival of conciliar government by Clarendon, the ministry of the talents represented by the cabal, and Danby's system of parliamentary management. Charles showed himself the ablest politician of his day (as of his dynasty). By utilizing the advantages presented to him by the irresponsible recklessness of the Whigs, he resolved the problem in a wholly monarchical sense with complete success.

In the election of 1678 the Whigs, at an enormous cost in beer and gold, swept the country.[51] Under cover of the Popish Plot, Shaftesbury undertook to achieve the exclusion of the duke of York from the succession to the throne. Charles threw Shaftesbury and his organization into some confusion by summoning him to head the privy council, remodeled according to a scheme of Sir William Temple to include all parties. When it failed to work, as Charles seems to have expected, Shaftesbury was dismissed.

On May 11, 1679, the Whigs introduced in the house of commons their bill "to disable the Duke of York to inherit the imperial crown of this realm." Shaftesbury and his followers had turned to the duke of Monmouth, who was reputed to be the son of Charles and even to be his lawful son and heir. The legitimate Protestant line was ignored because the Princess Mary and William of Orange showed as much reluctance as Charles to be the tools of a party or to participate in what they regarded as a diminution of their inheritance.

When the debate was at its height, a violent illness of the king con-

[51] M. Dorothy George, "Elections and Electioneering, 1678–1681," *English Historical Review*, 45 (1930), 552–78.

fronted the nation with the dreaded prospect of civil war. The government, which had been entrusted to Halifax, a clever and reasonable man, for his moderation called "the Trimmer," Essex and Sunderland, summoned James back from exile. When the king unexpectedly recovered, the rejoicings of the people gave pause to some of the Whigs. The Exclusion Bill was put through commons, but after an extended debate was thrown out by the lords, sixty-three to thirty. The fierce hostility of the London mob, completely under Shaftesbury's influence, and of the baffled Whig majority in commons, rose to new heights. Once more Charles dissolved parliament.

The new parliament was summoned to meet at Oxford, away from the London mob. Whigs came armed with bands of retainers but Charles, forewarned, had a regiment posted on the Oxford Road, and had once more been able to solve the problem of supply by giving up his alliance with the Spanish for 12,500,000 *livres* from Louis XIV. Thus when he faced his new parliament on March 21, 1679, it was with a feeling of adequate power to handle the situation. He offered a compromise by which James was to have the royal dignity while the real power was to be exercised by a regency under his elder Protestant daughter. For the Whigs, retreat was impossible. They refused the compromise and resolved instead to bring in another Exclusion Bill. On April 7, Charles dissolved his last parliament.

In the Whig program the logical step was an attempt to keep the parliament in being and to raise the country. Whatever the possibilities of the situation, they were lost by the confusion into which the opposition leaders were thrown. Within three months Shaftesbury was arrested and one of his followers was convicted and executed at Oxford on charges like those against him. London, however, was still a Whig stronghold, and the grand jury refused to find a true bill against him. Shaftesbury, broken in health, fled to Holland to die. Some of his followers organized the fantastic Rye House Plot to get possession of the king's person. The plot failed, but it gave Charles an opportunity to strike at the remaining leaders. The earl of Essex committed suicide, but Lord Russell, who had carried the Exclusion Bill to the house of lords, and Algernon Sidney, both members of noble families that had played large parts in Tudor and Stuart England, were convicted and executed. Titus Oates was turned out of his lodgings at court and forbidden the council chamber. Danby was released from the Tower on bail. Catholic recusants were freed from imprisonment in various parts of the country, but the justices of the peace, who associated the Rye House Plot with Dissent, were allowed to round up and punish ministers and teachers for breaches of the Clarendon Code.

Although the rights of juries to render their verdicts without fear of punishment had been established and the writ of habeas corpus had been made generally available by a statute of 1679, the courts had been brought pretty well to heel by the king's power to remove judges at his pleasure.[52] Most of the lawyers were antiprerogative, but Charles had been able to find enough competent and dependable judges willing to keep the courts subservient to his will.

The problem that remained was the control of parliament. Unlike the kings of France, the kings of England could not count on their "good towns" as natural allies in the development of monarchical power. The Corporation Act of the beginning of Charles' reign had already pointed the way to a method of controlling them. London itself, where popularly elected sheriffs had chosen juries brave enough to refuse to indict Shaftesbury and to acquit William Penn, was co-ordinated by a combination of force and fraud. In the summer of 1682, the lord mayor, who had been won over by the court, foisted two Tory sheriffs on the City and made sure that a Tory mayor would succeed him. The towns in general were brought into line by an extensive application of quo warranto proceedings. With pliant judges, the miscellaneous departures from the ancient charters which time, change of circumstances and usage had occasioned and even justified were exalted into reason for forfeiture. As many as sixty-six towns lost or surrendered their charters and passed under the control of the crown with new charters which gave the king effective control of their return of burgesses to parliament.[53]

In 1685, after a reign of twenty-five years, during which, except for Danby, he had been poorly served, Charles had achieved a control of England and of its constitutional machinery that in contrast with his situation in 1661 marked an advance in the position of the crown comparable to the work of the great architects of authority such as Louis XI, Henry VII, Richelieu and Mazarin. Charles died before the supremacy which he had won for the crown had received any normal test and his successor was no Mazarin, but rather a Marie de' Medici. Power passed into the hands of an oligarchy more corrupt and less open to the winds of doctrine than the feudal remnants and the privileged businessmen of France. Even in those days of primitive medicine Charles might be regarded as having a life expectation of some years. What would have been the course of English political development if he had lived as long as Louis XIV?

[52] J. C. Corson, "Judges and Statutory Tenure in England in the Seventeenth Century," *Juridical Review*, 42 (1930), 136–49.
[53] J. H. Sacret, "The Restoration Government and the Municipal Corporations," *English Historical Review*, 45 (1930), 232–59.

Chapter Four

LEVIATHAN: THE ORGANIZATION OF POWER II

I. THE CREATION OF A STATE: THE GREAT ELECTOR OF BRANDENBURG [1]

IN 1660 the Hohenzollern elector of Brandenburg, Frederick William, was lord of many lands by very diverse titles. In addition to the margravate of Brandenburg, he held the duchy of Cleves, the county of Mark and the county of Ravensburg, but the Dutch held Cleves in lien for the payment of an old debt. A heritage-fraternity and the death of the last of the Pomeranian line in 1630 had given the elector's father the right of succession to the Baltic coast, but Sweden had seized Pomerania in the Thirty Years' War and could not be dislodged. At the congress of Westphalia, Frederick William could secure only the eastern and poorer half, with most of the debt. As "satisfaction" he received the secularized bishoprics of Halberstadt and Minden and the "expectancy" of the archbishopric of Magdeburg. Last but not least, as the price of his services to the king of Poland, his suzerain for the duchy of Prussia, in the Northern War (1655–1660), he was freed of his nominal vassalage. The Treaty of Oliva (1660) sanctioned and consolidated his "supreme and absolute power" as duke of East Prussia.

Thus, by 1660 the Hohenzollerns were established on the middle course of each of the great north European rivers, the Rhine, the Weser, the Elbe, the Oder and the Vistula. Their possessions were geographically scattered and their titles to them highly diversified. The historical task of giving them the unity of a modern state was to extend over two centuries, but the fundamental pattern of the achievement was created in the lifetime of Frederick William, the Great Elector, and especially in the decades from 1660 to his death in 1688.

The instrumentality through which Frederick William built his state was his administrative system. Everywhere in his dominions at the begin-

[1] Bernhard Erdmannsdörfer, *Deutsche Geschichte vom westphälischen Frieden bis zum Regierungsantritt Friedrichs des Grossen, 1648–1740* (2 vols., Berlin, 1892–1893), Vol. I; Herbert Tuttle, *History of Prussia* (4 vols., Boston, 1884–1896), Vol. I; Albert Waddington, *Histoire de Prusse* (2 vols., Paris, 1911–1922), Vol. I; Otto Hintze, *Die Hohenzollern und ihr Werk: fünfhundert Jahre vaterländischer Geschichte* (Berlin, 1915); J. A. R. Marriott

ning of his electorate the functions of government were still feudally distributed, in the country among the lords and knights, and in the towns among the patricians (*Geschlechter*). Everywhere in the course of his reign he managed to establish agents and commissioners, wholly responsible to him through a hierarchy of superiors, who were able to take over the functions of the local dignitaries. The nobility, which he constantly favored, became a service nobility. The central element of the system was the privy council (*Geheime Rat*) of Brandenburg. Originally organized for the marks themselves and made up of Brandenburg nobles and gentry with the addition of some officials, it became the center at which all questions from any part of the dominions were decided and to which the various agencies of the elector were responsible. Although the commissioner for war and the finance minister were always members of the council, they retained a certain independence of it. Like the Tudors in England, Frederick William governed through his council. He did not hesitate to call to it subjects from any part of his territories or even foreigners with the qualifications he desired. If he drew his officials mainly from the nobility, he was quite ready to utilize also men from the upper middle classes, like Meinders and Fuchs, the "great men" of his last years. Like Charles II of England, Frederick William echoed Louis XIV. When he had reduced the high councilors (*Oberräthe*) of the duchy of Prussia to complete subordination he declared, "The High Councillors are councillors and servants who derive their power only from their lord; they have no power without his will and his approbation, to do or decide anything in his affairs, except in conformity with their instructions and commission. It belongs to His Electoral Serenity to make the decisions which he thinks best and most useful." [2] Nevertheless, it was but rarely and in crucial matters hardly ever that the elector took decisions against the advice of his council.

At the head of each province was a lieutenant (*Statthalter*) with whom was associated a collegial administrative group (*Regierung*), including the *Landräthe* or provincial councilors and the tax commissioners. The councilors in the country districts and the tax commissioners in the towns rapidly absorbed all the functions of the traditional local officials, leaving them only their perquisites. The towns retained an appearance of self-government, electing their own officials, but as a matter of practice

and C. G. Robertson, *The Evolution of Prussia, the Making of an Empire* (Oxford, 1915); F. Schevill, *The Great Elector* (Chicago, 1947); F. L. Carsten, "The Great Elector and the Foundation of the Hohenzollern Despotism," *English Historical Review*, 65 (1950), 175–202, and "The Resistance of Cleves and Mark to the Despotic Policy of the Great Elector," *ibid.*, 66 (1951), 219–41.
[2] A. Waddington, *op. cit.*, I, 356.

they were given specific instructions whom to elect. To Frederick William must be given the credit of laying the essential foundations of the Prussian civil service, with its traditions of pride, efficiency and honesty, even though in truth his inability to pay adequate salaries led in his time to much pluralism and nepotism.

The first step in the process of integration was to destroy or reduce to impotence the institutions of localism, particularly the provincial *Landtage*. The elector was of course obliged to recognize divergences of law and custom in his diverse possessions, but after the peace of Oliva he undertook to secure throughout his dominions a common obedience to his ordinances, administered everywhere by his own agents and commissioners, and to secure from all his territories adequate revenues to support the army necessary to defend his inheritance and to play the part of a European sovereign, which he had won with so little.

Legally and politically the position of the elector in 1660 was unpromising. As a result of the weakness of his two immediate predecessors, the nobles of Brandenburg, of Cleves-Mark and of Prussia claimed not only control of the purse, but of the administration, judicial and financial, of the army and of foreign relations. The nobles, however, were less effective in action than they were in appearance. In the first place, they were not in the least united. The elector was able to deal with each group separately and in turn, using forces from the other parts of his dominions. In Brandenburg and Cleves-Mark, during the War of the North (1655–1660), he did not hesitate to requisition the sums that the reluctant *Landtag* refused to grant him or to introduce into Cleves garrisons which no existing force was strong enough to expel. In Königsberg, where his lieutenant, the Lithuanian Prince Bogislau Radziwill, and his special delegate to the *Landtag,* Otto von Schwerin, had vainly attempted to overcome popular resistance to the new sovereignty under the leadership of Hieronymus Roth, Frederick William himself appeared in October, 1662, with two thousand men. At this show of force the disturbances died down, Roth was arrested and, when it proved impossible to secure a conviction by legal process, carried off to a castle in Brandenburg where he died in 1678, refusing to the end to make his submission to the elector. The "liberties" of the three cities of Königsberg were at an end.

An understanding was also effected with the Prussian nobility. By an *Assekurations-Akt* of March 12, 1663, the elector-duke confirmed the privileges of the estates, as he had ten years earlier in Brandenburg, insofar as they were consistent with his sovereign control, and the estates in turn recognized his sovereignty and did homage to him on this new basis.

A second conflict, which afforded an opportunity to settle matters with the Prussian nobility, arose in 1669 in connection with further demands of Frederick William for revenue. A part of the nobility still hoped for assistance from Poland against the rising pressure of the elector-duke and maintained a stubborn resistance under the leadership of Christian Ludwig von Kalckstein, who, as administrator of a district (*Amtshauptmann*), had already learned that the ducal authority was capable of enforcing criminal responsibility on faithless executives, even though noble. Kalckstein fled to Warsaw and there, without formal commission, treated with the Polish diet as the representative of the East Prussian nobility. He was an adventurer rather than a serious conspirator, but he was potentially dangerous as a link between the hostile elements of the nobility and the Poles, who had residual claims on East Prussia. An attempt was made to secure his extradition and when that failed, the Brandenburg resident at Warsaw had him kidnaped and delivered to Königsberg. He was then put on trial for high treason and, in violation of the privileges of the Prussian nobility, put to torture to divulge the names of his fellow conspirators. In 1672 he was convicted and executed. As in the case of the much more worthy Roth, the opposition collapsed and with it the hope of resistance based on Polish help. The government proceeded to collect taxes by requisition, independently of the *Landtag*. In 1674–1675 the war commissariat was established to enforce the collection of revenues. The commissariat was presently transformed into the war chamber, and, after the elector's victory over the Swedes in 1679, the last remnants of the old government by the Prussian estates were replaced by an unqualified absolutism.

In Brandenburg the advance of the elector's power was most gradual and least marked by open conflict. The privileged classes of the marches regarded the recess of 1653 as the foundation of the constitution of Brandenburg and as the bulwark of their privileges. This was correct as to the social ascendency of the nobility, but as to their political position, it really meant the end. The nobles still retained the right to be consulted in regard to external affairs, but this right had no practical significance in the case of a sovereign with territories from the Rhine to the Vistula and a European position to maintain. The grant of 150,000 thalers a year for the War of the North naturally had to be extended and as early as 1662 the estates had to recognize that the burden could never be lessened. Instead it was constantly increased and the principle that the elector's army must be supported by the country was gradually established. The revenue for the army, which in 1660 was still a special "contribution" during or in expectation of war, became a fixed burden, which from the end of the seventeenth century required no special grant.[3]

The *Landtag* itself disappeared. That of 1653 was the last general *Landtag* in the electorate. Thereafter the elector dealt only with committees and deputations made up of representatives from the various circles (*Kreistage*). In the late sixties these committees were put under the direction of a member of the privy council. As a final step, between 1682 and 1686, the representatives of the estates in the *Kreditwerk* (which had become the electoral *Landschaft*) were transformed into administrative functionaries. To the traditional sources of revenue was added the *Akzise*. The idea for this came from Holland and the name from France. It was not exactly an *excise,* but rather a complex of use taxes, occupation taxes and even some land taxes, the merit of which, from the viewpoint of the electoral government, was that it could not be evaded by the nobility, which was exempt from the "contribution." The aim of the elector was to have the *Akzise,* which in 1660 existed in some of the towns of the Mark, extended to the entire area, to take the place of the "contribution." The nobles defeated the first attempt in 1661, but in 1667 the *Akzise* was applied to all towns, though it remained "voluntary." In 1682 it was made a compulsory state tax, the surplus of which, above the obligation of the town for the army tax, flowed into the elector's treasury and not into that of the community. To keep the town clearly separate from the country, walls or palisades were built and close control kept over entry and exit. At the same time a new official, the war and tax commissioner, appeared, who became the instrument through which not merely the *Akzise* but the whole urban organization was reduced to the administrative control of the electoral government. An ordinance of 1684 laid the basis for the further development of the system.[4]

The generalization of the *Akzise* in the towns and the success of the nobility in preventing its extension to the countryside brought about a complete separation of interest, political and financial, between the nobility and the towns. It was a death blow to the old system of estates. The nobility faced the elector alone and found themselves unable to resist relegation to the limited and local affairs of the circles. In 1680 the nobility made an attempt to oppose the growing centralization.[5] They met in Berlin without the summons of the elector, as the *Landtagabschied* of 1653 authorized them to do, but this move only gave the elector the

[3] O. Hintze, *op. cit.,* 206.
[4] *Ibid.,* 208–9.
[5] A. Waddington, *op. cit.,* I, 347.

opportunity to abolish the last remnants of the *Landtag's* authority and independence. In 1683 he completed the task by demanding the presidency of the body for one of his councilors, which of course meant that the *Landtag* was thenceforth only another cog in the great machine of which the privy council was the motor.

In Cleves-Mark the conflict between Frederick William and the estates was more bitter than in Brandenburg. There, too, a constitutional agreement (1653) had in form stripped the elector of all power of independent action, but there, too, the nobility found themselves without effective means of resistance. They appealed to the Empire, and a decision of the Aulic council supported their claim to control the purse, but when the deputation returned, one of the leaders, Wilich von Winnenthal, was arrested and the estates of another confiscated. The nobles protested but surrendered. They ransomed Wilich by a grant of 150,000 thalers (October, 1655) which Frederick William was glad to accept in view of the approaching War of the North. During the war, in Cleves-Mark as in Brandenburg, he raised troops and contributions by force without heeding the loud protests that were raised.[6]

At the end of the war, a revision of the constitution recognized the changed position of the elector in Cleves-Mark. By the recess of March 19, 1661, the powers of the *Landtag* were sharply reduced. It kept the right to consent to taxes and, with due notice to the government, to assemble and even to raise and spend twelve thousand thalers independently of the elector. The *Indigenatsrecht,* the local nobility's monopoly of traditional offices, was confirmed and even strengthened. On the other hand, the right to negotiate with foreign powers, the right to appeal to the Empire, the oath of officials to support the earlier "recesses," the right to exclude troops of the elector, were all surrendered. The rights of the estates remained significant, but the possibility of effective opposition to the growing power of the state had disappeared. The contributions continued to be granted year by year, but like the army, for whose support they were intended, they became a permanent institution. In 1666 the termination of the provisional character of the Hohenzollern's position in Cleves-Mark (by treaty with Neuburg) removed the last element of instability from the position of Frederick William.

In the rest of the Hohenzollern dominions no serious resistance to the process of centralization developed. In eastern Pomerania, by the Ordinance of Government (*Regimens-Ordnung*) of 1654, the privileges of the nobility and the new governmental system were established to-

[6] *Ibid.*, I, 274.

1. Bernini: Bust of Louis XIV—"an expressive commentary on the age, the style, the artist and the subject."

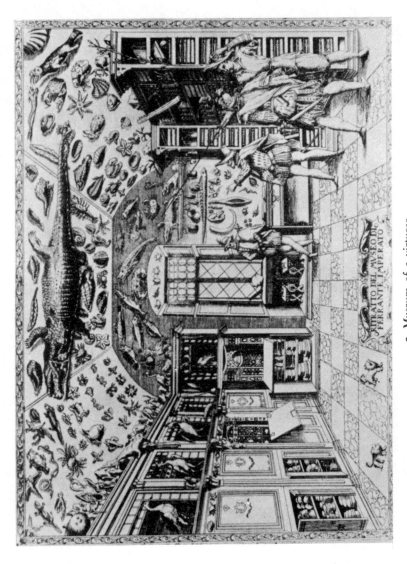

2. Museum of a virtuoso

(Ferrante Imperato, *Historia Naturale*, Venice, 1672)

3. Three views of a Leeuwenhoek microscope, Rijksmuseum, Amsterdam
Courtesy of *The Scientific Monthly*

4. The Magdeburg Hemispheres of Otto von Guericke
(A. Wolf, *History of Science, Technology and Philosophy, New York*, 1935)
Courtesy, The Macmillan Company

5. The Observatory, Paris
(A. Wolf, *History of Science, Technology and Philosophy,*
New York, 1935)
Courtesy, The Macmillan Company

6. The Observatory of Olaus Römer
(A Wolf, *History of Science, Technology and
Philosophy,* New York, 1935)
Courtesy, The Macmillan Company

7. Blaise Pascal
Bibliothèque Nationale, Cabinet des
Estampes

8. Louis XIV visiting the Academy of Science
(Denys Dodart, *Histoire des Plantes,* Paris, 1676)

9. Santa Maria della Salute, Venice,
by Longhena, 1632-1656

10. The Pesaro Palace, Venice, by Longhena, 1679

11. The Theatine Church, Munich, by Barelli, 1663-1675

12. Garden façade of Maisons Lafitte, François Mansart, architect, 1660

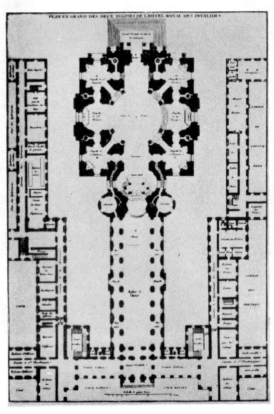

13. Church of the Hôtel des Invalides, plan
(Blondel, *Cours d'architecture*, 1698)

14. Rembrandt, etching: The Great Coppenal
(D. Ravinski, *L'œuvre gravé de Rembrandt,* St. Petersburg, 1890)

15. Rembrandt, etching: Abraham Receiving
the Three Angels
(D. Ravinski, *L'œuvre gravé de Rembrandt,*
St. Petersburg, 1890)

16. Rembrandt, etching: St. Francis Praying
(D. Ravinski, *L'œuvre gravé de Rembrandt,* St. Petersburg, 1890)

17. Molière at Versailles: *Le Malade Imaginaire*
(A. Felibrin, *Les divertissements de Versailles*, 1676)

18. Stage setting, Scipio's Palace, for the opera *Il Fuoco eterno*
(Vienna, 1674)

19. Baroque in Peru: The Adoration of the Magi
by an anonymous Peruvian painter, late seventeenth century
(Courtesy Mrs. Frank Barrows Freyer)

20. Merchants and bankers in a busy port
(J. Savary, *Le Parfait négociant*, 1675)

21. Amsterdam: The Herring-packers' Wharf
Contemporary print, Bibliothèque Nationale, Cabinet des Estampes

22. City planning: An extension of Amsterdam in the seventeenth century
(L. Mumford, *The Culture of Cities,* New York, 1938)
Courtesy Harcourt, Brace & Co.

23. The Fair of Saint-Germain
Bibliothèque Nationale, Cabinet des Estampes

24. Paris—the Pont-Neuf, late seventeenth century
Bibliothèque Nationale, Cabinet des Estampes

25. City planning—Paris, the Porte Saint-Denis
Bibliothèque Nationale, Cabinet des Estampes

Plus on a de moyens, plus on en veut *****
Ce pauvre apporte tout, bled fruit, argent ****
Ce gros Milord assis, prest a tout recevoir
Ne luy veut pas donner la douceur done ****

a la mouche
qui vole
il ne faut
peut dans

Il faut
paier ou
agreer

A tous
Seigneurs
tous
honneurs

Maigre
comme vn
leuorier
dataché

Le Noble — est l'araignée et
le Paisan la mouche

Plus a le Diable,
plus il en veut auoir.
l'laqud ***

26. "The Lord Is the Spider and the Peasant Is the Fly," a contemporary cartoon
Bibliothèque Nationale, Cabinet des Estampes

27. Frankfurt am Main, engraving by M. Merian, 1621-1687

28. Strassburg, engraving, late seventeenth century

29. A Russian town in the seventeenth century: Samara
(Van der Aa, *Galerie du monde*, n.d.)

30. The Leviathan of Thomas Hobbes: title page of the first edition

31. The oath of loyalty to Frederick William, the Great Elector, as sovereign Duke of Prussia, Königsberg, 1662 (Erdmannsdörfer, *Deutsche Geschichte*, Berlin, 1905-1911)

32. Louis XIV commanding the manual of arms
Bibliothèque Nationale, Cabinet des medailles

33. Louis XIV receiving the Dutch delegates suing for peace, 1673
Bibliothèque Nationale, Manuscrits françaises

35. John De Witt
(Erdmannsdörfer, *Deutsche Geschichte*)

34. William III of Orange
(Erdmannsdörfer, *Deutsche Geschichte*)

37. Frederick William of Brandenburg,
the Great Elector
(Erdmannsdörfer, *Deutsche Geschichte*)

36. Emperor Leopold I
(Erdmannsdörfer, *Deutsche Geschichte*)

38. Charles II in the robes of the Order of the Garter
(E. Ashmole, *The Institution of the Most Noble Order of the Garter*,
London, 1672)

39. Parade armor, worn by John Sobieski
at his entry into Vienna, 1683

40. John Sobieski as victor over the Turks at Chocim, 1673

NICOLAUS

Comes perpetuus à ZRINIO, etc. S.ª Cæs.ᵃ Reg. Maj.
à Consiliis, Interioribus, et Regnorum Dalmatiæ, Croatiæ et
Sclavoniæ Banus, Exercituumq; Regni Hungariæ Dux Generalissimus.

41. Nicholas Zrinyi, Hungarian rebel

Warhaftige Original=Abbildung Ungarischen
Feld=Herrn
Emerici Tököli.

42. Emmerich Tököly, Magyar leader against the
Hapsburgs

44. Raimond Montecuculli, Marshal of the Empire

43. George von Deflinger, Marshal of Brandenburg

45. Turenne, Marshal of France

46. Nikon, Patriarch of Moscow, with attendant clergy
(*Antiquités de l'Empire de Russie*, n.d.)

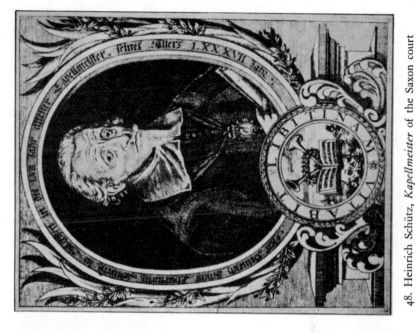

48. Heinrich Schütz, *Kapellmeister* of the Saxon court

47. Paul Gerhardt, German hymnologist

VITVS LVDOVICVS a SECKENDORF
SER. Ac POT. ELECT. BRAND. FRIDERICI III
CONSILIARIVS INTIMVS p VNIVERSITATIS HALENSIS CANCELLARI
NEC NON REDITVVM AC STATVVM PROVINCIALIVM IN DVCATV
ALTENBVRGENSI DIRECTOR etc
NATVS d 20 Decemb 1626 BEATE DENATVS d 18 Decemb 1692

FOLIVM EIVS
NON DEFLVET

49. Veit Ludwig von Seckendorff, Pietist statesman

gether. As in Brandenburg, the *Landtag* was displaced by the *Landstube,* a limited group of deputies from the circles. In Minden, Ravensburg and Halberstadt no opposition was encountered. The archbishopric of Magdeburg remained until 1680 in the hands of the elector of Saxony. The city, however, had for some time been attempting to separate from the archbishopric and to attain "immediacy" in the Empire. By the treaties of Westphalia, however, the elector, as the prospective lord, had secured the right to receive the homage of the city and to maintain a garrison there. These claims the city opposed. Frederick William thereupon turned against Magdeburg the army which he had raised with Dutch subsidies to keep the bishop of Münster from attacking the republic (1666).[7] The city was unprepared and unwilling to resist by force. It therefore surrendered to the elector's demands for the oath and a garrison. When the Elector August died in 1680, the archbishopric was taken over without difficulty and organized very much like Brandenburg.

Frederick William's position as a European potentate, his control and unification of his dominions, and his absolutism rested upon his army. In 1660 this army was still a poor thing, though it had enabled the elector to maneuver his way to considerable successes at the congress of Westphalia and in the negotiation of the Treaty of Oliva. It was then composed of feudal levies and militia (*Wybranzen* in East Prussia) under poorly trained or untrained officers, whom, to tell the truth, Frederick William was hardly able to pay even what they were worth. Although a standing professional army had been in his program since 1644, the army he had used so skillfully and with such effect in the last years of the Thirty Years' War never comprised more than eight thousand men.

The Northern War really saw the beginning of the professional standing army.[8] Frederick William still had to use the feudal services of his nobles (*Lehnspferde*) as late as 1678, but from 1661 onward he demanded in very positive terms the substitution of money payments for actual service. In his "paternal warning" of 1667, he recommended the same for the militia of Brandenburg and the *Wybranzen* of Prussia, which, he declared, were "no good for any kind of war."

The army gradually became more professionalized, though hardly stabilized. The great shortage of money made it necessary to allow numerous dismissals at the end of each campaign and to adopt a lower scale of pay for those retained in winter quarters. Nevertheless, in spite of

[7] O. Hintze, *op. cit.,* 217.

[8] Sidney B. Fay, "The Beginning of the Standing Army in Prussia," *American Historical Review,* 22 (1917), 763–77.

monthly and seasonal variations, the enlisted forces showed a steady increase throughout the elector's reign. After the Treaty of Oliva Frederick
William maintained from seven to eight thousand men. Then, in 1666, to
prevent the bishop of Münster from attacking the Dutch, he increased his
forces to ten thousand. In 1672, on the occasion of the Anglo-French attack
on the Dutch, he raised it to twenty thousand, but after the Treaty of
Vossem, by which he withdrew from the war, he demobilized almost all
of them. The largest force he ever gathered was forty thousand in 1678,
made possible by Dutch subsidies. After the Treaty of Saint-Germain
(1679), he again reduced his army, but French subsidies made it possible
to restrict the reduction. In the last years of the Great Elector's life, the
army numbered about thirty thousand. Such forces were beyond his
means and he was compelled to depend on subsidies from foreign powers,
such as the United Provinces, Spain, France and Austria.[9]

This fact explains much of the elector's foreign policy. He had to have
alliances that would take care of his expenses and, to a certain extent, had
to be satisfied with results that did not correspond to his military effectiveness. Yet despite these necessary mercenary considerations, Frederick
William, unlike some of his successors, always managed to use the army
in the interest of Prussia's power. The army had to earn its way, so to
speak, but the idea of power was there before the means to produce the
instruments of power were fully available. The idea of power became the
life-principle of the Prussian state. It necessitated a great cultural effort
to bring the economic resources of the state up to the level of its political
power and to adapt it to the heavy burdens which the power game involved.

As the army grew, Frederick William brought it more completely under
disciplinary control. Like the French army before 1660, the Brandenburg-
Prussian army was at first a collection of regiments furnished by colonels
who controlled them. Like Louvois, Frederick William gradually brought
the regiments, their recruitment, appointments and direction under the
control of the state. This process was complete by 1681. Experts such as
Lisola, the Imperial ambassador, and Rebenec, a French ambassador,
agreed that the elector's soldiers were the best in Europe. Discipline was
strict, but more rational and less brutal than in most armies. The technical services, the artillery and the engineers, were brought to a high level
of equipment and training.

Although he was cut off from the sea except in eastern Pomerania and
East Prussia, which were both poor bases for maritime activity, Frederick

9 O. Hintze, *op. cit.*, 221.

William, inspired by his Dutch experience as a youth and more specifically by two Dutchmen, the Admiral Gysels de Lier, and an adventurous businessman, Benjamin Raule, developed the ambition to have a navy. In 1675 Raule undertook to build him one on commission and did so. By 1684 the fleet amounted to one frigate and two little ships at Königsberg and seven vessels at Emden in East Frisia, mounting a total of 178 guns. This naval effort, like the effort to establish Brandenburg-Prussia as an oceanic trading power,[10] failed almost ridiculously in comparison with the military development. The strategic objective, however, was not ridiculous. Control of the Baltic would have solved the Swedish question.

To pay for a good army, Brandenburg-Prussia needed to be rich and it was very poor. During the Thirty Years' War Brandenburg had been ravaged by both sides to such a point that the approaches to Berlin seemed a desert. The elector was obliged to order the peasants to join in wolf hunts. The use of Pomerania and Brandenburg by Sweden in the War of the North (1655–1660) was no less destructive. Prussia was so ravaged by the raids of the Lithuanians and Tartars in 1656 that the high councilors in 1664 were still discussing the misery that resulted. Cleves-Mark was more fortunate. In 1660 it had been spared from war for more than ten years, but it was still not back to normal. In the circumstances, the only possible basis for the power which Frederick William intended to create was a drastic reconstruction. This Frederick William began after the Treaty of Oliva and this he never lost sight of to the end.

The elector interested himself personally in agricultural reconstruction. In addition to a policy of exempting from taxes for six years any peasant who would occupy and exploit an abandoned homestead, he brought seeds and livestock from East Prussia in quantity and distributed them generously. The most distinctive aspect of his policy, however, was his colonization program. From 1648 onward Dutch were settling in the valley of the Havel and after 1660 organized groups of Dutch and Germans from other parts of the Empire were established in Brandenburg and East Prussia. Persecuted Lutherans from the Palatinate and persecuted Calvinists from Saxony availed themselves in large numbers of the intelligent welcome of which they were assured. Even Swiss from the canton of Berne formed a considerable part of the immigration to Brandenburg. The largest contingent, however, and in nearly all respects the most important, were the Huguenots. Even before the revocation of the Edict of Nantes they were so numerous that by 1672 they had a church in Berlin, with services in French. After Frederick William's Edict of Pots-

[10] See below, p. 118.

dam (November 8, 1685), which, as a retort to the revocation, offered substantial advantages to the Huguenots who came to Brandenburg, the numbers rose to something like 150,000. Those who came were largely an urban group, but some turned to agriculture and established flourishing colonies, especially in Uckermark, making a profound impress on the agriculture and food habits of the region by introducing new culture such as tobacco, and setting a new standard of gardening.[11] The whole Moabit region, northwest of Berlin, became a market-gardening area producing peas, beans and asparagus. An exile named Ruzé became the gardener of the elector and covered the palace grounds of Potsdam and Berlin with flowers. Instead of the cheerless aspect of a desert, the approach to Berlin at the death of the elector presented the picture of an industriously exploited region. As good an index as any of the advance of agriculture was the increase in population. Frederick William himself evaluated it as one-third from the beginning of his reign to the end. In 1688 most estimates put the total at about 1,500,000.

Like his contemporaries, however, Frederick William counted on industry to enrich his states and labored unceasingly to develop it.[12] He used the ideas and institutions of his time with considerable effectiveness. While he maintained the gilds and crafts in the full enjoyment of their monopolies, he subjected them to the control of his administration and forced them to liberalize their terms of admission. He even carried the question to the diet of the Empire, but his modest proposals were too revolutionary for his contemporaries. His general industrial policy was one of extreme protectionism. He imposed numerous prohibitions in the interest of old or new industries, and an elaborate system of regulation for established industries. As elsewhere, wool production and the woolens industry were minutely controlled to insure the maximum utilization within his own dominions of the raw material produced. This system worked so well that at the end of his reign Frederick William was able to put his infantry into uniform blue produced by the textile workers of Stendal, Salzwedel, Brandenburg, Berlin and Frankfurt. The iron and copper of Mark, Halberstadt and Magdeburg was exploited by a substantially developed metallurgical industry, of which the principal center was Peitz. A cannon foundry was established at Königsberg. In Brandenburg as in London, brewing was becoming a large-scale industry; in 1669 the little town of Bernau sold over five thousand barrels of beer in Berlin and its suburbs.[13]

[11] A. Waddington, *op. cit.,* I, 390.
[12] *Ibid.,* I, 390.
[13] *Ibid.,* I, 393.

Generous inducements attracted industrial workers from various parts of Europe, especially from Holland. As in agriculture, the most massive and significant influx was the Huguenot immigration. It is estimated that among this group were about five thousand artisans. In addition to a general technical superiority, they brought in new lines of production, such as paper, tapestries, stockings, mirrors, gloves, candles. Though the attempt to introduce silk-growing and manufacture in Brandenburg failed, the Huguenot refugees successfully transplanted some of the most advanced types of French industry.

Under the direct impulsion of the elector, the means of communication were extensively improved between 1660 and 1688. The care and improvement of the roads were imposed upon the local communities and made the responsibility of an inspector in each circle. The rivers were brought up to a high standard of navigability. Between 1662 and 1668, under the direction of a Piedmontese engineer, Felipe de Chieza, the Elbe and the Oder were joined by a canal which utilized the course of the Spree and the Havel. The canal permitted the commerce of central Germany to outflank the Swedish and Danish tolls. It made Berlin one of the principal centers of commerce and prepared for this rather dismal village the metropolitan function it was to assume in the nineteenth century. The relatively poor ports of Outer Pomerania and of East Prussia were brought up to their capabilities; Königsberg was made accessible even to the largest vessels of the time. In 1682–1683 this port development was more than doubled by an agreement with the estates of East Frisia, which gave the elector's subjects the right to use the great harbor of Emden on the North Sea.

In 1654 the elector, in disregard of the quasi-feudal claims of the prince of Thurn and Taxis to a monopoly of the imperial posts, put the postal service of his scattered domains in charge of Michael Mathias. During his tenure of thirty years, Mathias established a rapid and trustworthy service between Berlin and all the other centers of the elector's possessions. The stages were short, about fifteen miles; passage to Cleves required only six days, to Königsberg five. The charges were relatively moderate and the secrecy of letters generally respected except in time of war. In 1687 the service was put in charge of the postmasters of Berlin, Cleves and Wesel.[14]

The removal of barriers to trade within the Hohenzollern dominions and within Germany was not foreign to Frederick William's mind but proceeded slowly and not very far. The canal of Mühlrose outflanked some Brandenburg customs, one series of which involved eighteen pay-

[14] F. Schevill, *op. cit.*, 248.

ments of one florin per ton between the Elbe and the Oder. Attempts to interest the Rhenish electors in the suppression of some of the Rhine tolls, the count of Oldenburg in the reduction of customs duties at Elsvliet on the Weser, and the Swedes at Stettin in freeing the navigation of the Ihna, proved vain. In this field, the elector was constantly hampered by his own pressing financial needs.

Abroad he met with little success. The Treaty of Westminster with Charles II of England gave Electoral and English subjects "most-favored-nation" status in the ports of the respective nations for ten years, but it was not renewed in 1672. Several approaches were made to France, especially after the Treaty of Saint-Germain (1679), but without success. The Spanish were equally unresponsive. The Electoral government turned to the "interlopers," furnishing them with legal authority to trade in the domains of the chartered companies of other nations. Much effort was expended to induce them to make Prussia, Pomerania or Emden (after 1682) their base of operations, but without much success. The elector long cherished the idea of an overseas establishment, and in 1661 attempted to promote an Imperial East India Company which came to nothing because Austria would not co-operate. After the Treaty of Saint-Germain he returned to the idea and, under the direction of Benjamin Raule, the Netherlander who had built his navy, sent out two expeditions to set up establishments on the African Gold Coast. The Dutch East India Company broke up the first effort on the ground that the vessels and crews were Dutch, but the second secured a slight foothold. An African Company was formed on capital furnished by the elector, by Raule and by the estates of East Frisia, with which a treaty was made providing for the use of Emden. This organization lasted until 1720 when King Frederick William I sold it to the Dutch. An East India Company was organized in 1684, but the death of its principal agent in Russia in 1688 ended its slight activity. The total positive result of these colonial enterprises was the advantageous foothold in Emden, which eventuated in the acquisition of East Frisia in 1744.

Frederick William imposed his authority as effectively in the realm of religion as in the realm of finance.[15] An exceptionally devout Calvinist, he nevertheless by principle and by policy used his power to enforce upon reluctant ecclesiastics the practice of toleration. "Like a father and without consideration of religion, you should love those whom God has given you as your subjects," he advised his successor. His subjects were

15 *Ibid.*, 249–53.

less tolerant. In the county of Mark, which was Calvinist, the elector had to protect Lutherans from persecution, while in Brandenburg and Prussia, which were Lutheran, he protected Calvinists. Paul Gerhardt, a pastor whose hymns are still sung, was exiled from Berlin for declaring from his pulpit that he could not regard Calvinists as Christians. In Prussia Frederick William intervened to save two professors of Königsberg, accused of "syncretism" because they advocated the union of all Christians. A decree of 1662 forbade candidates from Brandenburg to study theology at Wittenberg, because of its intransigent Lutheranism. Frederick William favored as much as he could the mission in Brandenburg of John Durie, a Scot who was the apostle of union among evangelicals.

As a good Calvinist, the elector was anti-Catholic. He was happy to see Brandenburg and Pomerania free of "the vulgar abominations and idolatry of papistry." [16] For a moment after the revocation of the Edict of Nantes, he resorted to reprisals, expelling some monks and forbidding Catholic worship. This, however, was only a momentary reaction. In various parts of his territories Catholic ecclesiastics themselves were glad to testify to the equity with which they were treated. Many convents remained open. In Halberstadt as late as 1808 the cathedral chapter still included four Catholic canons. In the duchy of Prussia the elector himself built some Catholic churches, while in the territories later acquired from Poland, bishops and curates were permitted to exercise lordship even over a Protestant population. Only against the Jesuits did the Great Elector maintain a constant ban.

The toleration which Frederick William exercised was so exceptional that it was supposed to conceal a predisposition to return to the Catholic Church. At least three missions were sent to Berlin to complete his conversion, but the man who had refused a chance to become king of Poland rather than abandon Calvinism was recalcitrant. Frederick William conceived his position with reference to religion as that of a universal bishop and he did not hesitate to prescribe specific additions to the church calendar, such as days of prayer and expiation, for Calvinists, Lutherans and Catholics alike. He rigorously restricted any appeal outside his territories, even in matters of faith.[17]

In view of the character of his principles it was logical that the elector's toleration should extend to lesser religious sects as well. The hated Socinians from Poland, the Vaudois from Piedmont, the Mennonites with

[16] A. Waddington, op. cit., I, 440.
[17] Ibid., I, 441.

their Anabaptist traditions, all found refuge in his dominions and protection against the clamors of the dominant groups. Even the Jews, who had been barred from Prussia and Brandenburg in the sixteenth century, were admitted in considerable numbers under the elector's *Schützbriefe.* Frederick William to be sure, charged them well for the privilege, but allowed the more wealthy to serve him as bankers with the title of *Hofjude.*[18]

The constructive work of Frederick William extended also to the intellectual life, and especially to the educational system. Although nothing was done for primary education, sadly reduced by the Thirty Years' war, secondary education, the essential for the training of future functionaries, was considerably advanced by the foundation of several new *Gymnasia.* Higher education received even more of the elector's attention. The University of Duisburg was founded in 1654–1655, and Halle, then a *Ritterakademie,* began to show some manifestations of its later development. Frankfurt an der Oder, which Frederick William held for "a precious jewel," received substantial subventions. At Königsberg, with its twenty-one professors, the salaries were raised and new funds established for the support of poor students. New professors were brought in from abroad.[19]

In general, however, the widespread poverty limited progress in education. The number of students was small and the general intellectual level remained low. As in the case of so much of the elector's work, the principal results were to be in the future. The universities ceased to be self-sufficient corporations and, reduced to state discipline, were susceptible to the impulsions that in later times made the German universities powerful agencies in the intellectual life of the nineteenth century.

Under the influence of a Swedish refugee, Benedict Skytte, Frederick William dreamed for a moment of creating a world university, the *universitas brandenburgica gentium, scientiarum et artium,* on the lines laid down by Bacon and Comenius, with personnel drawn from scholars exiled either for religious or political reasons. A decree constituting the university was prepared and circulars broadcast, but only a few English Nonconformists responded. The project had to be given up, but it reflects the revolutionary character which this state-maker shared with his contemporaries.

Frederick William was something of a virtuoso. He maintained a

---

[18] H. Rachel, "Die Juden im Berliner Wirtschaftsleben zur Zeit des Merkantilismus," *Zeitschrift für der Geschichte der Juden in Deutschland,* 2 (1930), 175–96.

[19] F. Schevill, *op. cit.,* 380.

chemical laboratory, unfortunately under the guidance of an alchemist. He patronized Otto von Guericke, who dedicated to him his book on the vacuum (1671). Surgery and medicine were backward, but a great step was taken in zoology when the first zoological garden was established near Cleves by John Maurice of Nassau, who was also the leading spirit in the organization of mineralogical, botanical and ethnographical collections. These were constantly increased by contributions from the elector's correspondents in all parts of the world. Libraries were established at Cleves, Königsberg and Berlin, but only the one at Berlin developed significantly. In 1688 it had 618 manuscripts and 80,000 books. Letters and the arts remained mostly a matter of importation and immigration.

The Great Elector succeeded in creating the state as machine, but not the state as organism. The scattered societies subject to his commands remained socially separated. The old medieval fabric, composed of a nobility imbued with prejudices of caste, a bourgeoisie dominated by petty local interest, and a peasantry despised and exploited by both, was not only maintained but even fortified during his reign. The people were to be loved, he told his successor, but for the powerful machine that he created they were objects and not participants. The state remained external like a Moloch, devouring and beneficent at the same time.

Brandenburg-Prussia had become a state. The process had been peculiarly abstract-mechanical, and of uniform simplicity throughout. An active administrative organization had gradually overlaid the local organizations. When resistance was provoked, it was obliterated by the use of force, by an army without local attachments. One looks in vain for indications of any social need to which the unity which Frederick William created was a response. Other than the interest of the state itself—and Frederick William much more appropriately than Louis XIV might have said, "I am the state"—no common interest of Cleves and Prussia, Brandenburg and Pomerania was existent, not to say operative, in the process. Such "nationalism" as there was, was German rather than Prussian. In a pamphlet which the elector had published in 1658 to rouse popular opinion against the retention of Pomerania by the Swedes, the changes were rung on the theme, "Remember that you are a German." [20] The pamphlet was popular and ran through a number of editions. Frederick William also protested against the *Rheinbund* because it "subjected weak German powers to strong foreign ones." When it seemed to serve his interests, on the other hand, he did not hesitate to ally himself

[20] A. W. Ward, "The Great Elector and the First Prussian King," *Cambridge Modern History*, V, 644.

with France (1679) and to lend some assistance in the "reunions" and the occupation of Strassburg. Correctly or incorrectly, the emperor distrusted him to such an extent that in 1682 he declined the elector's offer of twelve thousand troops to aid against the Turks.

It was, nevertheless, a beneficent rather than a merely exploitative state that Frederick William created. Over a wide range, he effected ameliorations that, taken separately and together, quite transcend the record of any of his contemporary fellow monarchs. Toleration was established as law; his economic promotion was successful; the standards of public service were raised; the army discipline was rationalized; educational institutions were strengthened; transportation and communication were developed; sanitation became an object of state concern. That, like his contemporaries, he failed egregiously in not including in his program the improvement of the social condition of the depressed peasantry and town laborers, only the sequel was to show.

II. THE EMPIRE, THE HAPSBURGS AND THE DANUBE [21]

The political history of Germany in the latter part of the seventeenth century presents a striking contrast between moribund and nascent institutions that vividly illumines the evolutionary problem of the absolute state.

The treaties of Westphalia marked the end of the ancient concepts of unity and catholicity of which the Holy Roman Empire had been the very imperfect expression. Even the remnants and vestiges of universality, which during the sixteenth century still clung to its name, became only a vague memory. The territorial independence of the princes was given the recognition for which they had been striving ever since the days of the Saxons and the Hohenstaufen. As interpreted by "Hippolytus a lapide" (Philip Chemnitz) the independence of the princes had become the cornerstone of Germany's constitution. His book, entitled *De ratione status in imperio nostro romano-germanico,* was devoted to the thesis that the power of the emperor was excessive and dangerous—the incessant quarrels of the emperors and princes proved it—and he therefore advocated the expulsion of the Austrians from the Empire as the holders of this dangerous power. The true interpretation of the constitution, he

[21] A. Huber, *Geschichte Österreichs* (5 vols., Gotha, 1885–1896), Vol. 6 (1648–1705) by O. Redlich (Gotha, 1921); Hugo Hantsch, *Die Entwicklung Österreich-Ungarns zur Grossmacht* (Freiburg, 1933); C. M. Knatchbull-Hugessen, *The Political Evolution of the Hungarian Nation* (2 vols., London, 1908); Dominic G. Kosáry, *A History of Hungary* (Cleveland, 1941); Louis Léger, *Histoire de l'Autriche-Hongrie depuis ses origines jusqu'à l'année 1878* (Paris, 1879; 6th ed., 1920).

claimed, vested sovereignty in the members of the Empire, meeting in a diet, the presidency of which carried with it the title of emperor, but in no sense involved actual sovereignty. The emperor's function was conceived of as purely ministerial. If he violated the laws, it was the business of the members to resist him.

The book of "Hippolytus a lapide" made a great impression in its day. It did more harm to the cause of Austria, people said, than the loss of several battles. In our perspective, it seems more likely that it stated fairly what had happened quite independently of its influence. The Empire was actually in such a confused state of disorganization that the more cautious Pufendorf (writing under the pseudonym "Severinus de Mombazano") could find no way of fitting it into any known classification; it was neither monarchy, aristocracy nor democracy; it was not even a mixture of these three types, but only an indefinite association "like that of the Greeks marching against Troy." Rome and its title to the sovereignty of the world was quite forgotten!

Nevertheless, the Empire persisted in spite of a constitution that seemed to doom it to disintegration. Two foreign monarchs hostile to its existence as a great power, the kings of France and Sweden, held parts of the German lands and participated in its politics. Two of its members, the emperor himself and the margrave of Brandenburg, were heads of major units of power outside the German lands and outside the Imperial organization. As in 1517, it seemed for a moment as though the imperial title itself was about to pass to the house of Bourbon. In 1658 Mazarin spared neither money nor diplomacy to bring about the election of Maximilian of Bavaria, but in spite of all he could do, Leopold I, the Hapsburg scion, was elected. It was an opportunity missed for the Empire to become European and for the lost unity of Europe to be reconstituted.

The diplomatic independence of the princes made it possible for the French to organize the anomalous League of the Rhine, composed of the French and Swedish kings, the electors of Mainz and Cologne, and the princes of Neuburg, Brunswick and Hesse-Cassel, to protect the "Germanic liberties" against the tyranny of Austria. In spite of the efforts of Leopold I to obtain its dissolution, it was renewed in 1660 and reinforced by the adherence of the duke of Württemberg in 1664.

The aggressions of Louis XIV in 1667 and 1668 alarmed the German members to such a point that they refused to renew the League, but the emperor was quite unable to convert it to his own purposes. The French government, by a judicious distribution of pensions, bribes and honors, succeeded in maintaining an effective group of princes, politicians and publicists as partisans of its policy. If French diplomacy failed to win the princes to action favoring France, it at least secured their benevolent neutrality. Louis XIV continued to wield an influence in Germany superior to that of the emperor as such.

The functions of the emperor were numerous but without importance. His revenues, almost equally numerous, had been adroitly appropriated by the states. The learned jurists who attended his courts attempted vainly to revive the authoritative traditions of the Roman law. Legislation was impossible and the Imperial courts gradually fell into desuetude.

The diet, composed of the college of electors, the college of princes and the college of towns, had functions which, though nominally important, were rendered nugatory by the lack of any disposition on the part of the states to act together. Agreement was extremely difficult to obtain and became more so when in 1663 the college of princes ceased to be the occasional gathering of the princes and became, instead, a permanent assembly of their representatives. The necessity of referring to the princes for instructions in regard to every decision made action almost impossible. The operations of the diet became slower than ever and foreign influences had every opportunity to intrude. The diet afforded a particularly convenient instrument for stirring up religious differences. The conversion of a Protestant prince to Catholicism, or the succession of a prince of a religion differing from that of his predecessor, were the subjects of unending discussion. The treaties of Westphalia had given the Protestants the right to vote as a separate corps in all matters touching religion: the princes used it constantly to defeat the proposals of the emperor and even to prevent the raising of forces at critical times.

The diet did function as an organ for the prevention of wars between members and in principle even effected an important reform in the military organization. The Empire was divided into "circles" to assure bringing together in the Imperial army soldiers from the same region with the same language and customs. Each circle had its own treasury, and a special treasury of the Empire was created, to be supplied by contributions from the states. The army thus based was to consist of 28,000 infantry and 12,000 cavalry in time of peace and could be doubled or tripled in time of war. Unfortunately for the Empire, this system was not kept up except in the "forward circles," that is those bordering on France. The other states soon made treaties merely agreeing to maintain certain troops.

The administrative machine was given a quasi-modern aspect by putting at the head of each of the ten circles a prince-governor. In theory, the Empire was to act effectively against any of its members. In reality, the "circles" were even more obstructive than the diets. Each of the 360 states, proud of the territorial sovereignty just won and anxious to preserve it, had its own diet or *Landtag,* as eager as the prince to prevent effective action by the Empire. The knights of the Empire, not themselves sovereign, but holders of lordships scattered throughout the Empire, might have been a valuable force for unification, had they recognized their true interest. Instead, they hampered unity by putting up barriers on their lands against the movement of commerce.

While the Empire and the Imperial idea were falling into desuetude, two great states of Germany were evolving from the confused aggregation of feudal lordships. The Hapsburgs and Hohenzollerns had been important and acquisitive dynasties ever since the thirteenth century. In our period, however, the dynastic aspect was fading out. Austria and Brandenburg imposed upon the diverse elements of which they were constituted a degree of uniformity and centralization hardly surpassed in Europe before the French Revolution. The meaning of the process became apparent from the codification of its results in each of these states in the early eighteenth century. Frederick William I of Prussia's Edict of August 13, 1713, declared the inalienability of any of his territories. The Pragmatic Sanction of Charles VI of Austria in 1723 set aside the old patrimonial idea and put in its place the idea of an indivisible state. The historical process of which these acts were the expression began before our period and continued after it, but in each state great advances were made between 1660 and 1685.

In Austria Leopold I, who succeeded as archduke and emperor in 1658, made far less of a reputation than Frederick William of Prussia (1640–1688), whom his own and succeeding generations have united in calling the Great Elector. Nonetheless, the sum of their achievements as state-builders was curiously equal.

For Austria as for Brandenburg the problem was the consolidation of the diverse dynastic possessions into a state. The nobility, about which the localisms organized themselves, had not wholly disappeared as a privileged and governing class, but it had ceased to be capable of effective opposition to the crown in the Bohemian and Austrian lands. The nobles sought honor and reputation in the service of the prince. Their only hope for power was to share it as a part of the court and of the administrative system. The court developed as the center of all that was modern and brilliant in all the Hapsburg lands. Relation to the court decided social standing. As in France, the crown had become the source of honor and reputation for the whole mass of subjects, who were classified according to their privileges and social position, but nevertheless all served the one master. About the Austrian court chancellery, which had been separated from the imperial court chancellery in 1620, a superior magistracy began to form which achieved an ascendancy over the local magistracies still existing in the several Austrias. More important, it assured the conduct of political affairs from the unitary standpoint.[22]

To a certain extent the Hapsburg administration was cosmopolitan. While the appointment of individuals to functions relative to their own homeland was not excluded, officials were commonly removed from their native regions to Vienna, where the chancelleries were located, and might expect to be active in any one or more of half a dozen parts of the domains. Germans, Italians, Frenchmen, Dutch, Poles, men with organizational talent from all over Europe found a ready welcome in Vienna. It is well known that the distinguished leadership of the Hapsburg armies (by whatever title they were brought together) was anything but Austrian. Charles of Lorraine, Montecuccoli, Eugene of Savoy, Caraffa, the elector of Baden and others made themselves famous as commanders of Hapsburg armies, to say nothing of the Pole, John Sobieski, who was a special case.

The same was true of the civil administration. Lobkowitz was a Bohemian *Freiherr;* Lisola was a Burgundian; Johann Joachim Becher came from Mainz. The legists came from everywhere. Even though some of their efforts, not in themselves discreditable, were doomed to failure, yet altogether they gave the Vienna service a cachet of distinction and of competence.

As archduke of Austria, Leopold I enjoyed an inheritance of remarkably complicated character. Austria itself was not one land, but three (Upper, Lower and Inner), each with its own feudal estates. To Austria had been aggregated certain other territorial lordships, such as Carinthia and Styria. The Tyrol had once belonged to the Hapsburg inheritance, but had been separated from it by Ferdinand I for the benefit of a younger line. It was the sign of an important change in political style when in 1665 it was reunited with the rest of the inheritance.

Politically the old hereditary lands offer little clue to the development of the Austrian *Reich.* The kingdoms to which the Hapsburgs had won election in the sixteenth century underwent a more critical development.

Bohemia had been completely subjected as a result of the misfortunes of the elector palatine—the Winter King—early in the Thirty Years' War.

22 Harry Schwartz, *The Imperial Privy Council in the Seventeenth Century* (Cambridge, Mass., 1943).

The old national religion had been proscribed. The old nobility had been completely destroyed and the new nobility had neither status nor historical sanction for resistance to the monarchy and its agents. All the essential decisions, the appointments to office and the administration of affairs were in the hands of the Bohemian court chancellery at Vienna, which had become the exclusive intermediary between the Hapsburg king and the Bohemian people. Although the chancellorship and other high offices might be held by Bohemians, the kingdom was ruled by men who, whether themselves Bohemian or not, saw Bohemia only as part of a larger whole, the Austrian state. Exclusive Hussite nationalism had no place in this scheme of things. German became an official language and the language of culture and politics. The Hapsburg king had become hereditary and had all power of legislation and control. In one part of his lands absolutism had been attained.

The critical problem of the late seventeenth century was the relationship of Hungary to the growing unity of the Hapsburg inheritances under the dominion of Vienna. Hungary had remained a separate kingdom and the kingship had remained elective. Even the Golden Bull of 1222 legalizing armed resistance to the king was still part of the law of the land. On the other hand, the Hapsburg kings had persistently ignored the demand of the Hungarian nobles for place and perquisites and had concentrated the management of Hungarian affairs at Vienna. The presence of the Turks in the valley of the Theiss, where they prevented the organization of Hapsburg power rather than ruling themselves, was of course disruptive to any coherent policy. The Hapsburgs actually controlled only about three-tenths of Hungary proper. In Transylvania the Hungarian nobles, by playing off the Turks against the Hapsburgs, had maintained substantial independence. This division did not prevent the Hungarians of all three sections participating in the politics of the remnant controlled by the Hapsburgs or from turning to the Turks or the Transylvanians, or even, as opportunity offered, to Louis XIV.

The political issues were complicated by religious cleavage. Protestantism had made a considerable place for itself among the Hungarians. In Transylvania Catholicism, Lutheranism, Calvinism and Unitarianism (Socinianism) enjoyed equal status. In Turkish Hungary the Moslem conquerors were quite indifferent to the variations of Christianity. In Hapsburg Hungary Protestantism had been deeply rooted by the end of the sixteenth century, but during the reign of Ferdinand II the dynamic propaganda of Peter Pazmany, a convert from Protestantism, brought many of the leading magnates back to the Catholic fold and restored

Catholic predominance in Western Hungary.[23] When Leopold I came to the throne in 1657, his *diploma inaugurale* pledged him to maintain the law of 1608 which guaranteed religious freedom. The Catholic nobility, however, despite the provisions of this legislation, assumed the right to convert churches on their lands to Catholic use and to force the return of Catholic deputies to the diet.[24]

At the very beginning of Leopold's reign the problem was somewhat simplified by the excessive ambitions of George II Rákóczy, the substantially independent prince of Transylvania. In 1657 Rákóczy, in alliance with Sweden, went to war with Poland, hoping to win the crown as Stefan Bathory had done in his time. Abandoned by the Swedes, harried by the imperial forces under Montecuccoli and by English, Dutch and Russians, George II offered a tempting opportunity to the Turks. Mohammed Kuprili, the old man who as grand vizier had been reinvigorating the whole Turkish system, sent tremendous armies to wipe out the independence of the Transylvanian magnates. Michael Apaffy replaced Rákóczy and accepted Turkish vassalage. By 1662 only two Hungaries were left, the Austrian and the Turkish.

The defeated Transylvanians appealed to Leopold I as king of Hungary, less because of any indicated sympathy than because he was the only recourse against the Turks, as the Turks had more than once been against the Hapsburgs. The tension characteristic of the Magyar diets had already begun. The Protestants were on the alert against any attempt of the Catholic bureaucracy from Vienna; the nobles cried out against the presence of "foreign" troops and against any attempt to use Magyar troops outside Hungary. In the diet of 1662 the Protestant nobles seceded. Leopold I had no reason to regard either the Hungarian Table of Magnates or the demanding Transylvanians as particularly helpful subjects.

When the grand vizier captured Ujvar (Neuhaüsel) and threatened to capture Vienna and complete the subjection of Hungary, the quarrels were appeased sufficiently to permit the organization of an effective army under Montecuccoli. In 1664, after the Magyar leaders had distinguished themselves in exhibitionist heroics, the brilliant tactics of Montecuccoli at the battle of Saint Gotthard drove the Turks back across the Raab.

At this moment Leopold as king of Hungary concluded the peace of Vasvár with the Turks because, as the head of the house of Hapsburg, the archduke of Austria and emperor, he was beginning to discern dan-

23 D. G. Kosáry, *op. cit.*, 123.
24 C. M. Knatchbull-Hugessen, *op. cit.*, I, 150.

gerous developments in quite another part of the continent. The Spanish succession was coming into question.[25] To secure peace, Leopold yielded territory (Hungarian) to the Turks. Thus, the peace of Vasvár from the Magyar point of view was a betrayal of the nation and a justification for rebellion. The Magyar nobility recognized at once that the advance of the Viennese bureaucracy was a threat to their own "liberties." It was whispered among the magnates that the courtiers spoke thus of the Hungarians: "We are going to throw their big hats and plumes in the mud and substitute lead for their gold and silver buttons." The restless Magyars of Hapsburg Hungary, under the leadership of several magnates who have become saints of the Hungarian political calendar, Zrinyi, Nadasdy and Vesselenyi, Tököli and, after 1666, another Rákóczy, the son of George II, revived their resistance to the Hapsburgs.

At the marriage of the young Rákóczy with a daughter of Zrinyi, arrangements were effected among the chief conspirators. Their hopes rested less upon their own power than upon the support of France, Turkey and even some of the German princes. Unfortunately for their combination, they were as jealous of each other as of the imperial power. When Apaffy, the prince of Transylvania, saw a Rákóczy, he saw a rival claimant to his throne. Zrinyi hoped for a kingship of the Croats and Slovenes, perhaps of the Hungarians, which did not fit with Nadasdy's ambition to succeed Vesselenyi as palatine. It was not, then, surprising that Lobkowitz, Leopold's chief minister, got all the information necessary to seize the principals and execute them.

The conspiracy was a godsend for the Viennese administration. A reign of terror followed upon the convictions. The nobles could only escape suspicion and trial by the most abject submission. The Protestants were punished for treason as well as for heresy and hundreds of their pastors were sent to the galleys of Naples to languish there until the Dutch Admiral de Ruyter released them when he conducted his Sicilian campaign in 1676. The traditional office of palatine, which had been held by a distinguished Magyar noble as the head of the diet, was abolished and the government at Pressburg was put in the hands of the high master of the German order as viceroy. Hapsburg Hungary seemed ready for the methods which had reduced Bohemia to absolute submission.

Unlike the Bohemians, however, the Magyars were able to obtain effective foreign support. Louis XIV, who had compunctions about supporting rebels, thought it right to do so when their prince was his enemy. The

[25] See below, Chapter Five.

part the emperor took in organizing the resistance of Europe to "devolution" ended his scruples. After 1664 he permitted his agents in Poland to lend support to rebels as they appeared.[26] The *Kouroutzes,* or crusaders, at last found a leader in Emmerich Tököli. Tököli was the son of one of the leaders of the earlier insurrection who had died while he was being besieged, the grandson of one of the three first executed, the husband of Helene Zrinyi, daughter of another "martyr" and widow of Francis Rákóczy, who had been spared for a few years of isolated life. Tököli was the heir of many hatreds and did not hesitate, when Louis XIV withdrew his assistance after Nimwegen, to turn to the Turks.

Leopold I had meanwhile revised his policy. He had decided to subordinate religious considerations to the unification of all his forces for resistance to Louis XIV. It had become obvious that the policy of harshness and persecution did not increase his power against his principal enemies, the French and the Turks. In 1679 he began by recalling the governor-dictator whose rule had become offensive to Catholics as to Protestants, and dismissed Lobkowitz, his chief minister, who had made himself hated for all time by the Hungarians. A few months later he made a truce with Tököli. In 1681, at the diet of Oldenburg, Hungarian constitutional life was restored. The office of palatine was revived and conferred upon Paul Esterhazy. The emperor agreed to govern Hungary with the advice of a Hungarian council. It was decreed that henceforth no Hungarian should be molested in the free exercise of his religion. A large number of towns and villages were permitted to erect Protestant churches. The landed classes recovered some of their rights as against the crown.

This settlement of Hungarian affairs would have been definitive but for the unsatisfied hatred of Tököli for the Hapsburgs. In spite of courtesies offered him, he refused to accept the results of the diet and took offense at the election of Esterhazy as palatine. In the last months of 1681 he sent three envoys to Constantinople to offer the sultan the suzerainty of Hungary. His forces joined the Turkish army in time to share in the disastrous defeat before Vienna. Thereafter he went from one reverse to another until the grand vizier imprisoned him as the source of the Turkish army's misfortunes. For some years Helen Zrinyi held out with a few of her husband's followers at Munkács, but in 1687 she and her children became the prisoners of the emperor. It was not until after the Treaty of Passarowitz (1699) that the troublesome pair were disposed of,

---

[26] J. Hudita, *Histoire des relations diplomatiques entre la France et la Translyvanie* (Paris, 1927), *passim.*

when they were interned in Asia Minor for the remainder of their lives in accordance with a special agreement between Austria and the Turks.

The fall of Buda in 1686, another bloody assizes at Eperjes like that of Pressburg, and another intervention of the emperor-king on the side of mercy, paved the way for the completion of the constitutional advance of the Hapsburgs. The diet of 1687, in return for a new amnesty which excluded only Emmerich Tököli himself, gave up the right of election and made the kingship hereditary in the Hapsburg family. The old right of rebellion, which dated back to the Golden Bull of 1222, was surrendered. Two important qualifications later created problems: one, that if the Hapsburg male line ran out, the right of election should be resumed, and the other, that the new sovereign, whoever he might be, should swear fidelity to the fundamental laws of the kingdom.

Thus Leopold I, in the face of tremendous difficulties, internal and external, had effectively shifted the whole axis of the complex of which his house had been and remained the leading element. The lordships of the family were transformed into a great co-ordinated state of which the family furnished the sovereigns. It is hardly necessary in this year of grace to attempt to analyze its importance as the organization of the Danube lands. It is well to recall that without destroying the local cultures of the areas included within it, the Hapsburg state functioned effectively for more than two centuries as the framework of diverse groups that now when it is gone find life dangerous and difficult without it.

III. ROYALIST REVOLUTIONS: DENMARK AND SWEDEN [27]

In 1660 the devolution of power in Sweden seemed complete. Charles X, who had initiated a program of undoing Christina's reckless dissipation of the royal domain, had died. He had left the succession to an infant son and the power of a council of regency completely in the control of the magnates, of whom Magnus de la Gardie was the leader. It was not even intended to be a strong government. The dissipation of the crown revenues continued and was intensified. Even the exploitation of Sweden's reputation for military invincibility declined to the level of mere bargaining for subsidies. By a political trick, Sweden was brought into the Triple Alliance of 1667. This brought some Dutch money into the treasury. The

---

[27] Carl Hallendorff and Adolf Schück, *History of Sweden* (Stockholm, 1929); A. A. Stomberg, *A History of Sweden* (New York, 1931); R. N. Bain, *Scandinavia, a Political History of Denmark, Norway and Sweden from 1513 to 1900* (Cambridge, England, 1905); W. F. Reddaway, "The Scandinavian Kingdoms," in *Cambridge Modern History*, Vol. V, ch. 18; C. Schefer, "Les états scandinaves," in Lavisse and Rambaud, *Histoire générale*, Vol. VI, ch. 17.

abortive effort of de Witt to strengthen the alliance after the treaty of
Aix-la-Chapelle brought the promise of further sums from Spain. The
more dependable and more generous offers of France, both to the government and to individual members, brought the council of regency back to
the policy of alliance with France.

The army had been allowed to fall far below the standards of Gustavus
Adolphus both in discipline and leadership. It was hoped that, as in the
Devolution War, Sweden would not be called upon to take any active
part in the war against the Dutch.[28] When the Alliance of the Hague was
reinforced by the participation of Frederick William, the French called
upon Sweden at least to threaten Brandenburg. A poorly equipped and
poorly led army was moved across the Baltic and into Brandenburg just as
Frederick William was being driven from Alsace by Turenne's famous
winter campaign, and just in time to lose to the elector the Swedish
reputation for invincibility at Fehrbellin (1675). Complete military disaster followed. The Danes and the Dutch got control of the Baltic at the
battle of Öland. Brandenburg besieged and captured Stettin and the
Danes invaded Halland and Scania. Only the reckless and untutored
bravery of the young King Charles XI saved the day. The regency received
an ultimate humiliation at the hands of Louis XIV. Without the participation of Sweden, Brandenburg and Denmark were forced by him to
return the conquests they had made at Sweden's expense.

The regency and the magnates whose instrument it had been were
thoroughly discredited. The king, on the other hand, had emerged from
the obscurity in which he had lived as the firm rock in the general debacle.
Schooled in the latter years by an extraordinary man, John Gyllenstierna,
he had learned the virtues of boldness and orderliness. With careful planning, and with the support of the unprivileged classes, he struck at the
regents in the *Riksdag* of 1680 and not only broke their power but ruined
most of the magnate class. The regents were called upon to render account
of their administration and to refund improper expenditures. The king
was given a free hand in the program of "reductions," the recovery of
crown lands, which had been practically suspended during his minority.
He was made independent of the council, which thenceforth had no
existence independent of him. Even the *Riksdag,* the lower house of
which had given the king such vital support, lost all power of control
over the purse and the administration. The officers of state were completely the king's servants. Like Louis XIV, the king made every act of
the government his own. He was completely successful in the financial

---

[28] See below, Chapter **Five.**

aspects of his government, but less so in the other aspects of administration. Nevertheless, when he died in 1697, he left his fifteen-year-old son a throne strengthened to the point of absolutism at home and respected abroad, financially strong and in complete control of all elements of the population.

In form, the Danish constitution at the beginning of our period was the same as that of Sweden: king, senate and diet. The elective character of the kingship had given the nobles a completely dominant position. The kingship was practically subject to them. On the other hand, the peasants had in effect been reduced to serfdom. Even the towns and the clergy were under the thumb of the nobility. The elective character of the kingship had been preserved and each successive sovereign of the house of Oldenburg had on election to sign a "capitulation" guaranteeing the privileges of the senate, the electing body. Nevertheless, the same forces that were changing Sweden were operative also in Denmark. Christian IV (1588–1648) was a man of superior type. If he was less fortunate than Gustavus Adolphus in his intervention in the Thirty Years' War, he created an army, exploited effectively the Sound dues, created commercial companies and advanced education by founding secondary schools. The limits of his power were demonstrated when he attempted to convoke representatives of the towns of Jutland to discuss with them some new commercial ventures: the nobility and the senate protested and the meeting had to be given up. All Christian's efforts to remedy the disasters of the war by economic reconstruction were resisted and he died in the midst of all sorts of difficulties.

Under the circumstances, his successor, Frederick III (1648–1670), had to sign a particularly restrictive capitulation. Two wars with Sweden worsened still further the condition of the kingdom and brought increasing hostility to the nobiliary regime. On the other hand, the prestige of the king and the self-confidence of the bourgeois had been advanced by the heroic defense of Copenhagen in 1660 against the Swedes. Thus the diet of 1660 suddenly turned into a rebellion of the clergy and the townsmen against the nobles. It had been summoned to meet the financial stringency and was presented with a proposal to establish a widespread system of indirect taxation. The nobles at once and during the whole negotiation with the other estates attempted to maintain for themselves and their villeins the exemptions to which they had become accustomed. Their intransigence served to solidify the somewhat uncertain combination of burghers and churchmen, who eventually forced them to surrender. With the support of Hans Svane, the bishop of Zealand, and of Hans

Nansen, the burgomaster of Copenhagen, Frederick III, student and alchemist rather than politician or soldier, resolved to follow up his advantage with a *coup d'état.* On October 8, 1660, the clergy and the burghers
in the diet offered the throne of Denmark to Frederick as a hereditary
kingdom. The nobles retorted by preparing to quit the diet. Frederick resolved to break the resistance of the nobility by force. The nobles were in
no position to resist and on October 13, 1660, Denmark legally became a
hereditary monarchy.

The intention of the revolutionists was not to establish absolutism.
Neither the *Rigsraad* nor the estates supposed themselves to be giving up
their constitutional place in the government. They had no more solid assurance, however, than the royal promise to rule as a Christian king to
the satisfaction of every estate. Frederick III proceeded to build up an
effective administrative machine and to destroy all elements of resistance.
A new nobility of service replaced the old nobility. Offices were opened to
talent without distinction of birth. No social change was contemplated or
made. The peasantry remained one of the most depressed in Europe. The
towns prospered. Copenhagen doubled its population.

Within five years the quintessence of autocracy was formulated in the
Kongelov or "King's law," which was not promulgated until the beginning of the next reign. It was the work of one of Denmark's greatest
geniuses, Peter Schumacker, a cosmopolitan young burgher of Copenhagen, who had studied his Hobbes. He rose to great heights and revo-
lutionized almost every branch of the governmental system. In 1670 he
became the real ruler of Denmark under Frederick's successor, Christian
V, and reeived the title of count of Griffenfeld.

Griffenfeld fell from power because he tried to establish peace, especially with Sweden. The turn in the Dutch War after 1674 presented itself to the king as an opportunity to win territory and glory at the expense of the old enemy, Sweden. Griffenfeld was not only degraded from
office but spent the rest of the king's reign in prison. The War of Scania
went well for Denmark in the military sense, but at the end the fiat of
Louis XIV took away all her conquests. Griffenfeld remained in prison
but his policy continued to develop. A basis for possible peace with Sweden was laid by the marriage of Ulrica Eleanora, the pious sister of
Christian V, to Charles XI. The taxation system of Denmark was made
the most scientific in Europe. Religious toleration was extended to Huguenots in spite of the opposition of the Lutheran clergy. In 1683, to the
great advantage of the absolutism and of the people, a codification of the

varying local laws, begun under Frederick III, established a common law for the whole country.

In principle and in reality Denmark had become the most finished example in Europe of the absolute state.

IV. HOLLAND: REPUBLICAN UNITY VERSUS ORANGIST UNITY [29]

The United Provinces of the Netherlands constituted the most considerable and most fully developed republican organization of the time. John de Witt, who as pensionary of Holland had made himself the effective boss of the Republican machine, declared that the United Provinces should not be spoken of as "a republic," singular, because each province was itself a republic. Everywhere the Republican or States party favored and preserved the old corporate autonomies. In the provinces the constitutions rested upon the medieval estates and corporations. In form the "sovereignty," which Bodin and Hobbes and the absolutist politicians were representing in unitary form, remained in the United Provinces almost as distributive as in Poland.

The republican program had an almost official manifesto. Pieter Delacourt's *The True Interest of Holland* (1661), inspired by de Witt and even written in part by him, accused the stadholders of uselessly prolonging the war with Spain, spending too much on military affairs, neglecting the navy and putting dynastic interest above that of the republic. For the republic, the book claimed credit for the reduction of financial charges and of the military burden, the plan for amortizing the debt, the peaceable solution of internal differences, the large increase of the naval force and the security it brought. The publication of these things, which touched the mystery of statecraft, created a furor in Europe. The book was sought after by all the statesmen and was translated and republished many times. The Orange party published a refutation and demanded prosecution of the writer, and the Synod of Leyden forbade him the sacrament and had the sale of his books prohibited.

John de Witt substantially controlled the whole Union. "John de Witt,"

[29] P. J. Blok, *History of the People of the Netherlands* (5 vols., New York and London, 1898–1912), English translation by O. A. Bierstadt and Ruth Putnam from *Geschiednis van het Nederlandsche Volk* (8 vols., Groningen, 1892–1908); George Edmundson, "The Administrations of John de Witt and William of Orange, 1651–1688," in *Cambridge Modern History*, Vol. V, 137–67; A. Hyma, *The Dutch in the Far East* (Ann Arbor, 1942); N. Japikse, *Jan de Witt* (2nd ed., Amsterdam, 1938); Mary C. Trevelyan, *William III and the Defense of Holland, 1672–1674* (London, 1930); B. H. M. Vlekke, *Evolution of the Dutch Nation* (New York, 1945); G. Edmundson, *History of Holland* (Cambridge, England, 1922).

wrote Chanut, the French ambassador, "is the most important person in the whole state, through the power of Holland over the other provinces and that which he possesses over the ten or twelve principal leaders of the governing party." Everywhere in the Union, in the numerous differences that arose, the support of de Witt and of Holland was available to the anti-Orange party.

The elements of opposition more or less centered on the house of Orange. The Orange cause had been radically weakened by the death of William II in 1650, just at the time when he had apparently destroyed the Republican leadership, and a few months before his son, William III, was born. The regents of Holland had a medal struck to celebrate the event: "The last hour of the prince is the beginning of freedom."

The offices which had been hereditary in the house of Orange, the captaincy general and the admiralty general, were suspended. The army, Orangist in sympathy, was weakened by giving each province control of its own troops. The Calvinist preachers, Orangist since the Synod of Dort, were refused support in their intolerant program. At the end of the First Dutch War, the states of Holland—but not the states-general—at Cromwell's demand, declared the prince of Orange ineligible as stadholder.

In 1660 the restoration of the young prince's uncle as king of England changed the picture. Nevertheless, de Witt maintained and apparently strengthened the Republican predominance. The "sovereignty" of the several provincial states enabled Holland to exercise a hegemony among them, corresponding to her actual economic superiority. The states-general began to depend entirely on the initiative of the states of Holland.

On the other hand, as William III grew toward manhood, it proved impossible to ignore him or brush aside his claims to power. In 1666 the states of Holland took over from his quarreling family the control of his education for the great charges it was "hoped" he would one day be given. In 1667, by the "Perpetual Edict," the states of Holland and of Utrecht abolished the stadholderate in their provinces, but the rest of the provinces protested. A "Plan of Harmony," which forbade the combination of stadholderates with the office of captain general or admiral general, was worked out and accepted by all the provinces between 1668 and 1670. The victory of Republicanism seemed complete and definitive.

By 1670 the cost of operating a minority control was coming home to de Witt. The burgher patriciate was losing its cohesion. For every appointment by which de Witt acquired a friend, he made ten enemies; for every job given a member of his family, he made perhaps twenty more. Amsterdam was in hostile hands. The powerful group that clustered about the pensionary Fagel was ready to do what was necessary to end de Witt's long domination. The council pensionary of Zeeland was elected as an Orange partisan and opposed every proposal of de Witt. The anti-Holland party in Groningen kept the upper hand in spite of every effort of de Witt to defeat it. Such division, however natural in the well-established constitutionalisms of, say, the nineteenth century, was fatal in the United Netherlands, where the vague constitutionalism of 1651 was still without a traditional sanction. The agricultural populations hated the cities. The nobles of the eastern provinces hoped for "glory" and "reputation" in a court or an army. The Calvinist ministers hated the tolerance of the plutocracy and hoped for another Synod of Dort. The army had been neglected for the navy. The bourgeois patriciate could not resolve these oppositions. It had no fundamental sanction. Saint-Évremond stated the basis of the republic in words beyond which it is impossible to go: "The magistrates like their independence because it enables them to govern those who are dependent on them; the people as a whole are disposed to submit more readily to the authority of a chief than to that of the magistrates, who are in reality but their equals."

As war approached, the antipathy of the population to its ruling coterie and the demand for the appointment of Prince William began to grow *pari passu*. In 1670, in spite of the opposition of Holland, the prince was admitted as a voting member of the council of state. Although the Plan of Harmony provided that he should not be named captain general until Novmber, 1672, de Witt was reduced to offering him a temporary commission to serve until the legal date. It was time to see, as Vivien had put it when he pushed his penknife through the draft of the Perpetual Edict, what steel would do against parchment.

The impact of war was fatal to de Witt's machine and to his ideal of government. As the republic faced the united power of France and England in 1672, the very joints of political organization were dissolved. The country as a whole refused to respond to the appeals of the Republican government. The demand for the prince of Orange rose in all parts of the country. In town after town the councils were forced by mobs to proclaim him stadholder. At last, on July 3, 1672, the states of Holland took the same step. A few days later, the states-general made him captain general and admiral general for life. "Here is the whole government of the country changed in a fortnight," wrote a contemporary, ". . . . [the prince] is sovereign in all but name."

The victory of Orange did not bring immediate civil peace. Mobs of townsmen and farmers held sway for weeks in Rotterdam, Gouda, Schiedam, Haarlem, Dordrecht and elsewhere. The alarmed burghers appealed to the prince, but, too good politician not to recognize the rebels as his friends, he declined to interfere and on occasion prevented effective action by the municipalities. In this atmosphere of hate and violence John de Witt and his brother Cornelis were done to death by a mob on August 20, 1672. The prince was shocked, but he accepted the situation. Within a short time each of the principal leaders in the affair was rewarded with an appointment or a pension.

Until 1678 the grim conditions of war enabled William III to exercise his undefined powers very freely. When the states of Friesland opposed the orders of the states-general to open the locks and flood the country, he wrote, "If they make trouble, have them shot on the spot. My authority is deeply involved in this." [30] When, after 1674, the occupied eastern provinces were recovered, he forced their reincorporation in their old status upon the states-general, which wished to treat them as conquered territories. Even more significant for our present purpose, he forced acceptance of the principle that the costs of the war were to be met by uniform taxation regardless of previous quotas paid or unpaid.

Most important of all, the stadholder was permitted to reorganize the three liberated provinces. Utrecht was given a new settlement that left nothing lacking to his power. In Gelderland the states proposed to make him "sovereign" by reviving the ancient titles, duke of Guelders and count of Zutphen. Only the opposition of fiercely republican Zeeland prevented the step. Even so, the three recovered provinces were effectively in the control of the stadholder. Holland and Zeeland were more nearly so than they have ever been. Amsterdam took over his father's debts to Holland. The East India Company granted him 1/33 of all its dividends to stockholders. Patronage was used even more unrestrainedly than before to build a stronger machine than de Witt's. In the East India Company, in the church consistories, in the governing boards, influence, intrigue and bribery determined all important appointments.

Nevertheless, the United Provinces continued to be very imperfectly united. Friesland and Groningen retained the youthful Henry Casimir of Nassau as hereditary stadholder, who was naturally jealous and hostile, since plans were openly discussed to push him aside and make William III stadholder in his place. The critical cleavage, however, came over the continuation of the war with France. The business interests demanded peace, even a separate peace. William III refused to abandon his allies.

[30] William III to John Maurice of Nassau-Siegen, June 25, 1673 (*Archives de la maison Orange-Nassau*, 2ᵉ série, V, 326).

Some of the leaders of the States party did not hesitate to open negotiations with the French. In these difficult circumstances, William cannily achieved the settlement of Nimwegen (1678) without too much sacrifice of his allies or loss of political strength at home or abroad. After the peace French diplomacy, with the aim of detaching the United Provinces from the enemies of France, played upon the internal differences. The French ambassador presented himself as ambassador to the states-general rather than to the stadholder. At Paris, Louvois offered substantial economic advantages and even a promise to let the Spanish Netherlands alone in case of war.

When Spain, aroused by the renewal of French violence in the Netherlands, appealed for help of the republic, the issue was fought out. When William III asked the states to authorize double the army promised by treaty, Amsterdam led a vigorous opposition to any new adventure. William III thereupon exposed the relations of "those Amsterdam rascals" with France and threatened to throw "the club into the street" as in 1672, to learn "whose head was firmest on his shoulders." Amsterdam obstinately held out and civil war seemed certain. The prince then went to work another way. In the states of Holland he overrode the protests of Amsterdam and Schiedam and declared a resolution supporting an increase in the army carried by a majority. The *liberum veto* of Amsterdam was ended for a while, and William had the resolution presented in the states-general as coming from Holland. At this point an intercepted letter of D'Avaux, the French ambassador, which spoke of some of the Amsterdam regents as well disposed, was communicated to the states of Holland. The Amsterdamers were put on the defensive, while similar methods were used with the opposition in other cities. Everywhere William III managed to establish his authority over the magistrates. Nevertheless, Spain had to wage its war with France alone.

William III seemed checked and defeated in his international aims by these internal divisions. The revocation of the Edict of Nantes operated catalytically to resolve the situation. The dissension between Amsterdam and the prince was settled by the mediation of the ambassador whom the Great Elector had sent to restore good relations with the republic. The city agreed to the maintenance of the army at a high level and supported the alliance with Brandenburg, including the subsidies. Henry Casimir was induced to pledge himself to support William III's policies, instead of opposing them.

William III was not a "monarch," but the absence of the title and status underlined the function he performed. As a kind of king, he and his successors were able to integrate the forces of Dutch society as the oligarchy of de Witt could not. In the Republican pattern, he had to use political methods. He outdid de Witt as builder of a political machine. No political psychology explains just how a hereditary sanction works, but it seems that with the sanction William could build his state more effectively than de Witt could without it. Orange remained and remains the effective symbol of Dutch unity.

V. THE NEGATION OF ABSOLUTISM IN SWITZERLAND AND POLAND

In two political societies of Europe, Switzerland and Poland, peculiar conditions of history and organization brought about the complete rejection of the Hobbesian state. To both of them devotion to the ancient "liberties" brought disaster before the end of the next century. The kingdom of Poland was destined to complete obliteration in the partitions of 1772, 1793 and 1795. The ancient Swiss Confederation succumbed to the Helvetian Republic imposed by the French conquerors in 1798.

Switzerland[31] was an anomaly in an absolutist world. From the three mountain districts which in 1291 had sworn mutual aid against aggression, the confederation had grown to thirteen cantons, bound together by widely varying pacts among themselves and associated in conflict and in treaties with powers and potentates outside the confederation. The process of growth and the changes of circumstance had brought heavy stresses. Most obvious was the religious cleavage which had come with the Reformation. Hardly less important and closely parallel to the religious cleavage had come a wide divergence in wealth, in social structure and in intellectual attitude. Some of the towns had grown rich and had begun that metropolitan financial function characteristic of Switzerland even in our own time. They were already capable of financing the heavy burdens of indemnity and the evacuation costs of German states at the end of the Thirty Years' War. In spite of their differences, however, the Swiss emerged from the war period with their confederation intact in principle and in territory and with the incidental and formal advantage of complete independence of the Empire.

It was generally recognized that the loose confederation in which the cantons had met and surmounted so many dangers was ill-adapted to the perils of the anarchic postwar period. In 1647, when the victorious French and Swedish forces threatened to engulf the little country, the hostility of

---

[31] W. E. Rappard, *Cinq siècles de sécurité collective* (Geneva, 1945); W. Oechsli, *History of Switzerland, 1499–1914* (translated by E. C. Paul from author's ms., Cambridge, England, 1922).

Catholic and Protestant and the jealous distrust of any infringement of the sovereignty of the cantons was temporarily suppressed. The Defensional of Wyl (1647) created on paper a standing army of twelve thousand, with corresponding reserves. When the danger declined, the support of the Defensional disappeared. When the advance of the Turks on Vienna in 1664 again threatened Swiss security, and again when the advance of the French into Franche-Comté in 1668 and 1674 created alarm, the Defensional was reconsidered and even renewed. Each time, however, once the immediate danger was past, the original Forest Cantons drew back and insisted on the restriction of their obligations to the original pacts of the fourteenth and fifteenth centuries.

As revived in 1668, the Defensional, with some revision in 1702, had a continuous life to 1798 as the constitution of such unity as the Swiss would permit themselves. Its provisions reflected not only the religious jealousy between the cantons, but also the political jealousy of any concentration of power. Quotas were meticulously distributed and the command of each army, a field army and a reserve army, was divided between a Protestant and a Catholic, each appointed by one of the four leading cantons. These officers were required to consult with the colonels from the cantons. This clumsy system was never severely tested, but when in 1676 the advance of a French army threatened Basle, all the cantons loyally fulfilled their obligations. The smaller cantons objected to maintaining forces in time of peace without the hope of booty, and even withdrew in 1680, but the threat to Constance from the French armies in 1681 and the occupation of Strassburg brought about a reconsideration and the Defensional survived. Even the Catholic cantons were alarmed by the revocation of the Edict of Nantes. The smaller cantons agreed to the passage over their territory of the contingents that had been raised by the larger cantons. Religious and political considerations made Geneva a peculiar problem, but the Catholic cantons loyally accepted the necessity of defending it and allowed Berne and Zürich to undertake a contribution of thirty thousand men in case of attack upon Geneva from Savoy or France.

Thus the attempt to create a confederal government, even for the special purpose of insuring security from external danger, was sharply limited through this period and, indeed, down to 1798. At the same time, the conviction of solidarity was so deep that at every external threat practical steps were taken to avert the immediate danger.

The failure of the Swiss illuminates by contrast the process of absolutism in the rest of Europe. The commonwealth existed. When Zürich and Berne made war on Schwyz because of that canton's persecution of Protestants, enough allies on both sides remained neutral to bring the conflict to an end in a few weeks. When, in 1653, the peasant populations of some of the cantons rose against the oppression of the urban patriciates, the governing groups of all the cantons except Zug freely joined forces to repress the outbreak. Switzerland was a commonwealth, but a commonwealth in which thirteen sovereignties asserted themselves. In 1655 Schwyz declared it would allow no one "to touch its sovereignty or its religion." The life of the confederation during the ensuing century was neither happy nor creditable, but it perished for its social rather than for its political sins.

Poland was an even greater anomaly than Switzerland.[32]

In 1660 Poland was an almost wholly agricultural country with a powerful nobility ranging from the great princes with private armies (the *pans*) to petty lordlings (the *szlachta*), united in defense of its "golden liberties." The bourgeois allies of the western kings were almost nonexistent. Bourgeois functions were performed by numerous Jewish refugees from Spain and Germany. The body of the population was the most depressed peasantry in Europe.

Poland was the most Catholic country of the continent. Protestantism, as such, had been wholly stamped out in the sixteenth century. In 1658 Socinianism (Unitarianism), which had continued to be cherished by some of the great families, was proscribed. The Jews, who had been attracted in great numbers to Poland from various European countries by a relatively generous toleration, were, like the peasants, tolerated, used, abused and despised. Some 650 monasteries maintained themselves in the 17 dioceses. The Jesuits enjoyed an easy predominance, especially in the upper levels of society, but the country was covered with a network of less intellectual or aristocratic orders which sent their friars everywhere, into the cabins of the peasants as well as the castles of the magnates. The Union of Lublin (1569) and Polish conquests in White Russia and the Ukraine had brought under the crown a considerable Greek Catholic population, much of which had been co-ordinated with the Roman Catholic Church in the form of the Uniat church, a combination of

[32] M. Korduba, W. Tomkiewicz, "The Reign of John Casimir, 1648–1668," and O. Forst de Battaglia, "Jan Sobieski, 1674–1696," in *The Cambridge History of Poland from the Origins to Sobieski (to 1696)* (Cambridge, 1950); O. Halecki, *A History of Poland* (New York, 1943); Sir R. Lodge, "Austria, Poland and Turkey" in *The Cambridge Modern History*, V, 338–71; Louis Léger, "La Pologne," in Lavisse and Rambaud, *Histoire générale*, VI, 627–55.

Roman doctrine, especially papal supremacy, with Greek ritual and discipline.

Poland still presented the appearance of a great power. Slavic in language and tradition, it was peculiarly susceptible to western education and cultural and literary standards. Poles had been prominent in the universities of Italy and Germany and in this period were especially so in the University of Paris. It was the frontier of the west toward Russian barbarism. It disputed with Sweden the control of the Baltic. In the days of its weakness it was still destined to play a high part in saving Europe from the Turks.

In fact, Poland represented the extreme case of feudalistic degeneration. The elective kingship and the *pacta conventa* (sworn agreements), which were the price of every election, gave the nobility and the greater nobility (the *pans*) in particular a complete ascendency over the kings, whom, in any case, they regarded as just one of themselves. In good feudal fashion, they disregarded majorities. As nobles they were all equal, and there was in their eyes no reason why any number of them should impose their will on any other number.

In 1648 John Casimir, the last of the Vasa dynasty, was called upon to take the Polish crown. He had a right to suppose that power would be granted him to meet his responsibilities, which were heavy. From all sides disaster threatened the very existence of Poland as an independent state. Charles X of Sweden attacked because John Casimir, as a Vasa, claimed the succession to Christina. Frederick William of Brandenburg joined in the Swedish attack to improve his position in Prussia. The Cossacks of the Dnieper, under Bogdan Chmielnicki, rebelled to shake off the Orthodox clergy, the Polish nobility and their revenue farmers, all of whom they hated. The Cossacks brought in first the Tartars and Turks and then turned to the Russian tsars. That Poland could emerge from this "Deluge," as the period is called by the Polish historians, with no more serious loss than the nominal suzerainty over Prussia and an even less substantial claim to Livonia and still retain a real influence in the Ukraine, testifies to the existence of substantial power in Polish society.

John Casimir attempted a threefold program: defense of the kingdom, alleviation of the lot of the peasants and settlement of the succession, but this was defeated in all its implications. Devoutly religious, the king, when Lwów was relieved of Russian attack in 1655, devoted the Polish nation to the Virgin and swore as a first duty to liberate the peasants from the oppressions under which they suffered, and which, according to contemporaries, were the worst in Europe. The satirist Opalinski (1610–1651) declared, "God punishes Poland for the cruel oppression of its subjects." The nobility had come to consider themselves a superior race and the peasants as children of Ham, destined to servitude. The same attitudes were displayed by the Polish *pans* in the Ukraine and evoked there the profound distrust and hate that made impossible the rational extension of the Union of Lublin by which the Ukraine, under an elective hetman, was to be a separate state under the Polish crown, retaining its Greek Orthodox religion (Treaty of Zgorovo, 1649). The nobility could not bring themselves to treat the Ukrainian peasants as freemen and the Catholic clergy would not tolerate the Orthodox clergy in equal status with themselves.

The *liberum veto,* which was only the medieval feudal concept of right, defeated every attempt to develop the power of the crown. Its anachronistic absurdity was demonstrated when, in 1652, a petty noble, obviously the tool of some of the great nobles, had by his single act of withdrawal imposed dissolution upon the diet. Educated Poles were fully conscious of the danger of the veto. "With a single word," wrote Vespazian Kochowski (1633–1699), "God created the world; with the single word, *veto,* we destroy Poland." It was very much like the "filibuster" in the senate of the United States. Majorities and minorities continued to co-operate, but in the long run any program that meant government by the crown could be defeated. Even when decisions were taken by the diet, it was impossible to secure their general execution. The dietines (the local assemblies of lesser nobles that elected representatives to the diet) and the "confederacies" of factional nobles that sprang up from time to time did not hesitate to impose local vetoes on legislation. What would now be called treason was rife. Opposition groups turned freely to the inducements and support offered by foreign powers to defeat particular policies or the development of power in the kingship.

The issue of royal power was fought out in connection with the question of the succession. When it became apparent that John Casimir would not have an heir, parties formed to secure the succession for one or another foreign prince—French, Austrian or even Russian. At the diet of 1661 John Casimir himself raised the question of the succession. In singularly prophetic words he forecast the ultimate dissolution of the kingdom unless the crown was assured continuity by election before the death of the reigning king. While the diet was lost in divisions over the various candidates, the question was settled by a rough veto. Taking advantage of an uprising of unpaid soldiers and of aid from Brandenburg and Austria, George Lubomirski, the grand marshal, rose in arms to defend the threatened "golden liberties." When he was condemned by the diet of 1664, he headed a second rebellion which did not end until the king renounced his whole program of reform and in particular the alteration of the law of free election.

When John Casimir, disgusted with the ungrateful burden of the kingship and widowed of the strong support of his French queen, left the throne to retire to France, the nobility after long intrigues in favor of various foreign candidates turned to one of their own number. Michael Wisniowecki was the son of Jeremy Wisniowecki, one of the leaders of the nobility in the repression of the Dnieper Cossacks, and was committed by birth and by the demand of the diet that elected him to the recovery of the Ukraine.

Like John Casimir, he found his support inadequate for his mission. A confederation of nobles under Czarniecki busied themselves with forcing the expulsion of the Polish primate, while French and Austrian parties in the diet defeated his domestic program. The Cossacks turned for aid to the Turks, who swept over the western Ukraine and over Podolia as well. When the Polish fortress-capital, Kamenets, was taken and Lwów threatened by the Turks, Michael was obliged to accept an ignominious peace that gave Podolia to the Turks and imposed an indemnity and an annual tribute on Poland. The shame of the treaty led to an upsurge of national feeling and an organized movement quite separate from the crown. Another confederation under John Sobieski repudiated the treaty and defeated the Turks at the battle of Khotin (Chocim) in 1673, but did not recover Kamenets.

Thus when Michael died, John Sobieski appeared as the only possible candidate and he was elected in 1674 amid general enthusiasm. Originally attached to France by his marriage and by a formal treaty (1675), John turned to Austria because of the Turkish threat. From a strictly national point of view, his immediate enemies were Brandenburg and Austria. It was wholly characteristic of the man and of his country that the problem was envisaged from a European rather than from a national point of view. The story of his intervention to save Vienna will be recounted elsewhere in this book.[33]

The victory of John Sobieski won him little gratitude at Vienna and little support in his own country. The Sapieha, a great noble family of Lithuania, proceeded to ruin all his attempts in the ensuing years to share in the sweeping Austrian demolition of Turkish controls. He was not even able to retake Kamenets. Austria, Russia, Brandenburg and France, however much they opposed each other in the diet, were united in de-

[33] See below, pp. 241–43.

fending the "golden liberties," that is, in impeding every reform designed to correct the weakness of the republic. They found ready instruments among the great nobles, who took their pay as readily as English parliamentarians and, similarly jealous of each other, were equally anxious to prevent any accession to the power of the crown in principle or to the power of John III in person. Like John Casimir, John III envisaged the establishment of his dynasty as the central point of a whole program of constitutional reform. His military failures after 1683, assured by the machinations of the parties in the diet, ended long before his death in 1696 any hope of passing the succession to either of his sons. His last years were filled with frustration, and on his death the diet turned again to a foreign prince, Augustus of Saxony. It was the beginning of the end. National and racial pride, community of tradition and economic solidarity, linguistic and religious unity were not enough to give Poland the cohesion necessary to survival in the anarchic power struggle of the eighteenth century. Like the Swiss cantons and only a little sooner, Poland was doomed as soon as the balance between her greedy neighbors was ended.

Before the end of the seventeenth century, absolutism was achieved in principle and in practice in Sweden and in Denmark. In Holland the controls which had been operated by the mercantile oligarchy had to be shared with William of Orange but, in spite of internal stresses among the governing elements, continued for some decades very much as before. In Brandenburg-Prussia the Great Elector had succeeded in crushing all forms of local resistance to the bureaucracy of which he had laid the foundations. In England Charles II had undermined the municipalities, gained control of parliament and approximated a monarchical absolutism, but the landlords and the financiers were too strong for his successors. In France the monarchy had assumed the responsibilities of absolutism without destroying the vested interests that could resist it. Through another century French kings and ministers were frustrated in repeated attempts to undo the negative results of the work of Louis XIV. It remained for the Revolution to integrate the French state.

It remained for the twentieth century to carry the process to its logical conclusions.

Chapter Five

ANARCHY IN INTERNATIONAL RELATIONS

THE absolutism of the states was a denial of the integrity and common law of Europe. The Thirty Years' War and the treaties of Westphalia had buried all ideas of general sanctions, authoritative or moral. Even before the Thirty Years War, Bodin, Grotius and their congeners had sought new sanction in the misty regions of the natural law and of history interpreted *ad hoc*. The sum total of their efforts had been a theoretical formulation that corresponded to the actuality: a recognition of the essentially anarchic character of the society of European states. That Europe was still a society was manifest in a community of religion that persisted despite all divisions and variations of belief; in a community of social standards which manifested itself in marriage, education, the arts, literature and clothes; in a community of economic standards which, while far short of its later uniformity, was actively developing. If Christendom was a less suitable name than it had been, Europe was still a society. Its essential and persisting unity as a society accentuated the anomaly of its segmented political structure.

The states of Europe, by history and by definition, lived in a perpetual battle royal, an anarchy untempered by rational arrangement, in which the part of each state was dictated by an unreflecting greed and limited only by the most obvious barriers. With what in perspective can be regarded only as naïveté and stupidity, the heads of ambitious states presumed that they could fall upon and destroy their neighbors without alarming other states which had only the same fate to expect when the first step was accomplished. Lesser powers, equally blind to their need for the protection of a common law, collaborated with even less compunction and restraint as opportunity offered to fall upon a neighbor attacked by a stronger power.

The society we are examining was prolific in genius, in common sense, in organizing ability. It could properly have been expected that intelligence, comprehension and high purpose would be applied to the control of human relations in general and to the relations between states and peoples in particular.

The fact was almost completely opposite. It was a period of marked unintelligence, immorality and frivolity in the conduct of international relations, marked by wars undertaken for dimly conceived purposes, waged with the utmost brutality and concluded by reckless betrayals of allies. Moral indignation is perhaps irrelevant and certainly supererogatory, but objectivity can hardly obscure the fact of shortsighted aims and badly calculated maneuvers.

The intellectual inadequacy of the statesmanship of the time was demonstrated by the tardiness with which the other states recognized the character of the French threat and by the uncertainty and haphazardness of the ultimate resistance to the Turks. It is hardly necessary to say that Louis XIV's program was unrealistic in its purposes and crude and self-defeating in its means. He fought for "glory." When in 1672 Colbert raised the question, what was to be done with Holland after the conquest, the collective wisdom of the king and his council could not provide an answer.[1] With all his European vision, William of Orange was equally capable of irrational choices. Thus in 1678 he attempted to sabotage the peace of Nimwegen and to renew the war by attacking the French army at Mons.

Diplomacy pursued frivolous ends, utilized frivolous means and, until the very end of the period, achieved no abiding alignments. French diplomats brawled in the streets of Rome and London over petty points of precedence. Although the outcome of the Fronde should have reminded the French king and his advisers that governments survive by satisfying the demands of dominant social forces, they still thought bribery could deter national groups from the courses dictated by their interest and prejudice. Indeed, it is apparent that French diplomacy ignored national interests other than those of France and, in a real sense, even those of France itself. As Lavisse points out, not one of the wars of Louis XIV can properly be called a war for economic ends.[2] A worthy objective found expression in the instructions to the French ambassador to Sweden in 1665: to prevent the domination of maritime commerce by any single power and to group around France the smaller powers in order to protect the liberties of the sea; but this proposal was not developed. Louis XIV was concerned with what he regarded as more important matters.

The Europeans had lost the catholic morality which as church, as feudalism, as economic community had at one time given them co-

---

[1] E. Lavisse, *op. cit.*, VII, Part 2, 343.
[2] *Ibid.*, VII, Part 2, 223, note.

herence. Power had become absolute and, as Lord Acton said long ago, absolute power corrupts absolutely. The intention of Acton's dictum was moral. It is more to the present point to say that absolutism corrupted the intellect. Hobbes, who reasoned so ably about the place of government within states, stopped reasoning when confronted with the problem of relations between states. His brief utterance may be taken as typical of the abandonment of the intellectual problem:

> But though there had never been any time, wherein particular men were in a condition of war one against another; yet in all times, Kings and persons of sovereign authority, because of the independency are in continual jealousies, and in the state and posture of gladiators, having their weapons pointing and their eyes fixed on one another; that is, their forts, garrisons, and guns upon the frontiers of their kingdoms; and continual spyes upon their neighbors; which is the posture of war. But because they uphold thereby, the industry of their subjects, there does not follow from it that misery, which accompanies the liberty of particular men.[3]

In a word, Hobbes evaded the problem. The Catholic tradition, as it now seems, offered him the precedent of an integrated European society. The miseries of the Thirty Years' War and the uncertainties of the peace of Westphalia presented a parallel to his Leviathan-creating society that to us seems inescapable. Nevertheless, Hobbes ignored the conditions in European society that he assumed had produced Leviathan in the particular societies such as England and France. On the other hand, it is equally obvious that at the time and later the Europeans as a whole made the same evasion and only in our day have come to recognize the need of Hobbesian integration of the whole society.

The peculiar irrationality of the dominant attitudes was accented by some of the glimmers of rationality that appeared sporadically during the period. The most conspicuous example was the proposal of Leibniz that Louis XIV use his dominance to give disorganized Europe leadership in asserting its power against the Mohammedan control of the eastern Mediterranean. Leibniz's *Consilium aegypticum* differed from other proposals of the same sort only in so far as it was couched in purely secular and cultural terms. In 1672 John Philip von Schonborn, the elector of Mainz, desperately seeking to avoid the choice between alliance with France and alliance with the Empire, formally proposed a similar plan to the French ambassador and was summarily rebuffed.[4] So was John Sobieski, king of

---

[3] Hobbes, *Leviathan*, ch. 51.
[4] C. Krappmann, "Johann Philipp von Schonborn und das Leibnizischer 'Consilium Aegypticum,'" *Zeitschrift fur Geschichte des Oberrheins*, 45 (1941), 185–219.

Poland, whose alliance Louis XIV was trying so hard to cultivate, when he made the same kind of proposal in the crisis presented by the advance of the Turks against Vienna in 1683. So was the pope in his attempt to organize Catholic Europe for the final expulsion of the Turks from Europe after their repulse before Vienna.[5] Our own age can hardly accept the distinctions of religion and culture upon which these projects were based, but they demonstrate the continued existence of a catholic European ideal and, at the same time, reveal how radically it had been weakened by the emergence of the Hobbesian state.

The moral issue was not wholly ignored. Both the English and the Dutch governments hired publicists to justify their respective positions in the Second and Third Dutch Wars. Charles II listed Dutch aspersions against him as one of his grievances in 1664 and tried to get Evelyn to retaliate in kind. In 1672 and 1673 William de Britaine and Henry Holland were paid to turn out war propaganda, including atrocity stories.[6] Much of Lisola's active career was devoted to propaganda against "the manifest design of the King of France [to establish] a universal monarchy."[7] Quite accurately, Lisola pointed out that after 1672 the French government did not attempt to justify its policy, apparently considering itself not responsible to public opinion. The Great Elector may not have been a sincere German patriot, but his appeal to German national feeling was neither frivolous nor deceitful.[8]

I. THE POWER PATTERN IN 1661 [9]

When Louis XIV undertook the task of ruling France, Europe was substantially at peace. The treaties of Oliva and Copenhagen (1660) and of Kardis (1663) suspended the aggressions of Sweden against Denmark, Poland and Russia, although the Poles and the Russians continued fighting. The Treaty of the Pyrenees (1659) had brought a truce in the long conflict between the Spanish Hapsburgs and the Bourbons of France. Across the oceans, however, the ancient disregard of

[5] See below, Chapter Eight, "The Expansion of Europe," pp. 241, 243.

[6] L. B. Schlatter, *The Social Ideas of Religious Leaders, 1660–1688* (London, 1940), 231.

[7] See especially his *Bouclier d'estat et de justice* (s.l., 1667); also A. F. G. Pribram, *Franz Paul, Freiherr von Lisola (1613–1614) und die Politik seiner Zeit* (Leipzig, 1894), 351–64; J. Haller, *Die deutsche Publizistik im dem Jahre 1668* (Heidelberg, 1892).

[8] See above, p. 121.

[9] E. Lavisse, "L'Europe en 1661," *Histoire de France*, VII, 2, 185–221; Max Immich, *Geschichte des europäischen Staatensystems, 1660–1789* (Munich, 1905); B. Erdmannsdörfer, *op. cit.*, I, 505–10; D. J. Hill, *A History of Diplomacy in the International Development of Europe* (3 vols., New York, 1914), III, 25–50.

treaties and of any kind of common law expressed itself in smuggling, piracy and freebooting. Furthermore, Europe and in particular the Eastern powers, Poland, Austria and Venice, continued to be threatened by the still vigorous Turkish empire.

Spain no longer enjoyed its century-long predominance in arms, in population and in economic power. It had had to yield to France small though important parts of the southern provinces of the Netherlands and, in the south, Roussillon and Cerdagne. It had successfully resisted the advance of French power over the Pyrenees into Catalonia, but was at the point of losing its last hope of holding Portugal and maintaining peninsular unification. It had lost Jamaica to the English, but it still possessed the most extensive colonial empire in the world. In spite of the flow of precious metals from the New World, it had suffered a radical economic decline. Since 1500 the population had fallen from about eight million to about four. It was still attractive to immigrating craftsmen and merchants. Genoese, English, Dutch and French financiers and merchants carried off the profits of overseas trade. A careful contemporary estimate put the number of Frenchmen in Spain in 1680 at 65,000.[10]

In Europe, Spain still held the southern Netherlands and Franche-Comté and easily dominated Italy by its possession of Milan and Naples. The Spanish were hated by their Italian subjects and feared by the other states of the peninsula. Louis XIV could appear as helpful ally and liberator. Savoy, Mantua, Parma, Tuscany were available to him as allies, strategically located and systematically opposed to Spain. Venice, still strong enough to resist the Turk in the eastern Mediterranean, generally favored French diplomacy. The papacy, however, remained under Spanish influence and antagonistic to French purposes in Italy.

Spanish power was still well based in northwestern Africa and in the Canaries. In Asia, the Philippines were undergoing Hispanicization as thorough and as permanent as Mexico, and in 1668 the Marianas were added to the empire. In spite of this wide base and a certain cultural vigor, Spain was destined to a drastic reduction of power in Europe.

The Austrian Hapsburgs, emperors, archdukes and kings, by their possessions in the Danube Valley, were bound to the heavy historical task of warding off the Turks and integrating central Europe. Still emperors, they did not fully perceive the logic of their losses in the

---

[10] A. Girard, "Les étrangers en Espagne en XVIe et XVIIe siècles," *Annales d'histoire économique et sociale*, 5 (1930), 578.

controls of German politics until the nineteenth century. The treaties of Westphalia had left them only rank and responsibility without corresponding power. As emperors they faced a congeries of constituent states that claimed the right each to go its own way in diplomacy and war.

As Hapsburgs, they were bound to the decaying body of Spain and wedded to the tradition handed down by Ferdinand and Isabella of defending and promoting Catholicism. The family heritage, Upper and Lower Austria, the Tyrol, Carniola and Carinthia, constituted the center from which certain adventitious acquisitions were governed. The kingdom of Bohemia had been inherited in 1526 and in the course of the Thirty Years' War purged of Hussism, Slavism and any trace of liberty. Hungary had nominally been acquired by election after the battle of Mohács (1526) but of the old kingdom only a third was directly controlled by the Hapsburgs and that constantly ready for rebellion. The Turks controlled the central third from Buda and Belgrade. Transylvania was substantially independent.

In Germany, the electoral duchy of Bavaria was dominated for two decades by French diplomacy. The elector of Saxony was beginning his maneuvers to obtain the Polish throne. Most importantly, Brandenburg, newly furbished with the sovereignty of East Prussia, under the leadership of Frederick William was to rise almost to the status of a great power. It was not yet that in 1661. The will to recover Pomerania from Sweden was to orient Brandenburg's foreign policy down to the death of Frederick William. Along the Rhine the great, rich, but militarily insignificant ecclesiastical electorates, Cologne, Mainz and Trier, were particularly susceptible to French diplomacy and formed with Louis XIV the League of the Rhine for mutual protection against the supposedly dangerous Hapsburg emperor.

France and Holland were the two greatest powers in Europe. France had combined diverse territories under diverse titles extending from the Pyrenees to Flanders and from the Rhine to the ocean. Its twenty million inhabitants were fairly productive as individuals and as a whole afforded a more nearly adequate base for supporting a government than any other people in Europe. The government was badly organized both economically and financially, but the complete collapse of the Fronde had paved the way for the development of an upper stratum of administrators, ministers, masters of requests and intendants, that partly compensated for the confusion of the mass below. France had just won a decisive victory over its traditional Hapsburg enemies, the kings of Spain, consecrated in the Treaty of the Pyrenees (1659). In the eyes of its young king and his ministers, it was ready for greatness on a new scale.

Amsterdam was the center of financial and commercial organizations that enabled Holland to draw strength from all of the European peninsula and from the four corners of the earth. Its bourse was open to traders from everywhere. They found a market provided with quotations of a wide range of products and even of securities. They found shipping services that enabled them to make contact with widespread outlets and sources of supply, covered by cheap insurance protection. Credit of all sorts at low rates of interest was readily available, centralized in the powerful Bank of Amsterdam. The East India Company, too, was already effective in funneling through Holland the products of the east. The West India Company, less effective as a business organization, at least facilitated piracy, smuggling and slave-trading in the Spanish seas. Amsterdam had become the metropolis of economic Europe.[11]

In the north, Sweden, at the cost of general hostility, had laid the foundations of a Baltic empire, comprising Scania and Halland on the Swedish side of the Sound, the archbishopric of Bremen with its control of the Weser, Pomerania with its control of the Oder, Livonia and Esthonia cutting off Russia from the Baltic, and Finland, long under Swedish domination. Sweden had become an army. War had been profitable and Sweden, in close alliance with France, did not fear the enemies which its conquests had made for it. The long minority of Charles XI from 1660 to 1675 involved a regency and that in turn involved a suspension of the efforts begun under Charles X to recover the extravagant grants of Queen Christina to her favorites. The treasury was empty and Sweden remained bound to France by its need for subsidies. In Denmark the absolutism which Frederick III established with such facility in 1661 ruled over Norway, Schleswig-Holstein, Iceland, the Fàröes, and Greenland, where some fishing, whaling and sealing were carried on from the western fiords.

The eastern part of the North European plain was occupied but hardly governed by Poland, the weakness and confusion of whose internal organization opened the way to the persistent intrusion of foreign agents into its domestic politics and made it an easy victim of the aggressions of its neighbors. Livonia had been lost to Sweden and East Prussia had been yielded in full sovereignty to the elector of Branden-

[11] Violet Barbour, *Capitalism in Amsterdam in the Seventeenth Century* (Baltimore, 1950).

burg as duke. Poland still retained Lithuania and the Ukraine, and to guard this immense territory required a large disciplined force. This the great lords, jealous of their liberties, refused to grant. The forces which they contributed on occasion could be effective, as the recovery of Warsaw from the Swedes and the recovery of Podolia from the Turks demonstrated. Poland was sought by France as an ally to the east of Germany, but it was drawn to the Hapsburgs by an awareness of the common danger represented by the Turks.

Beyond Poland, Russia was still quite detached from the power conflicts of the west. The Romanovs, established as the ruling dynasty only in 1614, were hardly able to face on equal terms the Swedes, the Turks or the Poles. Though they challenged Polish control of White Russia, the Swedes held the Baltic shores, and the Turks the Black Sea, and the Ukraine played off Poland, Russia and the Turks against each other in the effort to preserve a precarious independence. The Cossacks of the Volga, the Don and the Dnieper were in no real sense integrated with the tsardom. The measure of Russia's Europeanization in the political sense is indicated by the extraterritoriality which westerners still maintained in Moscow and Novgorod.

II. THE ANGLO-DUTCH WAR, 1664–1667 [12]

Europe's brief surcease from war was ended by the outbreak of hostilities between England and the Netherlands. This conflict illustrated perfectly the lawless and asocial character of the statesmanship of the period. "What matters this or that reason?" said George Monk, the duke of Albemarle. "What we want is more of the trade that the Dutch now have." [13]

Commercial jealousy had already brought on war between the English and the Dutch under the Commonwealth (1652–1654), a war that had resulted in the weakening of both powers without bringing about an abatement of the fundamental trade hostility between them. The common religious position of the two countries, which had influenced Cromwell in his policy toward Holland, was no longer of concern to the dominant forces in Restoration England. Friction between the

---

[12] K. G. Feiling, *British Foreign Policy, 1660–1672* (London, 1930), 83–201; P. J. Blok, *History of the People of the Netherlands* (5 vols., New York and London, 1898–1912), IV, 186–219; C. T. Atkinson, "The Anglo-Dutch Wars," *Cambridge Modern History*, V, 178–97; G. A. Lefèvre-Pontalis, *John de Witt, Grand Pensionary of Holland* (2 vols., London, 1885), I, 305–96.

[13] Quoted by J. A. Williamson, *A Short History of British Expansion* (London, 1927), 266.

Dutch and English trading companies strengthened the advocates of armed force. The Dutch left no stone unturned to discourage and ruin the trade of the Royal African Company; the English in clear peace seized New Amsterdam and renamed it New York.

When Charles II at last declared war on March 4, 1665, neither the English nor the Dutch were prepared. Feeble attempts had been made by the English diplomats to negotiate alliances with Spain, with Denmark, with Sweden, with Austria and with Brandenburg, but the only ally England had secured was the bishop of Münster, who was aggrieved because the Dutch refused to recognize his claim to the lordship of Borkelo.[14] In return for a substantial subsidy, he invaded Holland with eighteen thousand men in August, 1665. Münster's intervention served only to bring in the French on the side of the Dutch. In 1662 Louis XIV had signed an alliance with Holland by which he was pledged to aid the Dutch with twelve thousand men if they were attacked. Louis XIV's original purpose was to mediate the conflict. He was not disposed to see Dutch maritime and commercial power overthrown for the benefit of England, and in view of his designs on the Spanish Netherlands, he hoped to secure the neutrality of the Dutch. When Philip IV of Spain died in September, 1665, his purpose somewhat changed. He then desired to prolong the war in order to win a free hand in the Spanish Netherlands. Accordingly, he sent a force to the aid of the Dutch which, with some German mercenaries, drove the bishop of Münster from the eastern provinces and declared war on England in January, 1666. Denmark and Brandenburg also allied with the United Provinces. Sweden, which had been on the point of allying itself with England, declared its neutrality and offered to mediate. Münster, threatened by France and Brandenburg, made peace. Finally, Holland, Denmark, Brandenburg and Brunswick-Lüneburg formed a "Quadruple Alliance" for mutual defence. The isolation of England was complete.

Since both powers were too weak on land to strike an effective blow, they fought only on the sea. Their navies, however, were also far below what they had been. The Dutch navy was weakened by factionalism and jealousy and by the parsimony of the states-general. The English navy was starved in the literal and figurative sense. The provision of food was deficient and unpaid sailors rioted in the streets of London. The operations of 1666, though of some technical interest, produced no important strategic results, other than the negative but fundamental one,

---

[14] C. Brinkman, *Charles II and the Bishop of Münster in the Dutch War of 1665–1666* (London, 1906).

that both fleets remained in being and able to take to sea. Both sides soon wearied of the struggle.[15]

De Witt was concerned to end the financial and economic drain and to have his hands free to meet the problem emerging with the approach to maturity of the young prince of Orange. The English were hard hit by the Plague and the Great Fire, as well as by disaffection both in England and Scotland. Hence when Charles II made overtures for peace in October, 1666, they were favorably received and negotiations were begun. As a result of their financial and other distresses, Charles II and his council proceeded to save money by laying up the fleet, even suspending the works for the defense of the ports while the treaty was still being negotiated at Breda. De Ruyter was quick to take advantage of this slackness. Early in June, 1667, a fleet of some sixty-six sail left Holland and by June 10 Sheerness had been captured. The great naval station at Chatham was attacked two days later. The Dutch were thus enabled to secure favorable terms at Breda, retaining Surinam and Pula-roon, while the English Navigation Act was modified in their favor and the commercial treaty of 1662 reaffirmed. They gave up New Amsterdam, however, and recognized the right of the English to the salute on the four seas. De Witt had no intention of leaving the English with a sense of grievance.

III. THE DEVOLUTION WAR, 1667–1668 [16]

While England and the United Provinces were fighting their costly and unprofitable war, a more serious issue came to a climax as a result of the death of Philip IV of Spain on September 17, 1665. When Louis XIV under the terms of the Treaty of the Pyrenees married the Spanish Infanta, Maria Theresa, the royal bridegroom surrendered all claims of the bride to her Spanish heritage. This surrender, calculated by the Spanish statesmen to protect their country from absorption by France, was, by the skill of the French negotiators, attached to a simple but serious condition, namely, that the dowry of the princess should be paid promptly in three installments. As Mazarin had expected, the dowry of 500,000 gold crowns was not paid and the renunciation therefore (from the French point of view) was without force. The Spanish, however, argued that the renunciation on the part of the French queen was effective when it was made and created inalienable rights on the part of her

[15] A. T. Mahan, *The Influence of Sea Power on History, 1660–1783* (Boston, 1897), 107–32.
[16] E. Lavisse, *op. cit.*, VII, Part 2, 274–99.

younger sister. Louis XIV thereupon withdrew the aid he had been furnishing the Spanish king to recover Portugal or to fight the English, who were helping the Portuguese by raiding Spanish colonies in America. Indeed, he furnished financial aid to Portugal and to the English and enabled them to defeat the Spaniards when they attempted to invade Portugal in 1663 and 1665.

When Philip IV, by his will, made his son Charles II his sole heir and declared the Spanish Netherlands an indivisible part of the kingdom, while Maria Theresa and her heirs were "forever excluded" from any of the Spanish inheritance, the French king advanced a technical claim strong enough to enforce against a weak brother-in-law. French experts had discovered that in some of the provinces of the Netherlands customary law provided a right of "devolution," by which at the death of a parent all the children shared the inheritance. According to this, it might be argued that the French queen had the right to take possession of some of the domains where this was the law. French diplomacy went even further and claimed the whole of the Spanish Netherlands by this right of devolution. The French had already tried to get the Dutch to accept the French point of view but, as John de Witt said, the Dutch liked the French as friends but not as neighbors. The French had previously made one advance which alarmed them. Charles II of England, in need of money at the beginning of his reign, had sold Dunkerque (won from the Spanish by Cromwell in alliance with Mazarin) to the French king for five million francs.[17] The Dutch tried to arrive at some compromise arrangements or at any rate to keep the negotiation going, but Louis XIV ended the talks. "The true design of his Majesty," wrote Lionne, "is to keep himself free."

The Anglo-Dutch war began before Philip IV of Spain died, and the intervention of the bishop of Münster imposed on Louis XIV the obligation to support the Dutch. He did so but worked for settlement. To keep the Spanish occupied he married a French princess to Alphonso of Portugal and gave him almost two million *livres* a year to carry on his war. The Spanish hoped for assistance from the emperor, but the German states along the Rhine favored abstention and urged an agreement on the whole question of the Spanish succession. The League of the Rhine was not renewed, but separate secret alliances with the duke of Neuburg, the electors of Cologne and Mainz and the bishop of Münster

[17] Clyde L. Grose, "England and Dunkirk," *American Historical Review*, 39 (1933), 1–27.

gave the French a barrier that shut off the emperor from the Nether-lands.[18]

As long as the Anglo-Dutch war lasted Louis XIV had nothing to fear from Holland. Although at war with England, he was able to arrange a secret treaty with Charles II by which England was to receive colonial territory in the West Indies in return for agreement not to enter any combination against France for a year (April, 1667).

In May, 1667, the French king announced to the queen regent of Spain his intention to take possession of his wife's inheritance and at that time to present a document which would show his wife's rights in the matter. The publication "proved" the nullity of her renunciation and set forth her claims: the duchy of Brabant with its dependencies, Antwerp and Limburg, the lordship of Malines, Upper Gelderland, the county of Namur, Cambrai and the rest of Artois, the county of Hainaut, a part of Luxemburg and a third of Franche-Comté. The Belgian lawyers of the Spanish crown published refutations, but Louis XIV had an ap-pearance of legality, which sufficed for him. He proceeded to occupy the claimed inheritance.

In May, 1667, the king joined Turenne at Amiens and with over-whelming force the French advanced as the Spanish troops withdrew before them. Militarily the whole Spanish Netherlands was at their mercy.

The Dutch were involved in negotiations at Breda attempting to make peace with the English. To hurry them de Witt sent de Ruyter to the Thames. The peace was soon signed, July 7, 1667. The English and the French returned their respective conquests; the Dutch and the English each kept theirs.

Spain was demanding help against France, but de Witt knew he could not venture participation without allies. Louis XIV offered peace on moderate terms provided a treaty was signed before the end of March, 1668: if he could have Luxemburg and Franche-Comté, he would keep only half a dozen of the towns he had occupied. De Witt sought to turn the French toward the east and toward Italy and to induce them to give up all claims in the Netherlands, but Louis XIV refused to tie his hands.

The French had not only cut off the emperor by their alliance with Neuburg and the other Rhine states, but had also induced the elector of

18 A. Legrelle, *La diplomatie française et la succession d'Espagne* (4 vols., Paris, 1888), I, 101–48.

Brandenburg to adopt neutrality. The emperor himself was eventually persuaded to adopt a similar attitude by a French promise to divide the whole succession of Spain. The new king of Spain, Charles II, was a weakly degenerate who was expected to die soon and without direct heirs. The prospect of the vast inheritance evoked the cupidity of the various royal families related to the Spanish royal house and was destined to persist as a concern of European diplomacy through Charles II's unexpectedly long life, to be the subject of several partition treaties, and when Charles died in 1700 to bring on the first world war, the War of the Spanish Succession. This first partition was quickly worked out. The king of France was to have the Netherlands, Franche-Comté, the kingdom of Navarre, the kingdoms of Naples and Sicily, the *presidios* of Morocco and the Philippines. The emperor was to have the rest. Leopold promised to persuade Spain to accept the terms France had offered, as, indeed, Holland was already doing.[19]

Then Louis XIV tried to win over Charles II of England to make war on Holland and Spain and to take the Spanish colonies. Clarendon, however, had just been replaced by the cabal, which was hostile to France. Sir William Temple, who was by way of heading a pro-Holland group in the English government, was sent to Holland to negotiate an offensive-defensive alliance against France. De Witt refused, but easily came to an agreement to oblige Spain by armed mediation to accept one of the solutions already offered by Louis XIV in 1667, to defend Spain if Louis XIV nevertheless continued the war, and not to lay down arms until France had been reduced to the boundaries of the Treaty of the Pyrenees. The two powers also agreed to work for peace between Spain and Portugal. Sweden, which had been closely bound in alliance with France, promptly joined them. In the absence of La Gardie, a pro-Dutch party authorized the Swedish minister at The Hague to join the other two powers.[20]

Louis XIV was doubtless shocked to see the three powers act so independently of him after having been so recently his tools. At the moment, however, he wished to avoid a rupture and so began to conciliate the Dutch by sending his troops into Franche-Comté, which was easily conquered in less than three weeks.

---

[19] A. F. Pribram, *op. cit.*, 405–12.

[20] Mary C. Trevelyan, *William III and the Defense of Holland* (London, 1930), 48–58; P. J. Blok, *op. cit.*, IV, 342–46; E. Emerton, *Sir William Temple und die Tripelallianz vom Jahre 1668* (Berlin, 1877); W. Westergaard, *The First Triple Alliance: The Letters of Christopher Lindenov, Danish Envoy to London, 1668–1672* (New Haven, 1947).

The Triple Alliance was at the lowest terms a check to France and therefore angered Louis XIV. Others were presuming to determine the destiny of France. The Dutch re-equipped their navy, raised troops and hired mercenaries in Germany. The English parliament voted funds for war. The disinherited duke of Lorraine, restive under the provisions of the Treaty of the Pyrenees, made preparations. Even the Swiss showed themselves disturbed by the appearance of French power in Franche-Comté on their borders. Spain finally made peace with Portugal and seemed to take on a new vigor, though all she could offer the alliance was the promise of money from America.

Thus challenged from all sides, Louis XIV decided to accept peace. Spain agreed to surrender the towns and territories of the Netherlands, in part as revenge on Holland for imposing the peace. The terms were settled between the plenipotentiaries of France, Holland and Spain at Saint-Germain-en-Laye and then sent to a peace congress at Aix-la-Chapelle, to be signed without change. The final treaty was concluded May 2, 1668.

France acquired twelve towns, all she had conquered, in the Netherlands, including Armentières, Bergues, Lille, Douai and Tournai, with their dependencies. Franche-Comté was returned to Spain with all its strong places dismantled for convenient conquest at a later time.

The peace was in reality only a truce. Louis XIV had been stopped, but his pride had been injured. He had gained territory not only valuable in itself but strategically convenient for later advances. He had secured recognition of the rights of the queen and of his own. The problem of further advance seemed simplified; he had only to isolate and overwhelm the Dutch. Within four short years, he felt ready for the next step.

IV. THE FRANCO-DUTCH WAR, 1672–1678 [21]

The bases of a new war against Holland had already been laid. By the tariff of 1667 Colbert had followed the characteristically mercantilist aim of ruining Dutch prosperity. The Dutch had asked the king to "replace commerce, which is the soul of human society, in its former liberty," but Lionne had haughtily replied that the king would not change his tariffs. It was the beginning of a commercial war which, as de Witt saw, would lead inevitably to actual war. He therefore undertook to strengthen the Triple Alliance. The Swedes were alienated because Spain

[21] E. Lavisse, *op. cit.*, 2, 300–45; P. J. Blok, *op. cit.*, IV, 366–443.

did not pay the subsidies that had been promised. Spain was forced to pay and by January, 1670, the Dutch guarantee of the Spanish Netherlands was renewed, and the contingents of soldiers to be furnished by Holland, England and Sweden were fixed.

De Witt and his associates hardly realized the resources of French diplomacy and the cogency of its inducements in money and other forms. The emperor, who had just inflicted a severe political defeat on the French by preventing the election of the duke of Enghien as king of Poland, was pushed by his ablest adviser, Baron de Lisola, to join the Triple Alliance. The French ambassador reminded him of his secret treaty with France recognizing his claims to a part of the Spanish inheritance, showed him the gravity of an alliance between the Catholic and Apostolic emperor and three Protestant states, and made pointed references to the Hungarian rebels and the Turkish danger. Leopold disavowed Lisola and abandoned the alliance. In return he secured a free hand against the Hungarian rebels and some assurance against a Turkish attack.

In Germany, the alliances of France with the princes, especially those along the Rhine, were strengthened. Many of the princes were beginning to realize that their danger was not the Hapsburg, but the Bourbon. Louis XIV was a candidate for the imperial throne and an alarming one. The elector of Mainz therefore tried to organize a Union of the Electors (which was to include the emperor as elector of Bohemia). It was to be a vigorous military union for the defense of Germany, to obviate the delays and indecision of the diet. Louis XIV and his diplomats at once saw the danger. The elector of Brandenburg, hopeful of winning French support in getting Sweden out of Pomerania, succumbed to French promises, accepted French subsidies, and held aloof from the Union of Electors. The Treaty of Köln am Spree (December 31, 1669) bound him to stay out of the Triple Alliance, to renew the League of the Rhine and to furnish ten thousand troops to support the rights of the French king to the Spanish Netherlands. Louis XIV promised (and paid) subsidies and ceded to the elector some fortified places on the Meuse. Frederick William, however, despite his own grievances against the Dutch, refused to commit himself to war against Holland. Bavaria, under the influence of a French duchess and a Francophile minister, made a similar treaty, including a promise to vote for Louis XIV as emperor on the death of Leopold.[22]

[22] A. Legrelle, *op. cit.,* I, 216–37.

The diplomatic campaign of Louis XIV was somewhat disoriented by an act of violence. When the duke of Lorraine, a prince of the Empire, refused to disarm, as he was obligated to do by the treaty of Aix-la-Chapelle, a French force appeared without warning before Nancy and forced him to flee. The diet of the Empire protested, the electors of Saxony and Trier joined the anti-French Union of Electors and the emperor began again to consider joining the Triple Alliance.[23] Nevertheless, the lack of real union among the German lands and the local and personal grievances of some of the northern princes permitted the French to build up a line of communication through the Rhineland, Cologne, Liège and Münster, giving them a free road to the borders of Holland. Finally the emperor, aware of the successes of the French diplomats and concerned with his Hungarian and Turkish problems, agreed to disinterest himself in the fate of the Dutch on condition that the war be carried on outside the territory of the Empire (Treaty of Vienna, November 1, 1671).[24]

Meanwhile, by the secret Treaty of Dover, Charles II detached England from the Triple Alliance and, indeed, committed it to war against the United Provinces as the ally of France. This extraordinary reversal was originally motivated by the fear on the part of the English government and of Arlington in particular lest, in the expected partition of the Spanish empire, the Dutch by arrangement with Louis XIV might inherit the Spanish Netherlands.[25] Domestically, the failure of parliament to meet its responsibilities as Charles II saw them made it seem politially profitable for him to turn to Louis XIV. From the French king he might expect financial and political support for a policy that would integrate his divided kingdom and give it a primacy on the seas to match the primacy of France on land. The current of English politics in 1670 was neither parliamentarian nor republican. The ferocious repression which the parliamentary oligarchy exercised in defense of the Established church and the ruthless treatment of capitalists and peasants in Scotland and Ireland had led to threatening disturbances. On the other hand, in Sweden, in Brandenburg and in Bavaria the wealth of the French king had been used effectively to build up well-integrated structures of government, and had served as the lifeblood of many a German princeling's state and even of the stout cantons of Switzerland.

[23] J. Haller, *op. cit.*

[24] P. Sagnac and A. de Saint-Léger, *op. cit.*, 122.

[25] J. J. Jusserand, ed., *Réceuil des instructions données aux ambassadeurs e. :ninistres de France . . .* , *XXV Angleterre* (Paris, 1929), Tome II, 30.

Finally, as Cromwell had demonstrated, it was important for England to be prepared to take full advantage of the expected breakup of the Spanish empire.

Charles II, then, was neither violating his own principles nor running counter to the political morality of his time and place, when he turned to Louis XIV and negotiated the much discussed Treaty of Dover. With his sister Henrietta, duchess of Orleans, Charles handled the negotiations himself. He proposed larger terms than Louis XIV would accept, for he offered to assist Louis XIV with all his forces in return for the cession of Minorca in the Mediterranean, Ostend on the Belgian coast and all of Spanish America, as well as the islands of Walcheren and Kadzand off the Dutch coast and the port of Sluis. Louis XIV was shocked by such suggestions for a distribution of territories which he did not control and the negotiations languished for a while.

As signed on June 1, 1670, the treaty was much more restricted. The two sovereigns would make war on Holland, Louis XIV by land with the support of six thousand English troops, Charles II by sea, with the co-operation of thirty major French vessels; Louis XIV would respect the Spanish Netherlands, Charles II would receive three million *livres* a year during the war and, as his part of the conquests, Walcheren and Kadzand. Charles agreed to return England to Catholicism. At the opportune moment he was to be publicly reconciled with the Roman church, and was to receive an additional two millions and, if required, six thousand French soldiers to repress any resistance. If, meanwhile, new rights to territory were acquired by the French king, Charles II would assist him to take possession. Neither king would make any additional treaty relative to the subject except by consent of the other.

The "supersecret" Treaty of Dover was concealed by the pretense of another negotiation, carried on as though the real treaty had not been signed. The death of Henrietta necessitated putting this negotiation into the hands of the ministers, Clifford, Ashley and Lauderdale. The pretended treaty, similar to the official Treaty of Dover, but without reference to the king's conversion, was signed on February 2, 1671. It increased the share of England in the expected conquests so as to include two more islands off the coast of Zeeland. It set the date of war in the spring of 1672.[26]

France was fully prepared for war. Louvois, aided by competent lieu-

[26] A. Bryant, *op. cit.*, 203–11; Keith Feiling, *British Foreign Policy, 1660–1672*, 269–319; "Henrietta Stuart, Duchess of Orleans and the Origins of the Treaty of Dover," *English Historical Review*, 47 (1932), 642–45.

tenants, had been actively organizing the army and the northern bases. It was to be Louis XIV's first war on a grand scale and everything was designed to make it short and fortunate. Actually it was destined to be long drawn out and to involve almost all the states of Europe.

The Dutch were never worse prepared. Anti-Orange feeling and reluctance to incur heavy expenses had led the estates-general to neglect the army and the fortresses, and to dismiss most of the senior officers, replacing them with their own hangers-on. When at last the council took alarm at the rising threat of war, it was the navy rather than the army that commanded its attention. In spite of much jealousy and a lack of discipline in the higher ranks, the navy was equal to its task. One of the most serious deficiencies was the lack of an over-all command. To most of the Dutch the answer to this problem was obvious. The position of the republic and of de Witt had steadily declined as the nation turned to the prince of Orange, who in 1670 had been admitted to the council of state. On February 24, 1672, William was named captain general and admiral general, after efforts of de Witt and the oligarchy to impose constitutional conditions had failed.[27]

De Witt hoped the English parliament and nation would make it impossible for Charles to break with Holland. Charles II, however, strong in the expectation of French subsidies, had prorogued parliament. Meanwhile, as in 1665, every petty issue, such as the publication of books and medals celebrating Dutch victories over the English or a failure to salute the flag, was exaggerated into quarrels by Sir George Downing, who had replaced Sir William Temple as ambassador at The Hague. De Witt yielded all along the line. He agreed to the salute and even recognized the supremacy of the English in the four seas. Charles II had won a great victory without firing a shot, but his policy required not concessions but a rupture. Dutch ships were embargoed in English ports and Sir Robert Holmes attacked a fleet of sixty-six Dutch vessels on its way home from Smyrna (March 22, 1672). Nevertheless, Charles II had to declare war. He recapitulated all the petty quarrels of the past and in a letter to his nephew, the prince of Orange, alleged in addition the machinations of the bourgeois oligarchy against the prince. De Witt had been as submissive with Louis XIV as with Charles II, even offering to disarm if the king would give assurances of his peaceful intentions, but this proposal was summarily rejected. On April 6, 1672, the French king declared war. Mounted heralds-at-arms announced it on the streets of Paris.[28]

[27] Mary C. Trevelyan, *op. cit.*, 78–99; A. Lefèvre-Pontalis, *op. cit.*, II, 384.
[28] A. de Saint-Léger and P. Sagnac, *op. cit.*, 131.

The situation of Holland seemed hopeless. Against the combination of foes which French diplomacy had organized the republic could claim support only from Spain, which was threatened by a renewal of war with Portugal, and from the elector of Brandenburg, whose German feeling, Dutch sympathies, anti-Swedish focus and inability to win help from Louis XIV in the matter of Pomerania led him to agree to maintain, with Dutch financial assistance, an army of 20,000 of which 3,600 should be kept in his Westphalian fortresses to contain the bishop of Münster (secret treaty of May 6, 1672).

On the other hand, the French forces amounted to more than 160,000 men, well supplied, with the best artillery in Europe and with a brilliant galaxy of leadership in the high command—Turenne, Condé, Luxemburg and Vauban. The French navy was strong, too, but the naval part of the war was left to the English. The duke of York and his able secretary, Samuel Pepys, had done yeoman work in building up English sea power, though much still remained to be done. Popular support for the war, lukewarm to begin with, was radically diminished by the Declaration of Indulgence (March 15, 1672) and the Stop of the Exchequer (June 12, 1672). Sweden, after having extorted the utmost possible in the way of subsidies from Spain under the Triple Alliance, undertook to co-operate with France by keeping an army in Pomerania and thus counterbalancing the elector of Brandenburg.

The military operation against the Dutch, as the French expected, proceeded like a tranquil promenade.[29] The various alliances permitted the French to move along the Rhine and the Meuse against the relatively unguarded eastern frontier. By-passing Maastricht, some hundred thousand troops entered Holland and forced William III with his handful of troops to fall back to cover Amsterdam. Louis XIV wished to have the glory of taking some towns by siege, and was perhaps dubious of Condé's bold plan of leaving the small fortified places behind him. As a result time was lost by the French and enough gained by the Dutch to permit the opening of the dikes. Although in political and strategical terms the French had lost their war, the Dutch thought they were beaten and asked for terms. Louvois demanded everything: cession of all occupied territory, revocation of all measures of reprisal against French commerce, an indemnity of 24,000,000 *livres*, admission of Catholics to public functions and the free exercise of their religion, and even an annual embassy to the

[29] P. J. Blok, *op. cit.*, IV, 399–406.

king of France bearing a gold medal in recognition of the liberty which the king, despite their ingratitude, would deign to leave the Dutch.

These terms were enough to galvanize the remaining free areas of the United Provinces into the unity that was so lacking before the crisis. The de Witts and their party were swept away and William of Orange emerged as stadholder in the traditional position of leadership held by his ancestors.[30] He was hardly a good general in the military sense of the term—only a modest strategist and still less a tactician—but at the higher level of continental political strategy he was a master and he was favored by circumstances. Germany began to rise against the French. The elector of Brandenburg, disappointed by the inability of the Dutch to supply his ever deficient treasury and gratified to have them out of Cleves, had reversed his field and made an arrangement with the French, subject to his obligations as a member of the Empire. Then he turned to the emperor and made a defensive alliance with him. This was a threat to the allies of the French, Cologne and Münster, and to the French line of communications. Louis therefore divided his forces to meet the German threat. That gave William of Orange an opportunity to strike at Charleroi on the border of France, as usual in his case, not quite effectively. Only a desperate winter campaign by Turenne kept the bishop of Münster from surrendering "at the sound of the imperial trumpets." Nevertheless, the genius of Turenne and the effectiveness of his troops gave the French Maastricht (June 30, 1673) and effective control of the line of the Meuse. The fall of Maastricht seemed to Louvois to provide a basis for a peace congress, in the expectation that the Dutch would accept the conditions the king wished to impose. The Dutch, so abject a year before, refused them. In a few months the character of the war had changed. For France, it was no longer a problem of defeating the Dutch, but of facing a coalition of Europe.

On August 28, 1673, the emperor appeared before the diet to denounce Louis XIV as a threat to the peace of Christendom. This move marked the beginning of a complete revolution in the diplomatic and military situation. Within a few days, the emperor, the king of Spain and the duke of Lorraine were bound in an alliance with the United Provinces. On the other hand, the system of alliances which Louis XIV's diplomats had so carefully combined before the war was falling apart. The imperial forces easily took Bonn and knocked Cologne out of the war. Münster was likewise eliminated. The Palatinate, the archbishoprics of Trier and Mainz,

---

[30] M. C. Trevelyan, *op. cit.*, 213–35; A. Lefèvre-Pontalis, *op. cit.*, II, chs. 13, 14.

the princes of Brunswick, and, again, the elector of Brandenburg were successively drawn into the grand alliance of The Hague. Holland, isolated at the beginning of the war, was, by the end of 1674, the center of a great coalition. France, which had been so thoroughly armored with alliances, was isolated.[31]

In 1674 England withdrew from the war. Even at the outbreak of hostilities, public opinion had been skeptical of its possible results. The development of the French navy and especially of the merchant marine had aroused recognizable hostility even before the Treaty of Dover. The Stop of the Exchequer and especially the Declaration of Indulgence angered the parliamentary oligarchy. The Test Act of 1673 broke up the cabal and drove the Catholic duke of York from office. All these issues were sharpened by the marriage of the duke of York to the duchess of Modena, a Catholic princess. Shaftesbury, dismissed from office, began organizing the opposition. The advent of Charles II's nephew, the prince of Orange, as stadholder, had changed his attitude. He was constantly in touch with the prince almost from the beginning of the conflict. To avoid an open conflict with parliament, and, it may be presumed, to shake off the burden of a war no longer promising satisfactory results, Charles II made peace with the Dutch after less than two years of formal war (February 19, 1674).[32]

The position of England remained ambiguous. Powerful pressures from within and without were exerted to bring England into the war against France. French money, however, was still important to Charles II's aim to become independent of parliament. Louis XIV thought it worth while to pay as much for English neutrality as he had paid for England's participation in the war. Sir Thomas Osborne (later earl of Danby) reorganized Charles II's finances for him and by a skillful distribution of favors built up a fairly disciplined majority in parliament. In 1676 the two kings formalized their diplomatic alliance in another secret treaty which pledged each not to conclude any agreement—that is, under the circumstances, treaty of peace or alliance—without the consent of the other. Thus it seemed that France was assured of the friendly neutrality of England and of her support at the peace negotiations. That, however, turned out quite otherwise.

Thus the military problem had changed. For France the war had become defensive. Conquest at the expense of Spain was still possible. Franche-Comté was again quickly overrun, while Condé, in a particularly

[31] B. Erdmannsdörfer, *op. cit.*, I, 583–89; F. Schevill, *op. cit.*, 292–306.
[32] G. N. Clark, *op. cit.*, 77–79; M. C. Trevelyan, *op. cit.*, 340–47.

brilliant campaign, defeated William of Orange in the Spanish Netherlands. The Spanish lost towns in each successive campaign. Meanwhile the
Imperials under Montecuccoli invaded Alsace but were thrown back
beyond the Rhine by Turenne's clever winter campaign. In the summer
of 1675 Turenne won his last victory over Montecuccoli: at the battle of
Salzbach, he was killed in the moment of victory. Condé, recalled from
the Netherlands, was able to stop a new invasion.

The war at sea went badly for the French. The Dutch navy under
Tromp and de Ruyter re-established its dominance over the narrow seas
and the ocean and threatened landings (without success) all along the
Atlantic coast of France. Only in the Mediterranean did the French succeed in keeping the upper hand. A rebellion against the Spanish in Sicily
was seized as an opportunity to aid the rebels. The Spanish called upon
the Dutch for naval assistance, but the French Admiral Duquesne defeated the Dutch and de Ruyter himself was killed. The French victory
in the Mediterranean was complete but it was not followed up. Meanwhile Louis XIV's Swedish allies were losing control of the Baltic. When
Brandenburg and Denmark joined the Grand Alliance, Louis called on
Sweden to fulfill its engagements. The regency set the Pomeranian army
in motion against Brandenburg and Frederick William, who had just
been thrown out of Alsace, found himself momentarily isolated and in
apparently desperate straits. The Swedish army, however, was carelessly
deployed over a long line. Taking advantage of the situation, Frederick
William struck at the middle of the line at Fehrbellin (June 27, 1675) and
to the amazement of Europe defeated the reputedly invincible Swedes. It
was a small action and, in principle, strategically unimportant. It coincided,
however, with the defeat by Denmark of the duke of Holstein-Gottorp,
Sweden's ally on the border of Denmark. Within a year the Danes and
the Dutch had gained control of the Baltic (battle of Öland, June 1,
1676), cutting off the Swedish troops in Bremen and Pomerania from the
peninsula. The Danes even invaded Sweden, but Charles XI by bold, not
to say reckless, leadership evoked a surge of patriotism that enabled him
to expel the Danes and recover Scania. On the other hand, the Swedish
losses in Germany remained militarily irretrievable. Stettin, the last foothold of Sweden in Germany, capitulated December 27, 1677. The Poles,
on whom the French counted to stop Brandenburg, and the Turks, on
whom they counted to hamper the Hapsburgs, were unwilling to move
because of their distrust of each other and their concern with the Russians.[33]

[33] A. T. Mahan, *The Influence of Sea Power on History, 1660–1783*, 159–70; R. C.

From the standpoint of France the war was lost, so far as its original purpose was concerned, when the Dutch flooded their polders and the conflict became a general war of Europe against France. The conquest and humiliation of Holland was out of the question. The problem was rather to defend France and especially French gains by the treaties of Westphalia, the Pyrenees and Aix-la-Chapelle. Heavy taxation and general war weariness produced serious revolts in Normandy, Brittany and Guienne. The *parlements* of Bordeaux and Rouen were suspended because of their sympathy with the rebels. The French army—soldiers, equipment and leadership—continued to show itself immensely superior to any combination that could be brought against it, but the number of France's enemies continued to increase. Parliament and public opinion in England pushed Charles toward the Dutch side. Charles II and William thereupon negotiated the principles of a peace which Charles submitted to Louis XIV as an ultimatum.[34]

The Dutch too were weary of the war. Their purposes had been achieved when their territory was made secure and when they had reestablished their naval superiority. The unity which the crisis of 1672 had produced rapidly disintegrated. The Republicans were disinclined to fight for the recovery of Spanish losses or to help the emperor reduce the French position in Alsace. The stadholder, on the other hand, saw the problem as a European one, requiring the definitive reduction of French power. In spite of this cleavage, the Dutch managed to bring Spain to accept the loss of Franche-Comté and an adjustment of the boundary between France and the Spanish Netherlands.

On this basis the negotiation of the peace at Nimwegen began. The negotiations between Holland and France proceeded apace. The French agreed to return Maastricht and to remove the discriminations against the Dutch in the tariff of 1667. The Dutch announced their intention of signing the treaty "with such of their allies as were so disposed." They were willing to desert their allies, but Louis XIV was not. He announced his intention of holding Maastricht and the line of the Meuse until the Swedes had recovered their lost territories. Only a concession on the part of the Swedes prevented the renewal of the war by the Dutch, this time with the help of England. On August 10, 1678, the treaty of peace and a treaty of commerce between Holland and France were signed, to be effective when a treaty was concluded between France and Spain. The

---

Anderson, *Naval Wars in the Baltic, 1522–1850* (London, 1910), 104–27; L. André, *Louis XIV et l'Europe*, 170; F. Schevill, *op. cit.*, 313–37.

[34] C. L. Grose, "The Anglo-Dutch Alliance of 1678," *English Historical Review*, 39 (1924), 349–92, 526–51.

Spanish, encouraged by William of Orange and Sir William Temple, who were working to have the peace conference break down, held out for a while but presently gave in and ceded Franche-Comté and a number of towns in the Cambrésis, Hainaut and Flanders, as well as the whole of Artois, receiving in return a number of the towns yielded to France in 1668. At the conclusion of the Franco-Spanish treaty, the ratifications of the Franco-Dutch treaty were exchanged.[35]

. Thus the coalition was broken. The emperor still fought on, holding out for his interpretation of the position of Alsace under the terms of the treaties of Westphalia. The French refused to yield and inflicted several defeats in the field. Furthermore, the victories of the Great Elector over the Swedes, which carried him as far as Riga, began to alarm his fellow princes and the emperor. Leopold, who remembered that Frederick William had deserted him, now abandoned the elector. He made peace with France and Sweden (February 2, 1679). France gave up Philippsburg but kept Freiburg im Breisgau, a bridgehead across the Rhine. Lorraine was to be returned to the duke, but on conditions that he refused to accept, and thus it remained in possession of France.[36]

Brandenburg and Denmark attempted to hold the conquests they had made at the expense of Sweden. Frederick William was determined to retain Pomerania and the port of Stettin. But Louis XIV, despite Frederick William's efforts to replace Sweden as the northern hinge of French policy, was determined to protect his ally. He set his troops in motion and Frederick William saw that he had to surrender. Without Sweden's participation, Brandenburg and France concluded the Treaty of Saint-Germain (June 29, 1679), by which all Sweden's losses were returned. Denmark was similarly forced to make peace with Sweden.[37]

Nimwegen is often regarded as the apogee of Louis XIV's policy: actually it was its bankruptcy. He had made his bid for supremacy in Europe with what seemed to be overwhelming advantages. He had failed, and never again would he make the bid without evoking the same kind of coalition against him. In the end his diplomatic combinations, built up in blind disregard of the real national interests of the states concerned, could not hold in the face of stress. Perhaps the most fatal comment to be made is that Louis XIV did not recognize how complete his failure was. The Europe he wished to subject had produced a leader. William of Orange, although he did not know how to combine armies, did know

[35] E. Lavisse, op. cit., VII, Part 2, 339–43.
[36] B. Erdmannsdörfer, op. cit., I, 637–40.
[37] F. Schevill, op. cit., 335–36.

how to combine the powers of Europe. Brought up in a hard school, he learned to accept the fact of opposition and criticism, and to conquer by maneuver and compromise. Unsentimental, he may have had some Dutch patriotism. He used Dutchmen, Englishmen, England and Holland, as he used the rest of the states and peoples he variously combined as pieces of greater or lesser value in a complicated game the objective of which was European. Marlborough was his heir, and his European vision made possible the coalitions of European states that defeated Louis XIV at Blenheim and Ramillies.

The fatal consequences of Louis's expansion policy, so apparent to a later age, were not apparent to the king or to his contemporaries. Louis XIV's position and prestige in Europe seemed still overwhelming. In a letter to Schwerin (August 11, 1679), Frederick William declared, "In the present state of affairs, so far as human prudence can judge, it seems that no prince will henceforth find security and advantage except in the friendship and alliance of the King of France." [38] He had failed to humiliate or destroy the Dutch Republic, but in the treaties of Nimwegen he had made important territorial gains and his opponents generally had been diminished. The German princes were again content to take his subsidies and commit themselves to the support of his policies. To the electors of Mainz, Trier and Cologne, had been added the elector of Brandenburg and the elector of Saxony. Bavaria, however, began to orient its policy in the direction of Austria, especially after the death of the Archduke Ferdinand in 1679. Scandinavia was pacified by the influence of Louis XIV, but after some moves toward a triple alliance of France, Denmark and Sweden, Charles XI, aggrieved by the "reunion" of his hereditary duchy Zweibrücken and by French arrogance even in the return of Pomerania, turned away from France. In the east, Poland under Sobieski also turned toward Austria. Turkey thereupon became the best auxiliary of the French policy in the east. In spite of many difficulties with the sultan, arising from French action against the Barbary pirates, French diplomats kept up a good understanding with him. Not only was Constantinople (with Warsaw) used as a convenient base for support of the Hungarian rebels, but at least after 1676, the French government constantly encouraged the grand vizier to attack Austria. Only the compunctions of his council kept Louis XIV from forming an outright alliance with the Turks. In 1683 the French ambassador informed the Turkish

[38] L. André, *Louis XIV et l'Europe,* 184, note.

government that no objection would be made to a Turkish capture of Vienna.[39]

On the other hand, Louis's enemies were relatively weakened. Spain had sunk to its lowest point. The Dutch Republic, which had suffered immense damages to its soil by invasion and by flooding, was engaged in a slow and costly process of reconstruction. With the passing of the crisis the old divisions and the Republican distrust of Orange, in particular of his militancy, began to reappear. When the stadholder wished to ally with England, the states-general listened to the proposals of the French ambassador for an alliance with France. Holland was poorly regarded by the allies it had so cavalierly deserted at Nimwegen. England's position, too, was ambiguous. The course of politics had fortified the ancient Gallophobia: France appeared as a danger to parliamentary liberties and to the Protestantism not only of the church but also of the sects. What confidence there had been between Louis XIV and Charles II had been undermined by the willingness of Charles to go along with the anti-French program in 1678. Nevertheless, by 1681 the two sovereigns came to an agreement that again neutralized England.[40]

v. THE REUNIONS, 1678–1684

Between 1678 and 1684 Louis XIV was able to make peace as profitable in annexations as war. The coalition against him had been thoroughly disrupted by the successive desertions of the Dutch, the emperor and the Great Elector. The divided and confused state of these former allies opened the way for a series of operations of force and maneuver combined, which within their limits and from a purely technical point of view rank among the most adroit in the history of international relations.

The method used was essentially the same as that applied to the claims of Louis XIV to the Spanish Netherlands. A quasi-legal claim was formulated, suit was brought in the French courts, customary or special, and the inevitably favorable decision was followed by positive action with forces which the parties at interest were unable to resist. Arnauld de Pomponne, who as secretary of state for foreign affairs had negotiated the settlements of Nimwegen, was dismissed because he "lacked the force which ought to be shown in executing the orders of a King of France," because he was disposed to be satisfied with limited results and, possibly, because he was connected with the Jansenists. Colbert de Croissy, brother

[39] *Ibid.*, 201
[40] See below, p. 174.

of the controller general, who, as intendant of Alsace, had even before the Dutch War initiated procedure against some of the lords who had "usurped" rights claimed by the king of France, was appointed to direct, with Louvois, a vigorous policy of "reunion." [41]

The new rights of the king of France and the persisting rights of the emperor and the various German lords lacked clear definition. The ambiguous formulation of the Treaty of Münster left and leaves it still uncertain what the emperor ceded or what the king of France received.[42]

The emperor-archduke gave up everything, but many lords and cities retained their "immediacy," that is, their direct connection with the Empire. This immediacy, however, was not to detract from Louis XIV'S right of sovereignty (*omni supremi dominii jus*), already ceded. Respect for usage, to which the Hapsburg was bound, might have made such provisions workable, but Louis XIV was not so bound. His supreme dominion was new and had to be defined, and defined it was by his sovereign courts to support his unchallenged power. In Alsace, as in Franche-Comté, he was scrupulously respectful of existing institutions and rights, provided only his absolute supremacy was recognized.

The Decapolis, the ten towns whose "immediacy" to the Empire had been nominally preserved by the Treaty of Westphalia, were summarily ordered to take the oath of fidelity to Louis XIV. Great lords like the margrave of Baden and the duke of Zweibrücken (who was also the king of Sweden) were summoned to do homage. The same procedure was carried out in the three bishoprics (Metz, Toul and Verdun), and in Franche-Comté. The diet of the Empire protested. Louis XIV, aware that William of Orange had managed to organize a defensive alliance with England and Spain, responded in conciliatory fashion until he had worked out a new alliance with Brandenburg. In the hope of securing French support against Sweden in Pomerania and in return for substantial financial assistance the elector agreed to support all the rights which Louis XIV enjoyed or might enjoy under the Treaty of Nimwegen. The reunions were then resumed. The final step was taken in the reduction of Alsace to a province of France. The free Imperial city of Strasbourg, which had served during the Dutch war as a gateway for the Imperial forces, was suddenly surrounded and forced to surrender (October 23, 1681). Almost

---

[41] L. André, *op. cit.*, 188.

[42] J. E. Hamilton, "Alsace and Louis XIV," *History*, 13 (1928), 107–17; C. Benoist, *Les lois de la politique française et le gouvernement d'Alsace sous Louis XIV* (Paris, 1929); G. Zeller, "La réunion d'Alsace à la France et les prétendues lois de la politique française," *Revue d'Alsace*, 76 (1929), 768–78.

at the same time French troops took possession of Casale, the capital of Montferrat, on the Po, lying between Spanish Milan and Piedmont and dominating them both. These seizures illustrated the fact that France had other means of expansion than legalistic processes.

Europe was alarmed by the increasing prospect of a renewal of war. The process of "reunion" had been applied to the county of Chimay, which belonged to the king of Spain. The Spanish troops withdrew as the French advanced. The Dutch states-general refused to commit troops to help the Spanish defend the Spanish Netherlands, as the governor at Brussels demanded, but at the instigation of William of Orange they did undertake to reform the coalition which Nimwegen had broken up. Charles XI of Sweden, who was also duke of Zweibrücken and had refused to do homage to Louis XIV for the duchy, promptly signed with the states a treaty of association to guarantee the treaties of Westphalia. According to the Dutch, it was "a convention of a very innocent character, so pacific, so Christian, and so honorable, that no one could take exception to it." It was nonetheless the first step toward the League of Augsburg, which was in a few years to stop France at the cost of another great war. William of Orange attempted to bring in Charles II of England, but the latter refused because war would have meant a renewed dependence on parliament, which he had just gotten rid of. He did agree to make representations to Louis XIV, which that ruler took as occasion to suggest that he receive Luxemburg as the "equivalent" of some other claims to parts of the Spanish Netherlands. Charles II raised objections, but another million *livres* on his annual subsidy quieted them. He offered to arbitrate, but the king of Spain declined.

The seizure of Strassburg threw the German states into consternation. Louis XIV took advantage of the confusion to call a special conference at Frankfurt, where his representatives declared that he had no designs on Germany and offered to give up Freiburg im Breisgau, on the German side of the Rhine, if the emperor would return Philippsburg, a bridgehead on the Rhine farther north, to the bishop of Speyer. The greater princes generally, for one reason or another, favored negotiation. The ecclesiastical princes were thoroughly tied into the French system by their alliances. The elector of Brandenburg saw his great hope of gaining Pomerania in winning French support against Sweden.[43] On the other hand, a number of the smaller states, less moved by considerations of high statesmanship and greed, reflected their alarm at the threatening

[43] Frederick William to Schwerin, August 11, 1679 (L. André, *op. cit.*, 184, note).

advance of French power by forming the Laxenburg Alliance under the leadership of Waldeck, the friend and lieutenant of William of Orange, with the sympathetic support of the emperor and of Bavaria, newly anti-French under its young elector, Maximilian Emanuel. The Laxenburg Alliance lacked military power and was contemned by the French: it was a premonition of what they should have feared most, the development of Francophobia.[44] Nevertheless, at the moment, the emperor could not secure the support of the diet for an anti-French policy. He vainly sought a truce with the Turks and even formally adhered to the association of The Hague, but the Turkish advance forced him to turn his efforts to the east.[45]

With the growing Francophobia in Holland and England, the threat to Luxemburg, which was blockaded by French troops under Marshal de Créqui, became a critical issue. Charles II, anxious to avoid summoning a parliament, insisted that it should not be taken. Louis XIV, equally anxious that parliament should not have an opportunity to align England with the Dutch, decided to lift the siege. It was an opportune moment. He was being pressed by Poland and by the papacy to aid in the resistance to the Turkish advance. Without avowing his real reason, Louis declared that he was withdrawing his troops in order not to hamper the German princes in their support of the emperor against the Turks.[46] In view of the growing combination against him in Germany, he insisted that his proposals to settle the disputes with Spain and the Empire be accepted. The Spanish attempt to bring about a general congress was roughly brushed aside.

In this situation the Turkish attack on Vienna was made, resisted and defeated. By the French the victory of the Christian forces was regarded as a defeat: Luxemburg must counterbalance Vienna. The French found it easy to dislocate the combinations against them. The estates-general, in spite of William of Orange, accepted the idea of another settlement at the expense of Spain. The king of England remained obdurate in his determination not to get into war and so become involved with parliament. The Austrian generals demanded that the war against the Turks be pursued to the end. The stubborn resistance of Frederick William and the other princes defeated every attempt of the emperor to organize support for action in the west as well as the east.[47]

---

[44] B. Erdmannsdörfer, *op. cit.*, I, 667–75.
[45] See below, Chapter Eight, "The Expansion of Europe."
[46] Arthur Hassall, "The Foreign Policy of Louis XIV," *Cambridge Modern History*, V, 49.
[47] B. Erdmannsdörfer, *op. cit.*, I, 690–92.

Thus when Spain, rendered desperate by the renewed insistence of the French upon acceptance of their increasing demands, declared war, the hope of intervention by either Holland or the Empire had been defeated. The United Provinces and the English king were induced to undertake mediation to force the Spanish to yield. Louis XIV stepped up his military action against Spain and won easy victories. Courtrai and Dixmude were taken early in 1684. Luxemburg was besieged again, and after a strong resistance of some months fell in June, 1684. Catalonia was invaded. Genoa, which had served as a financial and shipbuilding center for Spain, was bombarded into surrender and compelled to accept a humiliating vassalage. The Dutch were induced even to withdraw the troops they maintained in the Spanish Netherlands. The emperor, unable to command support from the diet or from the Dutch, yielded to the demand of the diet that he negotiate with the French king. Spain was obliged to give up and left to the emperor the responsibility of securing as favorable terms as possible.

Spain was once more called upon to pay the piece of peace. At Ratisbon (August 15, 1684) the emperor for himself and for Spain agreed to a twenty-year truce, leaving Luxemburg, Strassburg and Alsace in the possession of France, while Courtrai and Dixmude were returned to Spain and Louis XIV agreed to make no further claims upon the Spanish Netherlands. Apparently the truce of Ratisbon was made with the expectation on each side that time would work in its favor: on the French side that the Germans would grow accustomed to the loss of imperial territory, on the German side that some later development would make it possible to renew the legal claims of the Empire to Alsace.

Militarily, with Casale, Strassburg and Luxemburg in firm possession, Louis XIV seemed to have guaranteed the predominance of France in Europe. Politically, French diplomacy and French gold had disrupted the bases of mutuality and confidence necessary for combination against France. Only Louis XIV himself could integrate the opposition of Europe and expose France to disaster by an act of arbitrariness and violence, the revocation of the Edict of Nantes.

VI. THE POWER PATTERN IN 1685

In 1685 the high aims which Louis XIV had pursued with such naïve disregard of opposing forces were less attainable than ever. France had gained territories but it had brought upon itself formidable and irreconcilable enmities. The net result of twenty-five years of a diplomacy based upon a sense of superiority was the union of all the potential enemies of France and the disaffection of its potential allies. Denmark and Brandenburg had been used for Louis's purposes and compelled to make peace when they attempted to realize the values of the alliance for themselves, Charles II of England had been held at the cost of his people's confidence in himself and his dynasty. Victor Amadeus of Savoy remembered the arrogant interventions of the French king for purely French purposes. The leadership of William of Orange was preparing the Netherlands to serve as a nexus about which a world alliance was to be formed against France. The house of Austria remained irreconcilable. Spain had had to pay for every peace by new territorial sacrifices. The emperor desired to recover Strassburg and, as Hapsburg if not as emperor, had new strength available as a result of the defeat of the Turks before Vienna. The Protestants, exasperated and alarmed by the revocation of the Edict of Nantes, combined with Austria against France as they had once combined with Richelieu against Austria. Sectarian rancor only reinforced the alarm generally felt at the apparent insatiability of Louis XIV after Nimwegen.

The intangibles of politics were beyond the range of baroque statesmen generally and of French statesmen in particular. The growing flame of hate fed by the numerous pamphlets of Lisola [48] and his emulators was not countered by any effort on the part of the French to make themselves loved or even acceptable. In his *Mars christianissimus* (Cologne, 1684), the very title of which is a volume of irony, Leibniz formulated the impact that such attitudes as the French made on a society without too much delicacy: "After 1672," he wrote, "the French decided the King did not need any longer to justify his enterprises to the world, as his ancestors did, by publishing superfluous manifestos." The conviction was quite widely spread among Frenchmen, Leibniz was convinced, especially among those who went among foreigners, that only their own people and those who "had French souls" could have more than common wit and polish. The ambassadors knew that the French were hated. Colbert de Croissy wrote from England of the universal aversion and distrust of the French felt by the English. The ambassador at Turin wrote that "nowhere are the French less loved." The hate of foreigners for the French was one reason why Turenne thought it important to develop the frontier defenses.

The imperial idea that might have served as a basis for the imperial ambitions of Louis XIV was lacking. As Lavisse says, it would have taken a very great man indeed to appreciate and follow the advice of Leibniz and to furnish the leadership of European advance in America, in Asia and above all in the eastern Mediterranean. It was a very mediocre man indeed who labored pompously through another thirty years of misfortune and disaster without any evident analysis or review of his motives, purposes and limitations. Louis XIV found it easier to go on fighting for glory and for territory than for any ideal standard of societal organization. His impulses remained feudal.

Nevertheless, without attributing to Louis XIV any advanced geopolitics, it is possible to recognize in his program potentialities that could have made a very different Europe from that which actually evolved through the eighteenth and nineteenth centuries. Considered as a program, projected, the pattern emerges: a French king, emperor, king of Spain, lord of the Netherlands, both Dutch and Belgian, master of Italy, ruler of great lands beyond the sea, master of the Mediterranean and champion of Christendom against the infidel. Such a world would have required bolder rationalizing than a Colbert or a Louvois could imagine, but in a century or two it might have compared favorably with the segmented Europe that actually persisted.

Chapter Six

THE SEARCH FOR GOD

Négliger les choses religeuses du XVIIe siècle ou les estimer petitement,
c'est ne pas comprendre l'histoire de ce siècle, c'est ne pas la sentir.

(To neglect the religious affairs of the seventeenth century or to rate them
as minor, is to fail to understand the history of that century or even to sense
it.) [1]

THE problem of religion as such dissociates itself from the problem of
power either in terms of ecclesiastical organization or of the religious
policy of a state. In that sense, the latter part of the seventeenth century
was marked by greater intensity of religious experience among individuals and by a highly diversified search for new forms and values in religious experience. It was the age of Bunyan, of Labadie and Spener, of
Pascal and Madame Guyon.

The Europeans were asserting in religion the principle of the baroque:
I will conform and I will be free. At the same time the intellectuals were
losing their sympathy for the theological fury and doctrinal disputes
that raged in Catholic, Lutheran and Calvinist pulpits. Many of them
sought in syncretism a practical reconstruction of the ecclesiastical unity
that Europe had lost in the sixteenth century, or in deism a generalization of religious values that aimed to transcend not only the sectarian
divisions but the historical limitations of Christianity itself. The Europeans had come in contact with many forms of religion far different from
the Christianity, Judaism and Islam with which their culture had developed. In general, they carried Christianity into all the new areas opened
up to missionary activity by exploration and conquest.[2] In this period,
however, the significant missionary achievement was almost wholly
Catholic. Although Spener and Fox recognized the obligation, even the
Pietists and the Quakers fell short of a sustained or extensive program.
The nationalized official churches lacked a world point of view. In the
Catholic church, on the other hand, the great missionary orders of earlier
origin, the Franciscans and the Dominicans, as well as the new orders

[1] Lavisse, *op. cit.,* VII, 88.
[2] K. Latourette, *A History of the Expansion of Christianity,* 3 vols. (New York, 1937–
1939), Vol. III, *Three Centuries of Advance.*

born of the Counter Reformation, such as the Jesuits, the Capuchins and the Lazarists, all carried on a world-wide campaign. In China and India this activity was perhaps more significant as a channel for the return of oriental influences to the centers of European culture than as an agency for the conversion of non-Christians.[3] In the expanding Spanish empire, on the other hand, the missionaries of the orders, recruited from all over Europe, were the agents of advance and organization on the frontiers and established Catholic Christianity as a phase of the ineradicable *Hispanidad* that still marks those areas.[4] The Society of Foreign Missions, founded in Paris in 1663 by Francois Pallu, formulated for the French missions and ultimately for the Congregation of the Propaganda the statesman-like aim of raising up an indigenous secular clergy.[5]

The strong fabric of Indian, Chinese and Mohammedan religion not only resisted the Christian propaganda, but reacted upon the provincialism of earlier Christian feeling so as to reduce its rigidity and intolerance. Along with other factors, both intellectual and economic, Christian contact with other religions operated to reduce the *odium theologicum*. Freedom became the norm of religious feeling and, to a considerable degree, of religious practice.

The religious life of the Europeans in the latter part of the seventeenth century may be comprehended under two diverse and ostensibly opposed tendencies, intellectualism and mysticism. The intellectual aspect ranged from the disputatious scholasticism of the Jansenists and their opponents to the Cartesian utilitarianism of the Deists and the Syncretists.

I. JANSENISM [6]

Jansenism had begun as a revival of the issue of grace and good works as means to salvation. At the hands of Antoine Arnauld and Pascal it had become an attack upon the morality of the Jesuits. When the pope condemned the Five Propositions alleged to be contained in the *Augustinus* of Jansen, the movement became an assertion of the irreducible freedom of the individual soul under God.

The ideal of Jansenism had been developed and represented principally by Port Royal, a small group of nuns under the leadership of

---

[3] A. Reichwein, *China and Europe: Intellectual and Artistic Contacts in the 18th Century* (translated by J. C. Powell, New York, 1925), 19–20, 389 *et passim;* see also B. Stankewitch, *La Chine en France au temps de Louis XIV* (Paris, 1910).

[4] R. K. Wyllys, *Pioneer Padre: The Life and Times of Eusebio Francisco Kino* (Dallas, Texas, 1935).

[5] K. Latourette, *op. cit.,* III, Introduction.

[6] A. Gazier, *Histoire générale du mouvement janseniste,* 2 vols. (Paris, 1922).

Mother Angélique, the sister of "the great Arnauld," with a convent in Paris but with another center at Port Royal des Champs in the country near by. With them were associated the Messieurs de Port Royal, a group of devotees who lived monastically but were not formally organized as a monastery. They conducted a school distinguished for its modern methods and its record of brilliant pupils.

The condemnation of the Five Propositions by the pope (1653) and the acceptance of the bull by the French assembly of the clergy (1656) led to the requirement by the assembly from all the clergy, regular and secular, of a Formula of Submission to the bull and its complete acceptance. The Jansenists refused on the ground that the Five Propositions were not in the *Augustinus* and that the authority of the pope did not extend to matters of fact. The upsurge of public opinion in favor of the Jansenists resulting from the *Provincial Letters* of Blaise Pascal, and intensified by a miracle at Port Royal itself, prevented effective action.

Meanwhile, Mazarin and Louis XIV grew increasingly hostile to Port Royal. Jansenism, to them, was, like Protestantism, a challenge to authority. More particularly, Jansenism and Port Royal attracted the support of several ex-*Frondeurs* such as the Cardinal de Retz and the Duchesse de Longueville. On December 13, 1660, the king ordered all the clergy and other religious persons in France to sign the Formula "purely and simply," not only submitting to the condemnation of the Five Propositions but admitting that they were in the *Augustinus*.

In spite of the earnest intervention of Harlay, the new archbishop of Paris, the nuns of Port Royal (although the Messieurs were more pliant) refused to sign and prepared joyfully for martyrdom. To their disappointment, they were merely scattered among other convents. Most of the Jansenists in the university and among the clergy of Paris and of Normandy signed. Four Jansenist bishops, however, successfully attacked the Formula as beyond the powers of the assembly of the clergy, which was in no sense a council. The king thereupon asked the pope to impose a formula by his authority.

By this time the Jansenist problem had become thoroughly involved with the emergent issue of Gallicanism. When the Sorbonne manifested its Gallican animus by condemning a book in favor of papal infallibility, the pope refused the king's request. When Louis XIV asked the pope to subject the four Jansenist bishops to trial by a papal commission, the bishops were supported by nineteen others in a protest against such intrusion of the pope in the affairs of the French church. The king and his ministers gave up. The problem became, in the words of Le Tellier, how "to disengage the king honorably from the steps he had taken at Rome." The nuns of Port Royal had been brought back to Port Royal from the convents to which they had been exiled and where they had been too active as propagandists. They were kept isolated, however, and the burden of the battle rested with the bishops.

The battle was temporarily quieted by methods more devious than honorable. Mediators undertook "to deceive both the pope and the bishop (Pavillon of Alet)," so that the pope could accept as "purely and simply" Pavillon's signature with reservations. The device succeeded and "the peace of the Church" was achieved. An *arrêt* commanded the king's subjects to desist from attacking each other, from using such terms as "heretic, Jansenist or semipelagian," and from writing about the connected issues. For a moment it seemed that Arnauld might become the real leader of the church in France, but as the king grew pious, the influence of the Jesuits increased. Thus, when Arnauld and Nicole renewed the attack on the morality of the Jesuits, Harlay, the new archbishop of Paris, once more evicted the pupils and lay persons who had again gathered at Port Royal des Champs and forbade the nuns to receive any more novices. Arnauld and Nicole fled to Flanders and several of the remaining leaders were committed to the Bastille. On the other hand, the Holy See, mindful that the Jansenists had been helpful in the matter of the *régale,* abstained from attacking them. It was not until the Oratorian Quesnel, in 1693, published the third edition of *A New Testament with Moral Reflections,* an outspokenly Jansenist work, that the battle was renewed.

The later tragic story of Port Royal and Jansenism came formally to a close with the dispersal of the nuns in 1709 and the bull *Unigenitus* of 1713, but Jansenism remained part of the antiauthoritarian ferment of the eighteenth century and even of the distinctive temper of present day French Catholicism.[7] In Germany and in England, with less political implication, it was a pervasive influence.[8] In Holland a Jansenist church continues to exist.

II. CARTESIANISM AND RELIGION

The spread of Cartesianism was a fact of religion as well as of science. In his *History of the Royal Society* Thomas Sprat admirably formulated the new point of view:

[7] A. C. Jemolo, *Il giansenismo prima della rivoluzione* (Bari, 1928).
[8] W. Deinhardt, *Der Jansenism in deutschen Landen* (Munich, 1929); Ruth Clark, *Strangers and Sojourners in Port Royal* (Cambridge, 1932).

And yet I should not doubt . . . to prove that even in Divinity itself they (the schoolmen) are not so necessary as they are reputed to be: and that all or most of our religious controversies may be as well decided by plain reason and by considerations which may be fetched from the religions of mankind, the nature of government and Scripture itself as by the multitude of authorities and subtleties of dispute which have been heretofore in use.[9]

As a historical phenomenon, Jansenism may be closely associated with the Catholicism from which it sprang and to which it so uncomfortably clung, with scholasticism, and with Cartesianism. The Jansenists, it is true, were humanist in their insistence upon the decisive authority of the ancient texts, but they were scholastic as any Thomist in the dialectic they applied to the text of Augustine. Their Cartesianism emerges in the distinction that was for decades their capital-in-stock, the distinction between faith and fact. The ambivalence is revealed in the words of Pascal—who, to be sure, was something more and something less than a Jansenist or a Catholic—when he remarked that God's purpose in establishing prayer was to establish in the mind of the worshiper the "dignity of causality." In a decidedly non-Jansenist phase, Pascal was being Cartesian when he said, "It is the heart that knows God and not the reason." He was associating himself, of course, with the great mystics, but he was also relying on the central thesis of Descartes, the distinction between the world of God and the soul on the one hand and the world of extension and motion on the other. By that test, the Jansenists, and Arnauld in particular, were being very imperfect Cartesians. They were applying reason to the world of God and the soul, where it did not belong. For the Jansenists, as for Sainte-Beuve, their great apologist,[10] Christianity was above all a body of doctrine and a rule of morality, rather than a religion. With a certain antiquarianism, they were attempting to base the religious life on an anachronistic intellectualism. The problem of seventeenth-century Europe was to dissociate its religion from the changing basis of its intellectualism and to find in human experience a new basis as firm as its increasing experience of the material world. In that sense it is possible to appreciate the severe judgment of a great religious historian, Catholic and French, when he says of Jansenism, "It long weakened the mystic impulse of our country by developing and organizing among us

[9] P. 22.
[10] Charles Augustin Sainte-Beuve, *Port Royal* (6 vols., plus index volume, Paris, 1840; 7th ed., Paris, 1922).

that sectarian intellectualism to which our national temperament is pre-disposed." [11]

Arnauld himself, who wrote many solid volumes of old-fashioned theological controversy, illustrated the new departure. Although highly competent and active as a defender of Jansenism and the *Augustinus* as doctrine, his best-known work, *The Moral Theology of the Jesuits,* in its various forms was essentially history, or at least, *histoires.*

A new standard, common sense, the judgment of the *honnête homme,* utilitarianism, was coming into the world. The virulence and pettifogging of the older generation was outmoded by a newer fashion best exempli-fied by Bossuet. His *Exposition de la foi catholique* (1668) and *Histoire des variations dans les églises protestants* (1688), to mention only the most significant of his works of controversy, raised directly the question of the relative effectiveness and appropriateness of Catholic and Protestant prin-ciples and disciplines.[12] It is hardly less significant that his *Exposition,* which was viewed with alarm by Protestant leaders even before its appearance, evoked correspondingly elevated responses from men like Pierre Jurieu, Ezechiel Spannheim, and William Penn.[13] The same urbanity and rationality was manifest in Dryden's two great religious poems, *Absalom and Achitophel* and the *Hind and the Panther.* Both Bossuet and Dryden appealed to human experience in the form of history. Bossuet certainly would have rejected the suggestion that he was being Cartesian and both would have repudiated Hobbes, but they were both relying upon the human utilitarianism employed by Hobbes and Des-cartes.

Recourse in argument to Scripture was being weakened on the one hand by the prominence of the Socinian argument that the Christian should use only what is positively taught in the Scriptures, and on the other hand by the development of criticism. When Richard Simon, a member of the Oratory, published his *Critical History of the Old Testa-ment* (1678) his intention was to convert Protestants by undermining their faith in the authoritativeness of the Bible as they knew it.[14] He demonstrated that Moses could not have been the sole author of the

[11] H. Brémond, *Histoire littéraire du sentiment religieux* (6 vols., Paris, 1916–1922), IX, 305; see also, IV, Preface, 256.

[12] A. Rébelliau, *Bossuet, historien du protestantisme* (3rd ed., Paris, 1908), 44, 69 *et passim.*

[13] *Ibid.,* 77, note.

[14] H. Fréville, "Richard Simon et les protestantes," *Revue d'histoire moderne,* VI (1931), 30–55; see also, Albert Monod, *La controverse de Bossuet et de Richard Simon, au suiet de la version de Trévoux* (Strassburg, 1922).

Pentateuch and that the Old Testament was a series of documents record-ing the experience of the Jews in the course of their evolution. Un-fortunately for his purpose, Bossuet not only entered the lists against his position, but had the book suppressed and Simon expelled from the Oratorians. A copy got to England, however, and the book was published in translation in 1682.

III. SYNCRETISM

The cleavage between Catholic and Protestant and between the Protestant sects was actively deplored by many intellectuals, who sought ways to bring about reunion. Syncretism was not new. It went back at least to the reforming cardinals Contarini and Pole of the sixteenth century. The council of Trent was originally designed to reunite the Church. The Union of Lublin (1569), which brought the Orthodox sub-jects of Poland under Roman obedience as Uniats, was one of the rare successful attempts at reunion. Early in the seventeenth century several national synods of the French Protestants had been devoted to finding a *modus vivendi* with the Lutherans, though without result.[15] The great representative of the Syncretist movement in Germany, George Calixtus, died just before 1660, but, inspired by him, the Great Elector actually brought Calvinists and Lutherans together to work out a form of union. This, too, proved futile. Frederick William discovered that long educa-tion was necessary in such matters. He gave considerable attention to John Dury, a Scot who was carrying on a voluntary mission for union, but did not become involved with his program. The German Lutherans and Calvinists were separated by a bitter *odium theologicum*. In spite of his Pietistic tendency, Paul Gerhardt flatly declared the Calvinists were not Christians.[16] One of the opponents of George Calixtus asserted that the yoke of the Calvinist anti-Christ was less supportable than that of the papal anti-Christ. In many points the Lutherans were closer to the Catholic than to the Reformed church. On the other hand, Jurieu, the Huguenot leader, was able, at least in retrospect, to regard union with the French Catholics as a practicable conception.[17]

In France, the first stages of Louis XIV's policy of extirpating Protes-tantism took the form of conferences between Catholics and Huguenots to find a basis for reunion. The differences resulting from more than a century of divergence proved too great. Both parties redoubled their

---

[15] A. Rébelliau, *op. cit.*, 27.
[16] See above, p. 119.
[17] A. Rébelliau, *op. cit.*, 27, 28.

efforts to win over converts of high social standing, so as to improve their respective positions. Much of the battle took the form of controversial publications. In the skillful *Exposition de la foi catholique* of Bossuet, the differences between the two faiths were so minimized that Jurieu, the Huguenot leader in exile, regretted that the issue had not developed according to Bossuet's plan. Bossuet actively concerned himself with finding a basis for reunion with the church of England.[18]

In principle, the English Act of Uniformity was an act of comprehension, but the new Prayer Book was designed to make it as difficult as possible for "tender consciences" to conform. Comprehension, the definition of doctrine and discipline in such a way as to make it acceptable for the largest possible association of Christians, had been given a significant formulation by Jeremy Taylor in his *Liberty of Prophesying* (1647), and by Edward Stillingfleet in his *Irenicon* (1662). Both based their arguments on the insecurity of tradition and authority. Stillingfleet went a step further and asserted the indifference of forms of church government as "a mere matter of prudence."[19] In Dutch and German Pietism, Spener and his group were quite lenient in regard to religious variations and the whole movement was strongly influenced by Catholic mystics, such as Antoinette Bourignon, von Spee and Madame Guyon.[20] At the very end of the period negotiations were carried on under the watchful eyes of Clement IX and Innocent XI by Leibniz and Bossuet, but political complications added to the theological difficulties soon brought them to an end.[21]

IV. DEISM

Deism was another aspect of the response of the intellectuals to the changing problem of religion. It was an attitude rather than a doctrine or sect and, like Pietism, hardly had a definite beginning. Lord Herbert of Cherbury in 1624 and Hugo Grotius in 1627 had formulated abstractions of religion as practiced among men. The universal reason of man, according to both, revealed the existence of God, a natural system of morality and the certainty of future rewards and punishments based upon conformity to it. This natural religion, they argued, was complete

[18] F. Puaux, "Les protestants sous Louis XIV," in Lavisse and Rambaud, *Histoire générale*, VI, 291; W. J. Simpson, "Bossuet's Interest in the Church of England," *American Church Monthly*, 26 (1929), 43–50.

[19] M. Kaufmann, "Latitudinarism and Pietism," *Cambridge Modern History*, V, 744–52.

[20] See below, p. 189.

[21] S. F. Smith, "Unions," *Catholic Encyclopedia*.

in itself; whatever went beyond it in Christianity or other religions was irrelevant, the mere product of superstition and human passions. God was thus converted to rationalism.

As an attitude Deism was characteristic of widely differing individuals attempting to adapt religious tradition to the intellectual position of the European world in revolution. In the broadest sense, the *Religio medici* of Sir Thomas Browne, the *Scepsis scientifica* of Joseph Glanvill and the *Christian Virtuoso* of Robert Boyle were Deist. In the narrower sense, the more radical representatives, who assumed the name, were hardly distinguishable from the "libertines," the epigones of Montaigne. They generally denied the validity of revelation and carried on an active debate with the more rational supernaturalists.

Something of the meaning of Deism and the general place of religion in the feeling of the period was revealed by the commotion attending the death of the earl of Rochester, one of the "wits," who had been a professing Deist. When the end approached, his wife, concerned with his welfare in the future world, offered to renounce her allegiance to the Catholic church, if he would renounce his Deism. He did so and she carried out her promise. Gilbert Burnet, the future bishop of Shrewsbury, seized upon the story and made an extraordinarily successful book out of it, *Some Passages of the Life and Death of the Right Honorable John Earl of Rochester* (1680), which in two centuries went through thirty editions and was translated into German, French and Dutch.[22]

The Cambridge Platonists were both mystic and intellectual. Strongly influenced by Plotinus, whom they did not distinguish too clearly from Plato, they were involved with cabalism and hermeticism.[23] On the other hand, they responded to the problems set by Descartes and Hobbes by making, as Tulloch says with some justification, "the first elaborate attempt to wed Christianity and philosophy . . . since the days of the great Alexandrine teachers." They conceived their problem to be the vindication of the supernatural and the spiritual against the monism and materialism of Hobbes. Without Hobbes's genius, either as thinkers or as writers, they contended with unequal weapons from the same armory. Hobbes himself declared that if he were not satisfied with his own philosophy, he would adopt that of Henry More, one of the most mystical of the Platonists.

The Cambridge group derived from Benjamin Whichcote, who con-

[22] J. H. Wilson, *The Court Wits of the Restoration* (Princeton, 1948), 203.
[23] J. Tulloch, *Rational Theology and Christian Philosophy in England*, 2 vols. (2nd ed., Edinburgh and London, 1874), Vol. II, *The Cambridge Platonists*, 14.

sidered religion "as the seed of a deiform nature" and the reason "as the very Voice of God." His most distinguished pupils, Henry More and Ralph Cudworth, "cried up Reason," as their orthodox critics complained, as a defense of Christianity against what they saw (not too accurately) as the materialism of Hobbes and Descartes. They furnished the intellectual starting point of the "new sect of Latitude Men," who as statesmen and preachers did so much to inculcate the ideal of moderation in religious difference and to encourage tolerance in practice.[24]

The Cambridge Platonists were neither great philosophers, great religionists nor great writers, but circumstances gave them more immediate importance than some much greater figures like, say, Pascal and Spinoza. Their principal merit was to furnish an argument, at once religious and philosophical, for tolerance. On the one hand, within the range of their influence, their teaching served to purify and elevate the religion of the generality. On the other hand, they formulated religion as a distinctive sphere of man's apprehension, a "deiform seed" in the soul. Their mission was a notable if not very clever protest against materialism.[25]

V. THE INNER LIGHT: QUIETISM, PIETISM AND QUAKERISM

The religious life of the Europeans during this period was at almost every point and in almost every aspect affected by mysticism. Mysticism is difficult to define. The experience of absolute knowledge of God, knowledge, that is to say, of a nonverbal character, precludes effective verbal definition. The problem of the seventeenth-century mystics was obvious. It was essentially the same as that of the mathematicians—to find adequate expression for the infinite God of an infinite cosmos. Pascal, the hero of mathematics, saw the problem more clearly than any other.

Mysticism was not new in the history of Christianity. Indeed, the latter part of the seventeenth century may well be regarded as the end of a long series of great mystic movements that in this period reached a climax, if not in individual experience, at least in influence and institutional form. No Tauler, no Thomas à Kempis, no Saint Teresa or Juan de la Cruz, no Jakob Böhme or Gottfried Arnold mark this phase of the long development. Nevertheless, a Pascal, wrestling with the problem of the intellectual face to face with the universe and with God, and a George Fox, with his strange spiritual force among men, are not to be

---

[24] S. Patrick, *The New Set of Latitude Men* (1662); M. Kauffman, "Latitudinarianism and Pietism," *Cambridge Modern History*, V, 753.
[25] J. Tulloch, *The Cambridge Platonists*, 470.

rated low among the great mystics. Who, indeed, has better stated the problem of mysticism than Pascal: "It is the heart that knows God, not the reason"? [26] In general, however, mysticism in this period was democratized in the form of societies and institutions rather than illustrated by the extraordinary experiences of individuals. The experience of God became a matter of *collegia pietatis,* of conventicles, of meetings, rather than of withdrawal into solitude and silence.

The Catholic church in France was still under the impulsion of the great saints, Francis de Sales and Vincent de Paul, and the great preachers, Bérulle and Olier, of the earlier decades of the century. Their institutionalization of "the sublime communication of the soul with God" in great organizations such as the Seminary of Saint-Sulpice, the Sisters of Charity, the Order of the Mission (known as the Lazarists) represented the disciplined response demanded by the Catholic ideal.

It was otherwise with Quietism. Derived from St. Teresa, this movement was developed for years without question by Miguel Molinos.[27] In 1669 he came from Rome to Paris, where Quietism became a cult and a subject of controversy. Quietism was an attempt to transcend the theological, the ecclesiastical and the social forms of Christianity and make of the Christian experience a purely personal matter, independent of doctrine, of priests and even of human association. It started with despair of the natural man and inculcated a completely passive dependence on God.[28] The final step in the Christian experience, as Molinos taught, is a state of quiescence in which the soul loses itself in God to the point of oblivion of doctrine, of works and even of its own salvation. As a contemporary put it, the love of God became so difficult that it could not be imagined that God had made it mandatory.[29]

When Molinos published his *Spiritual Guide* (1675), his doctrine spread rapidly in France, Italy, Scotland [30] and other countries. It was reinforced by the analogous teaching of Madame Guyon and her confessor Père La Combe. This was the doctrine of "pure love of God" in which the soul, mystically lost in God, without hope of recompense,

---

[26] *Pensées et opuscules,* 458. Brémond, *Histoire littéraire du sentiment religieux,* IV, 412.

[27] H. C. Lea, "Molinos and the Italian Mystics," *American Historical Review,* XI (1906), 243–62.

[28] R. M. Jones, Introduction to W. C. Braithwaite, *The Second Period of Quakerism* (London, 1921), XLII.

[29] H. Brémond, *op. cit.,* XI, 284.

[30] G. D. Henderson, "Quietist Influences in Scotland," *Church Quarterly Review,* 112 (1931), 281 ff.

without fear of punishment, becomes permanently detached from concern even with its own salvation.

Although Molinos had taught for years in Rome and Paris, his success alarmed the conservatives by its anarchic challenge to the discipline of the church. Molinos was condemned in 1687, but succumbed to mental illness. Madame Guyon was investigated and in 1695 imprisoned in the Bastille. A considerable controversy involving Bossuet and Fénelon, two great lights of the French church, ensued, but Fénelon, who had supported Madame Guyon, was eventually silenced.[31]

All forms of Protestantism, Lutheran, Calvinist and Anglican, underwent in these decades the revolutionary implantation of Pietism. Under this name may be gathered widely diverse groups and activities with the common character of devotion to an "Inner Light" as the ultimate Christian experience and the ultimate source of religious knowledge. Its boundaries were dimmed, however, by an unusual disposition toward a spontaneous syncretism. Heinrich Schlüter taught that there was no difference between the "reborn," whether Lutheran or Calvinist, and had to answer for it to the Synod of Wessel (1670) while his followers were imprisoned or deprived.[32]

The origins of Pietism are far to seek. Ultimately it had universities, distinguished leaders and a large literature. Its beginnings are lost in the indefinite and unorganized mysticism of the fifteenth century. The influence of the great Protestant mystics of the seventeenth century was patent and avowed. By a syncretism that was one of its best characters, Pietism also responded to the Catholic mystics, Antoinette Bourignon, Madame Guyon, the Jesuit von Spee. More specifically, it was a continuum with the *Freedom of the Christian Man* of the earlier, radical Luther and with the Anabaptism of the early Reformation, which, forced underground, continued without leaving vestiges from which a history can be reconstructed. Without a systematic theology, its documents were books of piety and hymns; its communal form was the conventicle.[33]

Its simple characters were expressed in the sects that pullulated in Republican Holland and Restoration England. In the Lutheran churches

[31] G. Joppin, *Fénelon et la mystique de pur amour* (Paris, 1938), 190 *et passim;* V. Giraud, "Évèque contre évèque: Bossuet et Fénelon," *Revue hebdomaire,* 39 (1930), 312–23.

[32] A. B. Ritschl, *Geschichte des Pietismus* (3 vols., Bonn, 1880–1886), I, 381.

[33] *Ibid.,* I, 5, 371; for the connection of Pietism with Anabaptism, see the thoughtful contemporary analysis of F. Catron, *Histoire des Anabaptistes, contenant leur doctrine, les diverses opinions qui les divisent en plusieurs sectes, les troubles qu'il ont causez, et enfin tout ce qui s'est passé de plus considerable à leur égard depuis l'an 1521, jusques à présent* (Amsterdam, 1699), Book IV, 207–80.

it was almost a party; in the Calvinist churches it was rather a pervasive influence. Its separatist forms, Labadism, Quakerism and English Dissent reached down into the lower strata of society. Its broad stream flowed in English Methodism and Baptism. The Great Awakening in America was Pietist in origin and expression.[34] Pietism was the dominant religious tone among the Europeans who settled the Mississippi Valley. The German, Scandinavian and Swiss immigrants carried Pietist books in their baggage and Pietist ideals in their hearts. More powerful than Puritanism, it effected the characteristic American translation of religion into conduct rather than theology. It provided the rule of life that governed nineteenth-century America, the sobriety, decency and simplicity, the rigors of the Sabbath, the bibliolatry that marked even the last generation of Americans. The midweek prayer meeting (*collegium pietatis*), common even now in smaller communities and definitely institutionalized as part of the discipline of some newer sects, is a mark of the pietistic heritage.

In view of the diffuseness and the organizational and ideological diversity of Pietism, it is necessary to limit this brief narrative to its forms and manifestations in the centers of its growth and its chief figures, especially in the German lands where, particularly, it had a habitation and a name.[35]

Pietism appeared about the middle of the seventeenth century in Holland. From the early days of the rebellion from Spain, the Netherlands had been characterized by a restless and complicated religious life which manifested itself in the formation of numerous groups and sects and in controversies without end. The social pattern itself was unfavorable to the development of effective control. Thus, when the Great Synod attempted to impose uniformity in the Presbyterian sense, the nobility and ruling merchant groups rose to defeat it. Reformism within the church itself and the influence of outside groups, such as, especially, the elements of English Puritanism that found their way to Holland, the Walloon communities and the French independents, constituted so many antecedents of Pietism. Outside of official Calvinism, the Lutheran communities, which were founded on complete religious individualism, the Mennonites, whose simplicity and antiecclesiasticism as well as their attachment to the Anabaptist tradition, and the Quakers, who came to the

[34] Wayland J. Chase, "The Great Awakening and its Educational Consequences,"*School and Society,* 35 (1932), 443–48.

[35] In general, A. B. Ritschl, *op. cit.*

Netherlands [36] in some numbers in the 1650's, also entered into the pattern out of which Pietism grew. The Collegiants, the little group of devotees with whom Spinoza found a refuge when he was expelled from the Jewish community, typified the vagueness of the movement and its intellectual simplicity. The common ground of Spinozism and Pietism was expressible as Quietism, the imperturbable tranquility of the mind in complete union with God. Even the great protagonists of the theological war that was rending Dutch Calvinism, Voëtius and Cocceius, put life above doctrine and turned to mysticism in order to raise religion above formalism.

Jodocus van Lodenstein is sometimes called the first Pietist, because he gave the movement something of the organization of a sect. His followers set themselves off in the Calvinist church as *"die Ernstigen," "die Feinen,"* (the devotees, the refined). Lodenstein himself, however, remained a loyal churchman to the end.[37]

Pietism also included religious extremists who felt obliged to separate from the established churches. Jean de Labadie (1610–1674), son of a French governor of Guienne, joined the Jesuits, left them, joined the Oratorians, left them, broke with both Jansenists and Jesuits, became a Calvinist, broke with the Calvinists of Geneva, went to Middleburg and found it necessary to leave there too. His personal charm and the intensity of his religious teaching brought him a considerable group of adherents who followed him in his peregrinations, ultimately to Herford in the Palatinate, where the Princess Palatine Elizabeth, abbess of Herford, gave the group shelter and economic support to build up a community of which Labadie was, of course, the autocratic leader. The death of the princess made it necessary to leave Herford and move to Altona, where Labadie died. His community broke up but for some time a group of Labadists persisted in Maryland, whither they had migrated.[38]

In spite of the smallness of the Labadist group and the political difficulties resulting from Labadie's uncompromising temper, he was a positive force and exercised a substantial influence on Pietist thought and feeling. His aim was a church—*"L'église à part"*—wholly detached from the world and devoted like the most rigid of monastic orders to a life of devotion. He carried into German Protestantism the ancient Donatist

[36] W. I. Hull, *Benjamin Furly and Quakerism in Rotterdam* (Swarthmore, 1941).

[37] A. B. Ritschl, *op. cit.,* I, 191.

[38] A. Salomon, "Jean de Labadie," *Bulletin de la société de l'histoire du protestantisme français,* 78 (1929), 7–41, 229–337.

ideal of a pure church, the rigorous Augustinianism of the Jansenists and the principles of mental prayer of Antoinette Bourignon. For Labadie piety was life and not a formula. His influence went far beyond his immediate group. Philip Spener was greatly influenced by him as a result of a brief period of contact while Labadie was in Geneva.

In Germany, especially among the Calvinists, Pietism took on the form of a schism. The Calvinistic Pietists were definitely anti-intellectual and antiorganizational. They produced a considerable literature of a maudlin type such as Nethenus' "The Sighing Turtle Dove and Zion's Banner of Tears" (1676). Calvinist Pietism dissipated its forces, but it is possible to recognize in the unconventional expression and the deliberate lowering of the theological level of their utterance one of the roots not only of later romanticism (beginning with Rousseau), but also of democracy.

Lutheran Pietism was kept more strictly within the bounds of orthodoxy and ecclesiastical discipline, and attained more definite institutional form. A Jesuit poet, Friedrich von Spee, like some of the French Quietists, *"enivré de l'amour de Dieu,"* popularized mysticism among Lutherans and Catholics alike and stimulated an intensely emotional religious hymnology. Paul Gerhardt, the Berlin pastor who declared that he could not regard Calvinists as Christians, wrote over a hundred hymns, which are still among the most popular in the Lutheran hymnbook.

Out of the mysticism and syncretism of the postwar period emerged Philip Jakob Spener to say effectively for all Protestantism that the primary element of Christianity is the religious experience of the Christian soul, to which all else, creeds and cults, are secondary. In 1675 he published his *Pia desideria oder wahre evangelische Kirche*. As much as anyone, he turned Pietism and Protestantism to Bible study. He promoted voluntary study groups (*collegia pietatis*) and Bible seminars (*collegia philobiblica*) for theological students. He taught a scrupulous respect for all sincere religious experience. He was influenced by Labadie and by the mystics, Jakob Böhme and Gottfried Arnold, but maintained toward them a benevolent neutrality. He was closely associated after 1681 with Veit Ludwig von Seckendorff.[39] Seckendorff illustrated the diversity of pattern in Pietism. A layman and a close friend of Spener, he was wholly nonmystical and nonseparatist. He used a succession of government posts in three small German states to promote practical education for clergymen and the social orientation of Christian effort. In

---

[39] Ernest Lotze, *Veit Ludwig von Seckendorff und sein Anteil an der pietistischen Bewegung des XVII. Jahrhunderts* (Quedlinburg, 1911).

1685 he published *The Christian State*,[40] in which he laid down social betterment as program for church and state.

Conservative elements began to react against Pietism as it grew more effective with increasing organization and practical bearing. In 1689 the orthodox drove Seckendorff from Zeitz, Spener from Dresden, and August Francke and Thomasius from the University of Erfurt. The tolerance and educational ambition which the Great Elector had left as a mark on the state he had created made it inevitable that they should turn to Berlin. There they were employed to elevate the academy at Halle to the status of a university. Under the leadership of Francke it promptly became a great Pietistic seminary and, for the time, a model of modern methods. For example, it was in Halle that Thomasius gave the first university lectures in German rather than Latin.[41]

The historical significance of Pietism in its organized form was not small, but its major impact lay in its extension beyond its own boundaries. As Quakerism, as Methodism and Baptism, as German and Swedish Lutheranism, it was carried over the whole world.[42]

Quakerism was the English twin of Pietism. It was and remained distinct by virtue of the special character given it by its great leader George Fox, by the testimony of his contemporaries a figure of extraordinary religious power, whom men followed gladly through suffering and persecution. Like continental Pietism, Quakerism had back of it a long historical background without organizational form. The particular mark that George Fox gave Quakerism was the avoidance of anything approaching ecclesiastical organization. Like the Pietists, the Quakers made "the Inner Light" the ultimate determinant of the religious life. It is possible also to recognize in some of their utterances a close kinship with Quietism in their emphasis on "the pure love of God." [43] The anarchic character of their association makes it difficult to attribute to them clear adherence to any of the warring creeds of western Christendom. A Scotch Quaker, Robert Barclay, attempted to formulate their position in his *Apology for the True Christian Divinity, as the same is held forth and preached by the People called in scorn, Quakers* (1678). Barclay arrived at a slightly diluted Calvinism, which probably defined

[40] *Christen Staat in drey Bücher abgetheilet* (Leipzig, 1685).

[41] L. Neisser, *Christian Thomasius und seine Beziehungen zum Pietismus* (Heidelberg, 1928).

[42] H. Pleijel, *Der schwedische Pietismus in seinen Beziehungen zu Deutschland* (Lund, 1935).

[43] R. M. Jones, *Studies in Mystical Religion* (London, 1909), 494.

correctly the intellectual position of most Quakers, but he missed the
revolutionary intention of the movement, which was to obviate doctrine
and discard the authoritative organizations based upon it. Some Quakers
were Socinians, some were Millenialists. Isaac Pennington (d. 1679)
paralleled the thought of Plotinus.[44] Although not a mystic or even acquainted with mystics, Barclay in his letters and writings often uncon-
sciously adopted phrases that connect Quakerism with the Quietists'
"pure love," "pure light," "pure motion." [45]

The Quakers believed that God continued to reveal himself to the
responsive soul and that the "Inner Light" was available to every human
being as a living and enduring personal experience.[46] Although Quakerism was anything but negative, it is convenient to express the spiritual
ideal in negative terms: no connection with the state, no infallible creed,
no hierarchy, no essential forms or ceremony, no organization as such.[47]

The positive aspects of Quakerism are to be sought rather in their
way of life. It was primarily an assertion of the divine worth of every
human being, man or woman, regardless of distinction of place, wealth,
color or creed. This meant resistance to oppression and injustice and
devotion to a program of social betterment. The ideal was complete sincerity of behavior, which led to such diverse practices as the refusal to
remove headgear for mere men and the fixed-price ideal in commercial
dealings. An ascetic element, common to Quakerism and Pietism, dictated plain dress and food and a rather hostile attitude toward art and
recreation.[48]

The Quakers were brutally harassed by the elements dominant in
English society after the Restoration. Religious fear of the radicals on the
one hand and of the Jesuits on the other gave the ruling classes a feeling
of insecurity that led them to extremes. In the panic of repression after
the rising of the Fifth Monarchy men, somewhat over four thousand
Quakers were imprisoned for four or five months. The Quaker Act of
1662 inflicted severe penalties on their meetings for worship, rising to
transportation for the third offense. About thirteen hundred were imprisoned under the act, but very few were actually transported. Their
willingness to endure martyrdom, the informality of their meetings for
worship and the social superiority of their leaders, such as Margaret Fell

[44] M. W. Hess, "A Quaker Plotinus," *Hibbert Journal,* 29 (1931), 479–86.
[45] R. M. Jones, Introduction to Braithwaite, *op. cit.,* XLIII.
[46] Luella Wright, *The Literary Life of the Early Friends* (New York, 1923), 29, 35.
[47] R. M. Jones, Introduction to Braithwaite, *op. cit.,* XXV.
[48] W. C. Braithwaite, *op. cit.,* 556.

and, after 1667, William Penn, made the act difficult to enforce. They were generally able to use all the resources of the law and to reach the politicians, parliament and court, including the king, and effectively challenged the laws under which they were being persecuted. Ideas of toleration, which the Quakers made a part of their religion, were growing in England on various grounds, mainly economic and political. The act *de haeretico comburendo* was repealed in 1663. As the original members of the Cavalier parliament died off, its temper grew less aggressive. Politicians like Shaftesbury and Buckingham were arguing that toleration would attract immigration, make commerce and industry prosper and raise land values.[49] Charles II saw in the domination of the parliament men, which the religious discriminations were intended to perpetuate, a division of the nation and a check on the power that he thought was rightfully his. Nevertheless, there were still five hundred Quakers in prison to be released by the Declaration of Indulgence in 1672. In the repressions of the last years of Charles II, the figures rose once more to nearly fifteen hundred, but this last persecution was avowedly motivated by Quaker support of the Whigs.[50]

The Quakers remained strong enough to carry on a vigorous expansion policy. Not only did their numbers rise in England but they formed interesting connections with the Pietists and especially the Mennonites in Holland and Germany. In the colonies they established themselves effectively on Barbados and Rhode Island, but their missionaries to Boston were hanged. Only the intervention of the king himself put an end to this particular barbarity. In 1682, under the auspices of William Penn, Philadelphia and Pennsylvania were established with a primarily Quaker and Mennonite population. Some brave souls among the Quakers felt themselves called upon to undertake the conversion of the pope and the sultan of Turkey, but their ventures were fruitless although they showed themselves skillful in carrying their message and getting back to England.

The expansionism of the early years soon ended. In spite of the solid coherence of the Society of Friends, the proselyting power which was so prominent a feature of Quakerism in the days of George Fox, Margaret Fell and William Penn seemed to die away. They had settled into a confirmed Quietism long before they discovered and used the writings of the great Quietists of France and Italy. Thus Quakerism, in contrast to the Pietism to which it had so strong a kinship, became a sect.

[49] J. H. Wilson, *op. cit.,* 65; see also, Frank Bate, *op. cit.*
[50] W. C. Braithwaite, *op. cit.,* 112–13.

The new world outlook of the seventeenth century had created a crisis for the traditional religion of Europe. That crisis was met and surmounted. Christianity adjusted itself to the dislocation of the ancient intellectual foundations. It found a refuge where the storms of reason and the tremors of world-shaking discoveries could not reach. That the problem of religion transcended the methods and instrumentalities of science and philosophy was the common theme of the learned and the unlearned alike, of Descartes and Molinos, of Malebranche and George Fox, of Spinoza and Bunyan. If this meant freedom for the scientist, it also meant freedom for the religionist. In the next century, reason and revolution quite generally shattered the material forms of ecclesiastical power, but, in spite of rationalists and revolutionists, religion in the form of traditional Christianity continued to exercise an undiminished power over multitudes of men. In religion, as in the mastery of the external world, these decades belong to a heroic age.

Chapter Seven

MAMMON: THE EVOLUTION OF THE
CAPITALIST ECONOMY

I. THE SOCIAL AND INTELLECTUAL ADVANCE OF THE BUSINESSMAN

THE latter part of the seventeenth century was the decisive period in
the accumulation of bourgeois wealth. The reconstruction after the
devastating period of war gave scope to the application of economic
energy. It was a period of realizations for the overseas ventures of the
English, the French and the Dutch. Though the lax Spanish economy
failed to realize profit for itself, the dynamic intruders upon the Spanish
exclusionist system reaped golden harvests that enabled them to extract
from the markets of the distant east and the Levant brilliant textiles and
exotic agricultural products.

The great town, in its ultimate development unique in the western
culture, broke the medieval pattern of the walled city. The towns of the
old dispensation were falling from their ancient glory, but the new centers were expanding and developing the embellishments and institutions
that would mark their dominance in this most urban of world cultures.
Their bourses, their books, their warehouses and agency services, their
operas and theaters, their newspapers and publishing establishments were
so many indices of a burgeoning life that was not by any means self-
contained but reflected an increasing productivity and a more elaborate
organization in the society as a whole. The demand of the town over-
whelmed the local village markets. The long lines of wagons carrying
grain from Bray to Paris, the long lines of Scottish runts, trudging to the
Norfolk cattle-feeders and thence to the butchers at Smithfield, were only
another reflection of the geographical expansion that was pushing Paris
into the fields of Saint-Germain and London into Bloomsbury and Tot-
tenham Court Road. The steady processes of usury were eroding the old
communal structure of the village and offering to many a Shakespeare,
for the investment of his urban gains, blocks of land to which the old
village custom was merely a dead form.[1] The riches under the earth
were being sought out by landlords, adventurers and technicians. Most

[1] Marchette Chute, *Shakespeare of London* (New York, 1949), 243–44.

importantly, the holders of capital were learning how effective it could be in the co-operative form of the stock company.

With the expansion of economic activity and its depersonalization in capitalistic forms, businessmen became magnates and magnates, businessmen. Businessmen held the places of power in Holland. Samuel Lamb explained to Cromwell that that was why Holland had grown so great. The Great Elector used bourgeois to manage his finances, to organize his navy, to create his postal system. The emergence of a powerful bourgeois aristocracy was an outstanding phenomenon of the seventeenth century.

As late as the end of the sixteenth century the commercial "upper crust" in France was largely foreign, consisting of Italians, Spanish and Portuguese Jews, Swiss and Dutch. By Richelieu's time Frenchmen who had started in life as peasants and shoemakers were buying marquisates and giving their daughters huge dowries. Some great fortunes were made in the overseas trade and lesser ones in the wholesale trade, but the most fruitful area was finance and especially public finance. The great fairs such as Lyons, Beaucaire, Saint-Germain, which had not yet declined, were great financial operations in which Frenchmen as well as the usual cosmopolitan group participated. Private banks were numerous but mostly in the hands of Italians.

The newly rich soon learned to live like lords. They built themselves great houses. They sent their sons to college with the sons of nobles and princes. Impoverished nobles counted themselves fortunate to marry into the family of a magistrate or a financier. Louis XI, Francis I, Charles IX and Louis XIII all conferred nobility for achievement in business. In the time of Louis XIV, to be sure, it was more difficult. Savary des Bruslons, in a late edition of his father's *Le parfait négociant,* recounted that in the case of certain founders of great industries, it required no less than three letters-patent to establish and maintain their nobility.

Government increasingly required businessmen. Colbert and the Le Telliers, if novel, were by no means anomalous figures in the great offices of state because of their bourgeois origin.[2] Colbert surrounded himself with men and women of business and technical skill. Bellanzini, who organized the first council of commerce, was an Italian, agent of the duke of Mantua. Camuset, a businessman, directed the French stocking industry. The brothers Dalliez promoted the forges of Burgundy and Nevers without giving up their interests in the Levant trade. Two Swedish brothers, the Besches, were rather unsuccessful as directors of mines and cannon

[2] L. André, *Le Tellier et Louvois* (Paris, 1942), ch. 1.

foundries. One of Colbert's most successful subordinates was Madame de la Petitière, who organized a school for lacemaking and embroidery at Auxerre.[3] Sir George Downing, who made a fortune in real estate, and Sir Josia Child, who made an even greater one in the India trade, played large parts in English politics and government. In Brandenburg the Great Elector, in spite of a deliberate policy of using the nobility as the principal support of his government, used able bourgeois in important ministerial offices.

On the other hand, the passion for profit did not fail to infect the nobility. Savary[4] tells us that most people of quality, lawyers and others, entrusted their money to wholesale merchants so as to make a profit from it. Maritime trade had long been permitted to nobles and *arrêts* of 1664 and 1669 renewed and extended the permission. An *arrêt* of 1701 permitted all nobles to carry on wholesale trade.[5] Mining, as in England, was developed and carried on by noble landowners.[6] Madame de Maintenon formed a partnership with a *menuisier* of the admiralty and an engineer to exploit a heating system. Her contribution to the partnership was "her favor with the King."[7]

Evelyn's diary reflects the growing social consideration of wealth in England.[8] He himself, friend of the king and familiar of great houses, attended the wedding (to her fifth husband) of the daughter of a broom man "whom God so blessed that he became very rich and was a very honest man." Other guests were the lord mayor, the sheriff of Middlesex, several aldermen and the chief justice, Lord Jeffreys. Evelyn was on good terms with Sir Josia Child, with Houblon, "a rich and gentle French merchant," with Pontaq, son of a rich winegrower from Bordeaux, and others. He himself was an active investor in real estate and interested in a project for briquetting coal. In England as in France the nobles were developing bourgeois interests. The Russells were active entrepreneurs in the draining of the Fens and in the development of suburban real estate around London. English stock companies attracted many investors from the upper social strata. It was estimated in 1660 that "over nine hundred considerable families" were interested in the East

[3] G. Martin, *La grande industrie sous le règne de Louis XIV* (Paris, 1898), 33–59.

[4] Quoted by É. Levasseur, *Histoire de commerce* (2 vols., Paris, 1911–1912), I, 380. See below, p. 216.

[5] P. Bellanger, "Jacques Savary," *Revue d'Anjou*, 5e année, Tome II (1856), 200–01.

[6] W. Sombart, *Der Bourgeois* (Munich, 1913), 79.

[7] Ch. De Boom, "Contrat passé par Mme. de Maintenon," *Revue belge de philologie et d'histoire*, V, 14 (1935), 456–60.

[8] s.d.d., March 16, 1683, July 13, 1683, December 5, 1683, *et passim*.

India Company, and in 1682 that over two hundred had more than one thousand pounds each in stock. In 1690 a number of lords and gentlemen participated in the formation of the Mine Adventurers' Company.[9]

Business had even become a proper subject for a learned treatise. In 1675 Jacques Savary published *Le parfait négociant (The Complete Business Man)*.[10] Savary had risen to fame as the prime author of the *Code de commerce* of 1673, and it was largely as a commentary on that "code" that his book was intended to function. Born in 1622 of a noble family, he had married a wealthy daughter of a bourgeois family and had prospered in business. After the manner of his time and class, he had entered the service of the king as a lieutenant of Fouquet and had fallen from grace with him. It was only in 1670, on the strength of two memoirs proposing reform of the business law, that he succeeded in winning Colbert's favor. With Pussort, Colbert's uncle, he was made a member of a commission to prepare a "code." The work was almost wholly his, as Pussort testified by calling it "the Code Savary." The prestige thus gained was enough to give his book a complete sanction in addition to its merits and to make him the chosen arbiter of the business world. The success of the book was immediate and solid. Before 1721 it passed through eight editions, and had been translated into German, Dutch, English and Italian. According to his son and biographer, Savary shared only with Cujas, the great Roman lawyer of the sixteenth century, the honor of being cited in the law courts while still living.[11]

Savary developed a large practice among businessmen as consultant and arbitrator and in later editions of *Le parfait négociant,* his *parères,* or decisions, were included as concrete guides for the businessman in the difficult questions especially of exchange and bankruptcy. Thus the Code Savary, supplemented by *Le parfait négociant* and the *parères,*

---

[9] E. Lipson, *The Economic History of England* (3 vols., London, 1937), Vol. II, *The Age of Mercantilism,* 292.

[10] *Le Parfait Négociant/ ou instruction générale, pour ce qui regarde le commerce/ de toute sorte de Marchandises, tant de France, que des pays étrangers/ Pour le Banque, le Change & Rechange/Pour les Sociétés ordinaires, en commandite & anonymes/ Pour les Faillites, Banqueroutes, Séparations, Cessions, & Abandonnemens de Biens/ Pour la manière de tenir les Livres, Journaux d'achapts, de ventes, de caisse & de raison/ Avec des formulaires de Lettres et Billets de change, d'Inventaire & de toutes sortes de Sociétez/ Et l'Application des Ordonnances/ & Arrêts rendus sur toutes les questions les plus difficiles qui arrivent entre les Marchands, Négocians, et Banquiers, sur toutes sortes de matières concernant le Commerce/ Par le Sieur Jacques Savary/ À Paris, MDCLXXV.

[11] J. Trouller, "Jacques Savary, le parfait négociant," *Économie nouvelle,* 27 (1930), 367–85.

served as the basis of French business law for more than a century and entered largely into the proposed revision of 1788 and into the Code of Commerce which a patient commission finally induced Napoleon to accept in 1807.

In addition to the legal commentary, *Le parfait négociant* included a geographical survey of French commerce in the areas with which Savary's extended experience had made him familiar. He purposely omitted the Levant and passed over interior Germany in silence, but for the rest—Spain, England, Holland, the North, the Americas, the Far East, he supplied an illuminating commentary. The sources of credit, the relation of the merchant to production, the forms of business association were only a few of the many subjects on which he wrote with intelligence and authority. Sometimes his geography was less than accurate: he seems to locate Archangel on the Baltic (Chapter 51) and to confuse Buenos Aires with Vera Cruz.

As ground-breaking effort, neither Savary's code nor his book proved definitive. The ordinance embodied much of antiquated practice that was about to pass from the scene, such as apprenticeship and the imposition of ferocious penalties for bankruptcy. The book was in many respects incomplete. For example, it threw almost no light on the problem of credit and, in particular, on the much noted question of usury. Nevertheless, it serves as a convenient monument of the enlarged position of the businessman as a major and powerful element in society, of the advancing technique of business as such and of the widening world outlook that business involved.

The code established double-entry bookkeeping as a general obligation of the more important businessmen, and the book, without serving as a manual, urged conformity. Double-entry bookkeeping was not new. Its origins went back to fourteenth-century Italy and it had spread among northern businessmen if not rapidly, at least steadily. By the seventeenth century, Holland had displaced Italy as the principal center of accounting techniques.

By modern standards, the practice was still low. In spite of Simon Stevin's introduction of the idea of the periodic balance, its use was still exceptional rather than routine. The English East India Company balanced its books in 1665 and probably not again until 1685. In the practice of the French India Company, the balance was apparently associated with filling up one ledger and opening a new one. As a result, gross errors flourished without control or correction.

It remained apparently for the Ordinance of 1673 to introduce the inventory. It enjoined upon all merchants and men of affairs "to keep a book which would show all their dealings, their letters of exchange, their debits and credits and the money invested in their establishments." [12] The 1693 charter of the English East India Company required "a book to be hereafter kept by the Company wherein the value of their stock shall be entered as attested by oath—and the like as to all mortgages, alienations, transfers and assignments." [13] Such prescriptions indicate the low state of bookkeeping but at the same time reflect a steady advance in the concepts. Capital was becoming discernible.

II. URBANISM AND THE ECONOMY

The pattern of urbanism in Europe was changing. Old towns were declining and new towns were growing and producing new types of institutions. Some of the greater towns of the preceding century, like Venice, Florence, Milan and Lisbon, were losing population. Antwerp had already lost its former primacy to Amsterdam. In the centers which were to perform the metropolitan function down to our own age, all the signs point to a steady and, as it seemed to contemporaries, all too rapid expansion. Repeated attempts were made to stop by fiat the expansion of London and Paris, but both grew to more than half a million by 1700.

London began spreading out into Bloomsbury, where the Russells were dividing the estate they had inherited from the Wriothesleys into building lots and streets that were to become so much part of the geographical framework of English literature and learning. By 1668 the leaseholds numbered 146 and provided a rent-roll of just over twelve hundred pounds.[14] Westminister and Southwark were essentially part of the town in the economic and social sense. Although in the middle of the seventeenth century the *haut monde* was still to be found in the City, Defoe a few decades later counted seventeen suburbs "all crowded and surrounded by fine houses or rather palaces." [15]

Paris was opened up by the leveling of the walls and the laying out of the *grands boulevards,* but the most rapid extension was across the Seine into the lands of the ancient abbey of Saint-Germain.[16] "It may very well be," wrote Dr. Martin Lister, "that Paris is in a manner a new city within

---

[12] Title III, arts. 1 and 3. Cf. W. Sombart, *Der moderne Kapitalismus* (3 vols., Munich, 1916–1927), II, 135.

[13] W. Sombart, *op. cit.,* II, 161–62.

[14] Gladys Scott Thomson, *The Russells in Bloomsbury* (London, 1940), ch. 3.

[15] *Tour of London,* quoted by W. Sombart, *Luxus und Kapitalismus* (Munich, 1912), 39.

[16] A. Descouriet, *Histoire des agrandissements de Paris* (Paris, 1860), 67.

these forty years. . . . In this age certainly most of the great Hotels are built or re-edified; in like manner the Bridges and Churches, the Gates of the City; add the great alteration of the Streets, the Keys on the River, the Pavements. All these have had great additions or are new." [17]

By 1667 Amsterdam had extended itself along the Amstel and the Y and had filled its recently acquired area with buildings, while the islands of the Y were filling up with a considerable working population.[18] Much of its growing wealth went into industry, some of it handicraft, but much of it utilizing wind power. Colonial industries, such as sugar-refining and tobacco manufacture, export industries, such as the finishing of textiles from various sources, luxury industries, such as silk-spinning and -weaving, were the characteristic forms. Type-casting and printing were export industries. In 1664 forty presses were issuing books, authorized and contraband, in all the literary languages known to Europeans. Storage warehouses, as indispensable to Amsterdam's commerce as the ships in the harbor, enabled the Amsterdamers to supply almost any demand at a moment's notice. Enormous sums were poured into the improvement of the port fortifications, a new city hall and the splendid private houses of the merchant princes.[19]

Naples, almost wholly a residence town, was growing to become by the eighteenth century the third largest town in Europe. New European towns were developing in the midst of ancient culture areas, such as Batavia, Goa and Surat. Even in the wilderness, Lima and Mexico, Panama and Acapulco, New York and Boston, were beginning to show urban character. Manufacturing towns like Birmingham and Solingen were "swarming with inhabitants and echoing with anvils." [20] The western ports of France were also prospering. In 1664 Nantes had not more than forty double-decked vessels; by 1713 its trade with Guinea and the Islands was "enormous" and it had many rich shipowners. Saint-Malo was rich with the profits of trade with Spain. Bordeaux and La Rochelle were transformed.[21] Bristol and Newcastle were still small but growing centers. Hamburg, free from the Hanse, was becoming a great port and financial center, hampered only by the disposition of its merchants to retire as early as possible.

[17] Dr. Martin Lister, *A Journey to Paris in the Year 1698* (London, 1698), 17.

[18] J. P. Hazewinkel, "Le développement d'Amsterdam," *Annales de géographie*, 35 (1926), 322–29.

[19] Violet Barbour, *op. cit.*, ch. 3, 88–89.

[20] Camden, *Brittania* (ed. of 1695), quoted by E. Lipson, *op. cit.*, II, 172.

[21] Henri Sée, *Histoire économique de la France* (edited by R. Schnerb, Paris, 1939), 247.

The great towns were less industrialized than now or even in comparison with some of the smaller centers. For a contemporary, London was "the mighty rendezvous of Nobility, Gentry, Courtiers, Divines, Lawyers, Physicians, Merchants, Seamen, and all kinds of excellent Artificers, of the most refined Wits and most Excellent Beauties." [22] Sombart has calculated that one-third of the London population made their living from the court and the government, one-sixth from administrative jobs, one-third from ground-rents and finance, and only about one-sixth from commerce and industrial activities.[23] After the Restoration London contained about three thousand merchants "known" at the Royal Exchange, two-thirds of whom were in foreign trade. The apprentices of this group were recruited largely from younger sons of country families, who paid as much as six hundred pounds to be articled with a strong firm.[24]

Of the working population of the towns, little is known. Although beggary and unemployment far exceeded any modern standards, everywhere a keenly felt shortage of competent workmen was indicated. Spain was undergoing radical depopulation and to supply its demand for labor and services welcomed immigrants from Italy, France and elsewhere. England was still importing German miners and Dutch drainage technicians. The silk and glass industries of France were built up by Italian immigrants. The van Robais were brought in from the Netherlands to establish the fine-cloth industry. Swedish iron workers were established in eastern France. The elector of Brandenburg welcomed trained workers in all industries (and agriculture) and from all countries. Russia attracted a certain number of workers. Holland, Sweden and especially Italy were the primary sources of technically qualified emigrants, but French Huguenots before and after the revocation and persecuted Protestants from other parts of Europe also furnished valuable personnel. Jews were welcomed in Amsterdam and in Brandenburg and made for themselves a large (but not a predominant) place in the growing capitalism of those areas. With less overt favor, they were making their way in England and the Rhine cities and, as well, in the colonies and overseas areas.[25]

The big towns were developing characteristic urban institutions. Pub-

[22] Edw. Chamberlayne, *The Present State of London* (13th ed., London, 1687), 200.

[23] W. Sombart, *Luxus und Kapitalismus,* 41.

[24] E. Lipson, *op. cit.,* II, 192.

[25] H. I. Bloom, *The Economic Activities of the Jews in Amsterdam in the Seventeenth and Eighteenth Centuries* (Williamsport, Pa., 1937).

lic transportation became available in Paris and London. Retail shops of a highly specialized character appeared in both cities. The directories of each listed twenty-six types, although the lists differed considerably. In England, the general store was becoming frequent even in villages. Hotels were numerous and quite luxurious in Paris, Lyons and London, and generally available along the more traveled routes through western Europe. In Germany the traveler still frequently had to provide for himself.[26] Amusements were available in commercial form. Opera houses in Venice, Hamburg, Paris and Vienna offered musical entertainment. Molière at least made a living from the theater for two decades in the provinces before he came back to Paris.

The conveniences of city life were developing. Meat was sold every day in the Paris markets.[27] Coaches were available in both London and Paris, but those of Paris were smaller, more easily managed than those in London.[28] Samuel Pepys was proud of the new pumping engines carrying up water from the Thames and declared that at an expense of 300,000 pounds London was as well supplied with water as any city in the world.[29] Street lighting was maintained in Paris at a cost of 500,000 *livres* a year.[30] In London it was the enterprise of the Convex Lights Company, founded in 1684.[31]

Free news sheets appeared in London in 1675 and 1679.[32] Local postal systems were a favored form of private venture but generally failed. Directories of persons, shops and transport organizations were not new, but much improved. Theophrastus Rénaudot operated in Paris a *bureau d'adresse,* where any and all "could give and receive notice of all the necessities and commodities of life," including lectures on the new learning. Bourses, exchanges for trade in goods, monies and bills of exchange, even stocks of the India companies and others were features of Amsterdam, Paris, London, Cologne and other cities. Sanitation and sewerage, however, were still far below the level even of the next century.[33]

The pressure of the town was wrecking the traditional local markets. The demand of Paris for grain created an extralegal, even illegal, prac-

[26] W. Sombart, *Der moderne Kapitalismus*, II, 272, 458, 459.

[27] A. Maquet, *Paris sous Louis XIV* (Paris, 1883), 83.

[28] Martin Lister, *op. cit.*, 12.

[29] W. R. Scott, *The Constitution and Finance of English, Scottish and Irish Joint-Stock Companies* (3 vols., Cambridge, 1910–1912), I, 276.

[30] Martin Lister, *op. cit.*, 24.

[31] W. R. Scott, *op. cit.*, I, 276.

[32] R. B. Westerfield, *Middlemen in English Commerce* (New Haven, 1915), 367.

[33] For a systematic account, see Sombart, *Der Moderne Kapitalismus*, II, 362–528.

tice of "country-buying." Advantages of price and convenience led the peasants to deal directly with the Paris buyers, who sought them out in their homes, instead of presenting their grain, as custom dictated, in the local market to supply the local demand. The merchants, the bakers, the merely well-to-do sought out the peasant producer and bought his output for speculation or for their own consumption. This undermining of the local market was most conspicuous in the Beauce. At Bray (in Brie), between 1660 and 1683, a real wholesale market, to which the grain flowed in anticipation of the metropolitan demand without any special canvassing of the local markets or farms got itself established. It still lacked the sanction of law and custom and it was still deficient as a price-making organization, but the idea had taken visible form.[34] The local producers who took their own grain, or grain they had purchased from their neighbors, to Bray were harassed by the local authorities. On the other hand, the Paris Châtelet, while it protected the Paris buyers and their agents against the local authorities, dreaded the possibility of combination among the Paris suppliers. Associations of any kind, even partnerships, in the grain trade were viewed with distrust and therefore prohibited. One Colmet was prosecuted for establishing control of the market at Bray in 1693, but he was able to demonstrate the necessity of organization.[35]

Colbert and even the king himself recognized the bad effects of existing restrictions on the grain market. Colbert isued general instructions to the intendants to promote freedom of trade in grain and indeed they generally did so, but in any crisis, such as threatened dearth, they were quick to support the local officials in establishing the old priority of the local demand.[36] Over most of France the restrictive custom of the old local markets continued to dominate and, as we can now see, to inhibit production.

In England the medieval tradition and form of the grain market was broken down in the same way.[37] The common law and English administration were less effective in hampering this inevitable development. In the grain trade as in other lines, "rings" and concentrations of control were common. The Grain Act of 1663 legalized, with certain restrictions, the practices of forestalling and regrating, but continued the prohibition

[34] A. P. Usher, *History of the Grain Trade in France* (Cambridge, Mass., 1913), 88.
[35] *Ibid.*, 316–17, 380 *et passim.*
[36] *Ibid.*, 96, 208.
[37] N. S. B. Gras, *The Evolution of the English Corn Market* (1915); F. J. Fisher, "The Development of the London Food Market, 1540–1640," *Economic History Review*, April, 1935.

of engrossing. As a matter of fact, the act broke down all controls and England had free trade in grain within the country down to the present century. An extralegal system of middlemen, broggers, mealmen and meal factors had developed. Most of the markets were operated by factors who sold for the owners on commission. The export trade was highly concentrated. Half of the grain exported from London between 1676 and 1683 passed through the hands of four exporters.[38]

In similar fashion the increasing demand of London for meat was surpassing the supply of cattle in near-by Norfolk and drawing as reinforcement the Highland cattle of Scotland, which moved along an organized chain of markets to feeding grounds in the Lowlands, to finishing establishments in Norfolk, and thence to the Smithfield butchers and the market.[39]

Expanding demand was also breaking down the old local markets in the English cloth industry.[40] There, as everywhere in Europe, putting-out was supplanting the old customer-craftsman relationship. The clothiers had for some time been using factors, who handled the sale of the products they had collected from the weavers. About 1660 these factors became the dominant element in the London cloth hall known as Blackwell Hall. By 1678 Blackwell Hall had become a woolens exchange. Responsibility was enforced by a system of registering the factors under an act of the common council of the City. In 1677 they numbered thirty-eight. They traded in cloth and concentrated the market for wool, both foreign and domestic. They used their position between the clothiers and the merchants to operate a usurious credit system at the expense of both. Typically, they grew rich. Fortunes of forty and fifty thousand pounds were reputed to have been made in Blackwell Hall. Under the circumstances the public market idea broke down just as in Bray. Instead of merely weekly market days, the operation became continuous and "private sales" soon involved the bulk of the trade.[41] By 1700 trading by sample was well on its way to standardization. The wholesale establishments were turning to the practice of settled warehousing, especially in Amsterdam. The factor, a stranger, not a servant, who undertook specific transactions for a client, and the broker, were becoming familiar figures in all kinds of business in the larger centers.[42]

---

[38] E. Lipson, *op. cit.*, II, 420–22.
[39] Naomi Riches, *The Agricultural Revolution in Norfolk* (Chapel Hill, 1937), 8–15, 147–50.
[40] W. Sombart, *Der moderne Kapitalismus*, II, 550.
[41] R. B. Westerfield, *op. cit.*, 279–81, 297, 302 *et passim*.
[42] W. Sombart, *Der moderne Kapitalismus*, II, 550–53, 941.

Combinations and rings were common in the iron industry and in the coal trade. The hoastmen of Newcastle had controlled coal prices after 1603 under a "limitation of vend." When the City of London assumed the power to fix prices at the time of the Plague, the hoastmen withheld their cargoes and forced the City to give up control. At the time of the Great Fire, Sir Edmund Berry Godfrey, whose later assassination made such a stir, sold coal at seventy-two shillings a chaldron (thirty-two bushels) for which he had paid only forty-one to forty-seven shillings. London was again directed to fix a scale of prices for coal.[43]

The great towns were usually centers of politically influential aggregations which used their power to win trade away from the smaller centers and thus aroused considerable hostility. Thus Amsterdam viewed with alarm the rise of Rotterdam and won away from it the English post in 1667. The East India interests centered at Amsterdam were frequently in conflict with those of Zeeland.[44] London was in constant conflict with the English provincial centers because of the attempt of the privileged companies, all centered in London, to force all trade to the metropolis.

III. THE TRANSPORTATION NET

The development of the towns was closely paralleled by a corresponding development of transportation. The seaways no longer held any mystery for the sailors. Little specific advance was made in the design and construction of ships as such, but something was being done to improve navigation, in particular, by premiums offered for the development of a reasonably accurate chronometer. Navigational aids were provided in some of the stream mouths that served as ports: Bremen could boast in 1679 that the Weser was the best organized stream in Europe. Amsterdam, Le Havre and Paris had quays along which small vessels could tie up, but typically the ocean-going ships loaded and unloaded while lying in the river or harbor.[45]

The size of the ships changed very little, the typical ocean-going vessel remaining at about 250 tons. The number of ships, however, increased radically. Although the statistical evidence is not dependable, it is estimated that the Dutch at the end of the seventeenth century had about 300,000 tons, or twice as much tonnage as the English, Germans and

---

[43] E. Lipson, *op. cit.*, II, 133, 147, 148, 151, 165.
[44] E. Baasch, *Holländische Wirtschaftsgeschichte* (Jena, 1927), 20.
[45] See frontispiece, J. Savary, *Le parfait négociant*, reproduced in F. L. Nussbaum, *Economic Institutions of Modern Europe* (New York, 1933), facing p. 116.

French combined.[46] Dutch vessels were not only built much more cheaply, but could also be operated more cheaply.[47]

Inland transportation was undergoing rapid and systematic improvement. In most countries road-building was energetically promoted, generally, however, with insufficient means. Colbert reconstituted the Administration of Bridges and Roads and planned and partly executed the improvement of the *grandes routes*. In England part of the post road from London to Scotland was built as "turnpike," that is, by private enterprise as toll road.[48] Stagecoaches appeared about the middle of the century. The *Mercurius Politicus* for April 1, 1658, carried the announcement of a triweekly service from London to thirty-nine provincial towns. The French system was uncertain and slow. It took eleven days to travel from Paris to Strassburg. Brandenburg developed a nonstop service from Berlin to Wittenberg. Magdeburg became the center of a great network.[49]

Freighting systems developed along with the passenger systems. A network of correspondents centering in Amsterdam and extending over France, Italy and Germany took over from the shipper responsibility for the delivery of goods.[50] In France the freighting system was organized as a royal monopoly in 1678. In England the services remained unconcentrated, but Thomas De Laune published a long list of "the carriers, waggoners and stage coaches that come to the several inns of London, Westminster and Southwark from all parts of England and Wales" in his book, *The Present State of London* (1676).

By 1660 the intercity postal network included every considerable market town in England. Ambrose Crowley, the great ironmaster, used circular letters to attract workmen from all over Europe to his establishment. Madame de Sévigné's famous letters were readily transmitted to and from remote parts of France.

Postal systems grew at the expense of the medieval monopolies of Thurn and Taxis in the Empire and at the expense of the university in France. In 1672 a monopoly of the French postal system was conferred for five years on Lazare Patin, but in 1676 the postal and freight systems

---

[46] H. Sieveking, *Grundzüge der neueren Wirtschaftsgeschichte* (5th ed., Leipzig, 1928), 127.

[47] V. Barbour, "Dutch and English Merchant Shipping in the Seventeenth Century," *Economic History Review*, II, 261 ff.

[48] E. Lipson, *op. cit.*, II, 444.

[49] W. Sombart, *Der moderne Kapitalismus*, II, 264–65.

[50] *Ibid.*, II, 339.

were combined in the hands of a farmer-general.[51] In Brandenburg-Prussia, one of the most brilliant achievements of the government of the Great Elector was the organization of the postal system under Michael Mathias. Statistically, the sending and delivery of letters was a very small matter by modern standards, perhaps all told less than the circulation through an American second-class post office, but by the end of the century all the principal towns of western Europe were connected and within the principal states, all the market towns.

Because of the generally poor character of the roads, the inland waterways were proportionately more important than later and as a matter of fact were more successfully developed. In England much agitation for the improvement of the rivers was carried on by the economic pamphleteers, including Sir William Petty. Before the end of the century six rivers had been made navigable and eight of the previously used streams had been improved.[52] In France Colbert put through considerable improvements on all of the great rivers and effected the completion of the canal of Languedoc. In Germany, up to 1688, canals had been built to the extent of 185.50 kilometers, and rivers had been canalized for a distance of 529.70 kilometers. Nevertheless, since waterways were limited, down to the eighteenth century the bulk of goods freighted was still carried by pack horses and wagons. A century was to pass before the great wave of canal-building would begin.

IV. MONEY AND CREDIT

The institutions of money and credit were still in a formative stage. In the last half of the seventeenth century the problem of money supply to carry on the growing economic life was being relatively well solved, for expansion of the money supply was made possible by a continuing inflow of silver from America. Although the heroic period of Spanish-American mining had closed by the middle of the seventeenth century, production was still substantial. Furthermore, the activities of the English and the Dutch on the west coast of Africa brought in an additional supply of gold. The inflow of the precious metals into the European peninsula was complicated, however, by the extension of the American market in the Spanish colonies, the West Indies and North America, which opened up channels of illegitimate trade, smuggling and buccaneering. From Europe much of the American silver flowed out to the

[51] H. Sée, op. cit., 222–23.
[52] T. A. Willan, River Navigation in England, 1600–1750 (London, 1936).

Near East and the Far East. The French Levant trade flourished only on the basis of Spanish piasters. Between 1658 and 1681 the English East India Company carried £5,000,000 in coin and bullion to India in a total export of £6,500,000. This outflow was not very large in proportion to the total import of American metal, but it served as a safety valve against potential inflation.[53]

In spite of the formal restrictions, elaborately organized, by which the Spanish government undertook to confine the trade with America to Spaniards, most of the American bullion flowed out from Spain through legitimate and illegitimate channels to Holland, France and England. The decline of Spanish industry made it necessary to import most of the products needed for the American markets. Before 1660 this lucrative trade had been almost monopolized by the Dutch. In 1659 the Treaty of the Pyrenees gave the French most-favored-nation status in Spain; the treaty of 1667 similarly opened up the Cadiz market to the English. The advantages of the legitimate market, however, were considerably extended by the general practice by which foreign merchants used the names of Spanish subjects to cover the shipping of their goods to the great fairs at Vera Cruz, Havana and Porto Bello. Nominally the returns in the form of bullion were even more narrowly controlled, but for very modest fees established service organizations would smuggle any amount of bullion to foreign ships. The vigorous consular service established by Colbert had excellent connections with the high Spanish nobility, and even when Spain and France were at war, commanded the protection of the dukes of Medina-Sidonia and Medina-Celi for the export of bullion on French ships. English exporters loaded their bullion on royal packets and claimed diplomatic immunity from search and seizure.[54] These forms of illegitimate trade in Spain were supplemented by the very considerable development, in this very period, of smuggling and buccaneering in the West Indies.

As a result of these activities, legitimate and illegitimate, Holland, France and England were well supplied with cash. Gold from Africa and silver from Spain flowed in enormous quantities to Amsterdam, from trade and from shipping services, and for the maintenance of Spanish balances or for the account of French and Belgian merchants. Every year thirty to forty Dutch vessels carried silver from Spain to Holland

---

[53] A. V. Judges, "Money, Finance and Banking," in E. Eyre, *European Civilization* (New York, 1937), V, 409.

[54] A. Girard, *Le commerce à Seville et Cadix au temps des Habsbourgs* (Paris, 1932), 170–300.

amounting, it was estimated, to half the product of the American mines.[55] Only half of it belonged to Dutch merchants. According to an official survey in 1680, precious metals entered France to the value of twenty million *livres* in 1679.[56] Because of the primitive character of French financial institutions, much of this "treasure" was handled through Amsterdam rather than Paris, Lyons or Saint-Malo. As a consequence, in spite of a growing export balance, French exchange remained throughout Louis XIV's reign at a discount in the world markets.

Holland and England benefited also from the immigration of refugees with money. Those who came to England from Portugal and France seem to have been particularly well supplied.[57] It was, however, rather the development of a free market in money and money metals, in Holland from 1647, in England from 1663, that gave those countries the predominance they were in turn to enjoy. The Dutch manufactured quantities of trade money for export to various areas—leeuwendaalders for the Levant, ryksdaalders for Poland, ducats for Russia, ducatoons for India and China. To the end of the republic only Spanish coins were more widely distributed about the world.[58]

In England a similar increase of the money supply followed when in 1663 the bullionist principle was in effect abandoned by parliament by the grant to the East India Company of full liberty to export ingots to India.[59] It is estimated that the flow of bullion to England rose from about £60,000 a year in the first years after the Restoration to about £373,000 a year between 1667 and 1680.[60] Reinforced by a considerable increase in the export trade and by the attraction to England of a particularly well-to-do stratum of immigrants from France, Portugal and Spain, the sums of money that flowed into England equaled by 1685 and later surpassed the sums flowing into Holland and France.[61] The committee of trade claimed in 1688 that England "hath of its own growth, manufacture and produce always enough to oblige the importation of money and bullion upon all occasions beyond any nation whatsoever in

[55] J. Van Dillen, "Amsterdam marché mondial des métaux précieux au XVIIe et au XVIIIe siècle," *Revue historique*, 152 (1926), 194 ff.

[56] A. Girard, *op. cit.*, 170, 300.

[57] W. Sombart, *The Quintessence of Capitalism* (translated by M. Epstein, London, 1912), 315.

[58] J. Van Dillen, *op. cit.*, 194 ff.

[59] J. Morini-Comby, *op. cit.*, 21.

[60] W. R. Scott, *op. cit.*, I, 283.

[61] W. Sombart, *The Quintessence of Capitalism*, 315.

Christendom." [62] In 1689 the increase in the volume of money during the two preceding decades had curtailed the practice of doing business "on time." [63] Free trade in coin was, however, restricted in one respect. In order to stifle the growing competition of Massachusetts, the committee of trade and plantations had cut off the export to the colonies of coin, and the settlers in the colonies were often forced to resort to wampum, commodity money and debased currency.[64]

The credit system of Europe was, in general, still comparatively undeveloped, but the use of credit instruments was expanding. Bills of exchange became flexible and were adequately legalized. Increasingly protected by the municipal law of the several states, bills were exchanged by simple endorsement instead of by separate documents and through the eighteenth century they continued to serve as a principal means of payment in interregional trade. The Code Savary of 1673 gave legal sanction to "inland bills," but it was only in the next reigns that this step was accomplished in England.

The private bankers of one sort or another, in view of the uncertainties of the business, charged heavily and aimed at high profits. The problem which the business communities hoped the new banks could solve and which the private bankers could not solve arose from the extraordinary multiplicity of coinages resulting from the cosmopolitan extension of trade, and was complicated by the various forms of debasement practiced by sovereigns and clippers. What the banks of the seventeenth century, new and old, undertook to do was to make available an ideal money, not coined, which would have the merit of stability and certainty. This "bank money," in good times at least, was serviceable, but the involvement of some of the banks with the lending business at times brought disaster.

In spite of the unfavorable conditions created by the violent and irresponsible gyrations of the money policy of the Spanish crown, the Bank of the Deposit and the Bank of the City survived at Barcelona.[65] In Genoa the Bank of St. George, in Milan the Bank of St. Ambrose, and in Venice the Checking Bank had evolved from medieval antecedents into serviceable stabilizing institutions.[66]

[62] Minutes, Br. Mus. Addl. Mss. 36,785, quoted by W. R. Scott, op. cit., I, 266.

[63] R. B. Westerfield, op. cit., 384.

[64] C. Nettels, op. cit., ch. 8.

[65] A. P. Usher, The Early History of Deposit Banking in Mediterranean Europe (Cambridge, Mass., 1943), 486–504.

[66] M. Sanchez Sarto, "Les banques publiques en Espagne jusqu'à 1815"; H. Sieveking,

The Bank of Amsterdam, founded in 1609, had from the start taken a leading place in the organization of European finance and credit. The freedom which the policy of the bourgeois republic assured enabled the bank to adjust readily to changing circumstances. In spite of some extra-legal involvements with the Loan Bank and with the East India Company, it confined its business to deposit banking and to the supply of good bank money. As the bank of the municipality, it was obliged to provide for its credit requirements. At the moment of the French invasion of 1672 it seemed about to fall with the republic, but it promptly recovered and continued to serve to keep Amsterdam in the forefront of international finance, as a principal source of credit and as the principal bullion market of the world in the eighteenth century.[67] Its services were used not only by every considerable Amsterdam businessman, but by governments such as Spain and Venice, by merchants from Cadiz to Moscow and by politicians of various countries uncertain of their futures.[68]

On much the same model, the government of Hamburg had established a bank in 1619, and Nürnberg one in 1621. The Hamburg bank prospered as did Hamburg, but the Nürnberg bank could not recover from the disasters of the Thirty Years' War, though it lingered on as a bureau of the town until 1831. In Sweden a Livonian of Dutch extraction, Hans Wittmacher (or Johann Palmstruch, as he is also known) established a bank in 1656, which succumbed after a few years. It had the distinction of having issued the first true banknotes, but this, combined with an unduly liberal loan policy, brought it to a crisis. Nevertheless, it had served so well to overcome the disadvantages of the Swedish copper currency that in 1668 it was taken over by the three upper estates of the states-general.[69]

In France and England the involvement of powerful financial interests with the governments served to prevent or delay the organization of banking as a public service. In France, in addition to the services of some private banks, usually Italian, the treasurers and receivers of the royal revenues constituted a network of lending units throughout the country, which, like the farmers-general, had the advantage of not re-

---

"Das Bankwesen in Genua"; G. Luzzato, "Les banques publics de Venise," in *History of the Principal Public Banks*, collected by J. G. Van Dillen (The Hague, 1934).

[67] J. G. Van Dillen, "The Bank of Amsterdam," in his *History of the Principal Public Banks*, 79–124.

[68] Violet Barbour, *Capitalism in Amsterdam in the Seventeenth Century*, 45–47.

[69] E. Heckscher, "The Bank of Sweden," in Van Dillen, *op. cit.*, 161–99.

quiring capital of their own (aside from the purchase price of their offices) and did business on the comfortable basis of the king's revenue. In England the goldsmiths had taken on the function of safe-deposit about the middle of the century and had very quickly developed as loan banks. Unfortunately their best customer was the king. They bought exchequer bills at discounts that sometimes amounted to 12 per cent and more. When in 1672 the king used his power to suspend payments—the Stop of the Exchequer—it threw this imperfectly organized system into considerable confusion, that was compensated for, according to contemporaries, by a great flow of specie into the country.[70] London was becoming a good money market. In 1681 the East India Company was able to float a loan of £550,000 at from 3 to 5 per cent.[71] It is apparent that it was a borrower's rather than a lender's market. In France the network of hostile interests prevented even the development of plans for banks. Colbert did not include banking in his program. Professor Paul Harsin[72] was able to discover records of three projects for giro banks more or less under influence of the Italian example. None of them came to anything. In England, on the other hand, projects were numerous and at least one, a materials bank, which gave credit at 6 per cent interest up to two-thirds of the market value of commodities pledged, was in existence from 1676 to 1683.[73] It was alleged that of all loans made less than one-tenth were to businessmen for carrying on their affairs.[74]

Ways of getting other people's money for use in enterprise did exist. "Grubstaking" mining enterprises, which had been so profitable for the Fuggers, persisted. The Neusohler and Schmolknitzer copper mines were financed by Dutch businessmen.[75] The Royal African Company took the bonds of Jamaica and Barbados planters for Negroes, "executing their securities with the utmost rigor."[76] Public works, such as river improvements, and local industries were sometimes financed by loans from interested muncipalities.[77] The silent partnership[78] was much used in France to bring upper-class money into the wholesale business. In the

---

[70] See above, p. 213.

[71] E. Lipson, *op. cit.*, II, 293.

[72] *Credit public et banque d'état en France* (Paris, 1933), 10–15.

[73] R. B. Westerfield, *op. cit.*, 380–81; R. D. Richards, "Early English Banking Schemes," *Journal of Economic and Business History*, I (1928), 36–76.

[74] R. B. Westerfield, *op. cit.*, 383.

[75] W. Sombart, *Der moderne Kapitalismus*, II, 710.

[76] Charles Davenant, *Works* (ed. 1771), II, 38, quoted by E. Lipson, *op. cit.*, II, 356.

[77] E. Lipson, *op. cit.*, II, 120–21; T. A. Willan, *op. cit.*, 70, 71.

[78] Above, p. 200.

Spanish colonies the church and especially the monasteries were often lending establishments. As late as 1716 Mexico had only two banks.[79]

V. THE STOCK COMPANY

Even more indicative of the future were the new companies that were becoming a common form of association in business activity. The old notion of the occasional, personal association was giving way to the concept of the stock company, a permanent association of credits, in which the property of the stockholder was merely a share in the company, not a claim against the company.[80] Association, of course, was not new but, aside from simple and occasional partnerships, it had generally served for purposes of mutual defense against competition, political action or even physical force rather than for a sharing of profit and loss. In the last half of the seventeenth century, partnerships became numerous, as the directories of London and Paris testify. Savary and his contemporaries thought partnerships, associations of several persons to share profits and losses, the most natural, the "ordinary" form of association. In *Le parfait négociant,* Savary distinguished two other types—the *société en commandite* in which one or several members furnish sums of money without participating in the transaction of business, which is carried on by one or several others, and the *société anonyme,* which he described in terms that indicate he was less than familiar with it in actual practice. He conceived the *société anonyme* as an association in which each member carries on his affairs, as in the medieval associations, and then reports his gains and losses for division among the group. The actuality had gone beyond that. In 1657 the English East India Company had become a consolidated fund with centralized management. Up to that date membership in the company had meant simply the privilege of participating in the successive annual ventures, the returns of which were completely distributed when the goods were sold. The new feature was what today is familiar. The company became a continuous firm and the members became stockholders. From the balance-sheet point of view, the change enabled the company to use the rather cheap credit available and thus by "leverage" pile up some attractive dividends. Between 1682 and 1693 it paid out to stockholders 400 per cent on its capital at the earlier date. The Hudson Bay Company, newly organized (1670) on a similar basis, in the same period paid a total of 275 per cent.

[79] C. H. Haring, *The Spanish Empire In America* (New York, 1947), 191.
[80] W. Sombart, *Der moderne Kapitalismus,* II, 150 ff.

The stock company retained for a long time the character of an arm of the state rather than that of a form of private business. It was chartered, regulated, favored with monopolies, politically dependent. The English East India Company under Sir Josia Child had become so involved with the Stuart regime that after the Revolution of 1689 a hostile parliament tried to supplant it with another company.

In France Colbert created numerous companies quite simply as organs of the state to develop colonial and maritime trade. Thus in 1664 he formed the French East Indies Company and the West Indies Company. They were not successful, primarily because they did not attract sufficient capital, despite Colbert's persistent demands, and because they were not primarily designed for profit. Colbert, for example, insisted that the Compagnie du Levant should trade only in Carcassonne textiles: it was only when the trade was freed and the merchants allowed to use Spanish piasters that the Levant trade prospered.

The Company of the North, although it showed ability to compete with the Dutch in the Baltic, failed for lack of sufficient capital to handle all the business it was offered and was dissolved in 1679 as a useless burden on the northern trade.[81] What a private company free of governmental control could do in France was demonstrated by the Compagnie de la Mer du Sud, founded and directed by Dancyan, a shipowner of Saint-Malo, which was organized to exploit the smuggling trade on the Pacific coast of South America.[82]

Marine insurance was highly developed. Amsterdam remained the unchallenged capital of the business. Its insurance chamber maintained sixty warships to protect its customers from pirates in the Baltic.[83] Savary reported a widespread practice in Paris among "not only businessmen, but gentlemen and judges," of insuring goods coming from or going to foreign countries. In Marseilles, according to Seignelay, "there is no one who isn't in the insurance business."[84]

In 1668, by *arrêt* of the French government, a chamber of insurance was established at Paris which, according to Savary, did more business than all the maritime towns put together.[85] In its original form it was

[81] P. Boissonade and P. Charliot, "Colbert et la compagnie de commerce du Nord," *Revue d'histoire économique et sociale*, 17 (1929), 5 ff., 156 ff.

[82] E. W. Dahlgren, *Les relations commerciales et maritimes entre la France et les côtes de l'océan Pacifique* (Paris, 1909).

[83] Jacques Savary, *Le Parfait Négociant*, II, 11.

[84] J. Savary, *op. cit.*, II, 113; Paul Masson, *Histoire du commerce français dans le Levant au XVIIe siècle* (Paris, 1896), 482; W. Sombart, *Der moderne Kapitalismus*, II, 309.

[85] W. Sombart, *Der moderne Kapitalismus*, II, 152.

only a society of privileged persons, but in 1686 it became a stock company. Hamburg developed an extended system of reinsurance, which enabled it to handle larger risks than other centers. The cost of insurance in general had declined from 10 to 15 per cent to 8 to 10 per cent for European voyages. Lloyd's of London did not emerge as a distinct entity before 1696, but specialists in marine insurance had operated in England for some decades. Fraud and war and the absence of an adequate statistical basis for calculating risks and premiums made it still a highly speculative business, but some of the fundamental problems had been recognized and even solved.[86]

Fire insurance and life insurance were becoming more clearly defined. Fire insurance early took the form of company organization. Life insurance was being rationalized. The letters of Huygens and the legislative proposals of John de Witt were the first evidences of the attempt to apply the calculus of probabilities to annuities, but the full recognition of the problem had to await the mortality tables of Halley (prepared for a Dutch group) in 1690 and the work of Bernoulli in the next century on calculus of probabilities.[87]

VI. THE ADVANCE OF AGRICULTURAL TECHNIQUES

Although the towns were growing rapidly, Europe remained through the seventeenth century overwhelmingly an agricultural economy. From 80 to 90 per cent of the population was rural and even that index is to be further weighted by the persistence to a degree now unfamiliar of agricultural activity in the towns, even in the great towns. The system of agriculture remained essentially that of the medieval communal operation, but manorial lordship had been generally commuted to money-rents. In some very limited areas special crops such as wine and olives required more individualized operation, as did the truck gardening in the Netherlands. Capitalistic exploitation of the land had in a very minor degree modified the open-field system in England. The drainage of the polders in the Netherlands and of the English Fens involved large-scale financing and definitely capitalistic forms of ownership, control and operation. These new forms, however, were marginal to the great body of European agriculture.

[86] Violet Barbour, "Marine Risks and Insurance in the Seventeenth Century," *Journal of Economic and Business History*, I (1929), 561–96.

[87] G. Castelnuovo, "Sulle prime applicationi de calculo della probabilità alla statistica et l'attuaria"; L. Amoroso, "Il periodo eroico della formazione della compagnie di assecurazione." *Atti dell' Istituto nazionale di Assecurazione*, II (1930), 9–15, 31–44.

Technique was correspondingly static. In spite of the notable contributions of Bernard Palissy, Olivier de Serres, Gabriel Plattes, Samuel Hartlib, all of whom flourished in the century before 1660, the old ways, the traditional crops, the customary sequences remained predominant in practice and in social sanction. The new developments which were beginning to manifest themselves were to require two more centuries to establish themselves as the general pattern.

Nevertheless, in agriculture, too, the system of production was being altered. According to Samuel Hartlib the highest standards were attained in Flanders. Urban demand, combined with the high cost of land and high wages, had created a specialized agriculture, emphasizing garden crops and dairy products, which were sold in the towns and even exported to England and the Rhine towns. Much larger cattle were produced than elsewhere by stall-feeding with fodder crops. Tillage was marked by the consistent plowing under of cover crops.[88]

In France the technological level of agricultural production remained low. Dearth was common. Hundreds and even thousands of deaths from starvation were from time to time reported by the intendants. Physical barriers to transportation were still high and customary and legal barriers contributed to make the toll of starvation a heavy one. The peasants seem to have been helpless victims of crises arising from bad crops and war, accentuated by the burdens of the royal fisc and of a clumsy and outworn seigneurial regime. As Robert Schnerb has pointed out, since the French nobility has never been studied closely in its relation to the land, the seigneurial regime of the seventeenth century is less well known than its medieval antecedents.[89] It would seem that, unlike their English counterparts, the relation of the French nobles to the land was largely parasitic, as Arthur Young thought it in the next century.[90] Enclosure was known only where the population was sparse. A large proportion, probably two-fifths, of the arable land remained uncultivated. Some three-fourths of the tillage was carried on with oxen.

In Spain agriculture, like other forms of economic life, was at a low point. The most interesting feature was the Mesta, the great organization of the sheep growers whose privileges, connected with the passage of their great flocks north and south with the seasons, weighed heavily on western Spain. There "sheep ate men" more truly than in England in the time of Sir Thomas More. As a matter of fact, the Mesta had long been

[88] W. Sombart, *Der moderne Kapitalismus*, II, 636–37.

[89] Henri Sée, *op. cit.*, 192.

[90] H. B. Hill, "French Constitutionalism," *Journal of Modern History*, 21 (1949), 222 ff.

in decline from its high point of 1526, when it had about 3,500,000 sheep. Its high favor with the Cortes and the royal council—doubtless connected with the "alms" and annuities it dispensed so freely—enabled it to increase its controls. Thus the pragmatic of 1633 (renewed in 1680) gave the Mesta full jurisdiction over the entire pastoral industry and discretionary power to sweep aside all local restrictions that interfered with the movement of the sheep. This and other legislation designed to aid the Mesta in its difficulties was so anomalous that it was time and time again laughed out of the high courts. The long war with Portugal (1640 to 1665) exposed the old privileged roads to raids and forced the migrating flocks to use routes further east, where bridge and ferry tolls were multiplied and collected, regardless of the Mesta's privilege, by church and other local authorities. From a level of thirty-five to forty million maravedis in the early 1630's, the general level of the Mesta's surplus sank steadily until it disappeared intermittently during the reign of Charles II. It political influence declined in corresponding degree. The attempt of the royal council in 1677 to re-establish the summary juprisdiction of the Mesta's officials was totally ignored. In spite of the general expansion of European trade, the flocks of the Mesta never rose in number above the average of the sixteenth century. From 1685 on its accounts indicated imminent bankruptcy. Yet it managed to survive through the eighteenth century and even for a moment in 1750 to enjoy an extension of its privileges.[91]

English agriculture was on the whole more responsive to change than French agriculture, although the modernization of the whole system was to require a long-continued and energetic propaganda in the next century. Gabriel Plattes, a Dutchman, found a ready welcome for his propaganda for Dutch methods. Sir Richard Weston before the Civil War and Samuel Hartlib down to the Restoration continued and extended his influence. New products were making their way. Much of the open field tillage was employed in the production of beans.[92] Clover and other artificial grasses, turnips and even potatoes were not unknown.[93] Agriculture even attained the intellectual level of a dictionary: *Dictionarium rusticum.*[94]

[91] Julius Klein, *The Mesta* (Cambridge, 1920), *passim*.

[92] Henry Homer, *An Essay on . . . the Inclosure of the Common Fields* (2nd ed.); 17, 22. Quoted by E. Lipson, *op. cit.*, II, 410.

[93] John Foster, *England's happiness increased, or a sure and easier remedy against all succeeding dear years, by a plantation of the roots called potatoes* (London, 1664).

[94] G. E. Russell, "Eighteenth Century Agricultural Dictionaries," *Bulletin of the Institute of Historical Research*, 7 (1930), 144–48.

The assured prosperity of the English grain trade under its new freedom led to a demand for enclosure of the open fields. Sir William Petty declared that enclosure of the waste and its cultivation would do away with beggary.[95] In 1681 John Houghton proposed a general enclosure act.[96] Another pamphleteer advocated a statute to compel the minority to accept the decision of the majority in each village.[97] Their arguments were highly individualistic and capitalistic—that productivity would be increased, that persons displaced would be available as labor for the expanding woolen industry, that landholders should be free to do as they would with their own. Nevertheless, it was not until 1688 that would-be enclosers were enabled to petition parliament for private acts. Only a few enclosures were accomplished through the slow processes of chancery.

VII. THE TRANSFORMATION OF INDUSTRY

The handicraft system remained the dominant industrial form. It had been radically altered in England by the Elizabethan Statute of Apprentices and, in the France of Louis XIV, by Colbert's subordination of the corporations to his all-inclusive system. Internally the gild had become something far different from the fellowship it had once been. The increasing differences in wealth made the masterships unattainable to the ordinary journeyman, and, in effect, the gild had become the monopoly of the sons and sons-in-law of masters. Externally it was falling short of the new types of demand that were developing. Bound by the very principles of its being to traditional ways it could neither produce the new kinds and qualities of goods nor the quantities required by the armies, cities and colonies. The entrepreneur emerged belatedly, after his function had long been prepared for him.

In the latter part of the seventeenth century the typical form of enterprise in industry was the vaguely and variously named domestic system, otherwise putting-out or, in German, *Verlag*. In general, the putter-out organized craftsmen working in their own shops or homes by supplying raw materials or machines or both to the workers, whom he usually sought outside the towns, outside the areas where gild regulations had force. Jacques Savary summarized the organization from the entre-

---

[95] *Economic Writings* (edited by C. H. Hull), II, 475–76.

[96] "Husbandry and Trade Improved," in his *Works* (1728), IV, 16, quoted by E. Lipson, *op. cit.*, II, 418.

[97] Worlidge, *Systema agriculturae* (1669); cf. Roger North, *A Discourse of the Poor* (1683).

preneur's point of view: he must know his raw materials, he must understand the processes of manufacture and he must know how to sell the product. The putter-out did not supply the locale or the specific supervision nor did he concentrate his workers. His function was limited to organizing supply to meet an enlarged and geographically expanded demand.

The factory system, which in this time was developing at a relatively rapid rate, was as old as the smelters, the shipyards, the sugar refineries and the other large-production processes requiring combinations of capital and labor force beyond the range of either the gilds or the putters-out. Mining was such a process. There were still many "free" miners in England and coal mining around Liège in Belgium was carried on by a complex of gild organizations, but in general the rising costs of deep shafts, drainage and transportation systems necessitated venture capital in relatively large quantities. It was a much favored field of investment in England at this time, but the investors were generally less than fortunate, usually because of deficient funds or credit.[98] The Swedish iron industry, which was conquering the European markets both because of the superiority of its product and because the Swedish forests seemed to furnish an inexhaustible supply of fuel, had been given a thoroughly capitalistic organization by Louis de Geer, a Dutchman in the service of Gustavus Adolphus.[99] The Russian iron industry, which supplied iron of a lower quality, was also capitalistically organized. In England Ambrose Crowley, the greatest ironmaster in the country, set up a capitalist-philanthropic establishment at Sunderland (1682) that anticipated the more famous New Lanark of Robert Owen by a century. An elaborate system of regulation not only controlled the working hours of his employees but provided for their health, the schooling of their children and their behavior off duty.[100]

The textile industries enjoyed a dominance in size and geographical extension that gave change in that area a greater social significance than more radical novelties in other areas. The combination of various technical processes under a single management was fairly frequent in the latter part of the seventeenth century, although it is to be remembered that most of these concentrations consisted of a group under one roof surrounded by an even larger group of outworkers. *The Discovered Gold*

[98] E. Lipson, *op. cit.,* II, 112–84.

[99] A. A. Stomberg, *A History of Sweden* (New York, 1931), 377–78; C. Hallendorf and A. Schück, *History of Sweden* (Stockholm, 1929), 228–29.

[100] E. Lipson, *op. cit.,* II, 178–83.

Mine (1685) recounts how "manufacturers at great cost built whole great houses, wherein the wool-sorters, combers, spinners, weavers, pressers, and even dyers work together." A Glasgow woolen mill in 1700 had fourteen hundred employees, one at Saptes in France, eight hundred.[101]

A whole series of industries escaped entirely the gild system, both because they were necessarily large units and, particularly, because they were new. Most of these were based on colonial raw products—sugar, tobacco, chocolate, cotton. These concentrated inevitably in the colonial ports, Amsterdam in the first place, and then in London, Bordeaux, Marseilles and Le Havre. The sugar industry was typical. The investment required ran to several thousand pounds and in the nature of the processes required a disciplined and co-ordinated, if not very large group of workers.

Much industry was leaving the town for the country. The putter-out (*marchand, marchand-manufacturier, Verleger*), who grew increasingly important through the seventeenth century, sought his workers in the country, away from the restrictive regulations of the gilds, which were localized in the towns. In spite of Colbert's disposition to favor concentration of workmen, he found the French workers reluctant to enter his *ateliers* and was obliged to depend on the *marchands*. Even a century later, English spinners and weavers clung to the cottage industry long after it had ceased to be economically feasible.[102]

The hosiery (frame-knitting) industry in England was a striking illustration of the deurbanizing operation of the putting-out practice. Because the stocking frame was invented too late to be included in the Statute of Apprentices of 1597, hosiery had never been officially a gild industry, but it had become localized in London, which had about 400 frames as against about 250 in the rest of the country. To preserve the ascendency of the London hosiers, a hosiery company was organized in 1657, with the usual monopoly and rights of inspection. Nevertheless, the country industry continued to grow at the expense of London. By 1727 London had 2,500 frames and the provinces, 5,500; a few decades later the hosiery industry had practically disappeared from the city.[103]

The social problem arising from the new forms of industry had as yet hardly emerged. In the Netherlands the textile workers manifested enough discontent to lead the employers to form an intercity organization to

[101] W. Sombart, *Der moderne Kapitalismus*, II, 730–99.

[102] Witt Bowden, *Industrial Society in England toward the Close of the Eighteenth Century* (New York, 1925), ch. 4.

[103] E. Lipson, *op. cit.*, II, 104–09.

control them by means of a common labor policy.[104] In France the Company of the Holy Sacrament and Vincent de Paul's Sisters of the Poor aimed to improve the condition of the workers. A great saint of the Catholic church, Jean Baptiste de la Salle, gave up a promising ecclesiastical career to devote himself to free education of the poor. In 1684 he founded the Institute of the Brothers of the Christian Schools, generally known as the Christian Brothers and today the largest of the teaching orders.[105] Ambrose Crowley's utopian organization of his ironworks stands quite alone in England.[106]

Europe was becoming rich. The vast flow of goods-capital from overseas and the increasing output of European craftsmen, miners and peasants sufficed to maintain a vastly increased apparatus of government, armies and intellectuals. The productivity of the society was still far from adequate to sustain the growing population without various degrees of starvation, but luxury was increasing among the rulers and the aristocracy and descending to ever lower levels among the bourgeois. Ever wider physical and organizational means of transport and communication combined with elaborated systems of finance to transform the simple localized agricultural diversity of an earlier time into a complex and unified whole. The new metropolises centralized and co-ordinated the worldwide commercial activities of the culture. Europe was becoming an economic system.

[104] Violet Barbour, *Capitalism in Amsterdam in the Seventeenth Century*, 72.
[105] W. G. Battersby, *De La Salle: A Pioneer of Modern Education* (London, 1949).
[106] Above, p. 223.

Chapter Eight

THE EXPANSION OF EUROPE

EXPANSION has been a continuing and complex phenomenon of Europe's history from its inexplicable beginnings in the tenth century to our own day. The latter part of the seventeenth century, however, was a critical phase of the process.

The problem has been disoriented by a certain obsession with the questions of political control and conflict. It was not without importance that the Leviathans sought to conquer and rule over large segments of territory overseas. Nevertheless, it is even more important to recognize that the expansion was more than colonialism and that it was a phenomenon of Europe rather than of its political segments. As a human group, the Europeans were increasing in number; they were intensifying their exploitation of their resources; they were spreading out to new parts of the world; as Christendom, they were pushing back Islam; and as the West, they were replacing vanished Byzantium in Russia.

The Europeans who carried out the expansion came from all the nations. Italians, Austrians and other Germans furnished much of the missionary personnel that was extending the bounds of Spanish America.[1] Germans without political backing constituted an important element of the new society in Pennsylvania. Scotch, Irish and Germans settled the Shenandoah Valley. Jews were conspicuous as traders and planters in the growing British colonies in the Caribbean.[2] Germans, Poles, Frenchmen and Italians drove the Turks down the Danube. In Moscow and Kiev Russians learned western ways from Italians, Germans, Englishmen, Greeks and Poles. Even the Russians on the distant Amur were responding to the demand for furs in the capitals of the West. The expansion of Europe, in short, was the cosmopolitan expression of the whole culture.

This expansion was in the first place internal. In spite of war and pestilence the population of Europe showed unmistakable indices, such as growing towns, new areas of occupation, more specialization of func-

[1] R. K. Wyllys, *op. cit.*
[2] W. S. Samuels, *A Review of the Jewish Colonists in Barbados in the Year 1680* (London, 1936), *passim.*

tion, of increase in a fairly constant progression, at least in the seventeenth century. While London, Bristol, Norwich, Paris, Lyons, Bordeaux, Rome, Amsterdam, Rotterdam, Stockholm, Berlin and Magdeburg, not to mention the "cities in the wilderness" overseas, grew visibly by immigration, it is impossible, in the absence of statistics, to believe that the essential basis of urbanism, a productive population in the country, was being diminished. Indeed, the statisticians, working with the scattered indications available, generally agree that the population of Europe west of Russia grew from something of the order of 76,000,000 in 1600 to about 100,000,000 in 1661 and to something over that figure in 1700.[3]

Statistics are equally lacking on the side of productivity. Agricultural productivity seems to have been static in comparison with the eighteenth century, but new areas were being added to the productive area in England, Holland, Prussia and overseas, and Russia was just beginning to be recognized as a source of agricultural supply for Europe. Coal and chemical products were expanding in use and in production. Products such as Silesian linen, French brandies, Swedish steel were increasing their foreign markets.[4]

The intensification of organization, which has been the subject of several previous chapters, itself was connected with an expansion in the character and number of problems. Kings were multiplying their boards and councils, their bureaucrats and judges, their soldiers and sailors. Churches and universities were increasing the specialization of their different organs, as the Benedictines of Saint Maur were specializing in history and Halle in the promotion of Pietism and educational reform. Businessmen were becoming differentiated into various types of middlemen, according to the areas with which they dealt, the kind of goods they handled, the size of their transactions. Specialized subsidiary services, such as brokerage, transport, news publication and hotel-keeping, were beginning to be offered.[5]

The facts of internal expansion are obvious from the story that has already been told. Here it is possible only to refer to its function in relation to the process it is convenient to call external expansion: the expansion of

---

[3] A. N. Carr-Saunders, "The Growth of the Population of Europe," in *Economic History of Europe Since the Reformation* (Vol. V of *European Civilization, Its Origin and Development*, edited by Edward Eyre, New York, 1937), pp. 326–47. See also Julius Beloch, "Die Bevölkerung Europas zur Zeit der Renaissance," *Zeitschrift für Sozialwissenschaft*, III (1900), 765; W. F. Wilcox, "The Expansion of Europe in Population," *American Economic Review*, V (1915), 742 ff.

[4] See above, Chapter Seven.

[5] R. B. Westerfield, *op. cit.;* Werner Sombart, *Der Moderne Kapitalismus*, II, 1, 422–530.

Europe over areas and among peoples that hitherto had been not-Europe. Europe expanded culturally to include Russia; it expanded militarily to push back the Turkish power; it expanded demographically across the seas to establish new centers and areas of European settlement.

I. THE EUROPEANIZATION OF RUSSIA [6]

Europe was spreading into the Slavic lands that we have come to know as Russia. Russia was the child of Byzantium and, by the advance of Islam, it had been orphaned. The social sanctions which it had derived from Byzantium had in the main been dissolved. The whole sixteenth century and the Time of Troubles were filled with the attempt to find new sanction, and the main theme of the history of the next two centuries was the naturalization of new sanction in the form of western cultural standards. Peter the Great and Catherine the Great have become symbols of this process, but, without minimizing the scale and effectiveness of their achievement, it is necessary to recognize that in essence this process had begun with the accession of the Romanovs in 1614 and had been substantially developed in the reign of Tsar Alexis (1645–1676) and even in the confused period between his death and the assumption of power by Peter the Great (1689).

Russia was still barbarian. The uneducated masses had made of Christianity a mere system of magic objects, words and acts. Trade was almost wholly in the hands of the westerners. Drunkenness and immorality, violence and filth shocked western travelers. Intellectualism had been formally barred by the church in the Council of a Hundred Chapters (1551). Nevertheless, humanism made its way and, a century later, westernism in various forms had penetrated to the very center of Russian culture.

The process was closely connected with the function of Kiev as a channel of western influence. As the metropolis of the Ukraine, it had been incorporated in the Lithuanian state in the fifteenth century and after the Union of Lublin had become a focus of Polish power and influence. The Polish *pans* used their predominance to establish themselves in absentee lordships, which they exploited through Jewish fiscal agents. A

---

[6] V. O. Kliuchevsky, *Kurs russkoi istorii*, translated as *A History of Russia* (5 vols., London, 1911–1931); P. Miliukov, C. Seignobos and L. Eisenmann, *Histoire de Russie* (3 vols., Paris, 1932–1933); K. Waliszewski, *Le berceau d'un dynastie: les premiers Romanovs, 1613–1682* (2nd ed., Paris, 1909); R. N. Bain, *The First Romanovs 1613–1725* (London, 1905); P. Miliukov, *Outlines of Russian Culture*, edited by M. Karpovich (3 vols., Philadelphia, 1942).

Ukrainian folksong alleges that even the churches were farmed, so that the peasant had to pay the Jewish farmer when he wished to have his child baptized.[7] The Jesuits established schools and churches and carried on a vigorous propaganda for the Uniat church. Kiev became a western colony with an active group of merchants, with western architecture and music. An ecclesiastical school developed in which the classical languages and grammar were taught.

Some of the graduates were admitted to a printing house, established at Moscow in those days, as editors of sacred books. They found many errors and proposed their correction. This simple and natural proposal evoked violent condemnation from the xenophobic heirs of the Josephite movement. The proponents had studied Latin, they were South Russians who had accepted union with the west, they had consulted Greek books printed in Latin countries and therefore were imbued with the Latin heresy. The party of "Zealots of the Faith" easily defeated the first advocates of revision and in 1652 Nikon, one of the "Zealots," became patriarch. Nikon himself had been an ardent opponent of revision and had been associated with a group of "Zealots" who were close to Tsar Alexis. These men were moved by a sincere religious zeal and had introduced preaching into the church service with remarkable effect. Their successes with the congregations won them hostility among the rank and file of the Moscow clergy.[8] On the other hand, under the leadership of the archpriest of Iuriev, Avvakum, the Zealots became the most vigorous opponents of Nikon, when from conviction he adopted a program of revising the service books to conform to the Greek practice. The revision was not of a very high order. Five hundred manuscripts had been provided by Greek scholars, but only seven were used and the missal was actually corrected to conform to a Greek missal printed in Venice in 1602.[9] Nikon went over completely to the Greeks and introduced a whole series of Greek practices. In 1656 he declared, "Although I am a Russian and the son of a Russian, my faith and convictions are Greek." [10]

The result was a bitter struggle that has colored the relation of church and state to the present day. On the one side was Nikon, armed with the authority of the other eastern patriarchs and supported by Tsar Alexis;

[7] Antonovitch and Dragomanof, *Chansons historiques du peuple russe*, II, 21–22, quoted by A. Rambaud in Lavisse and Rambaud, *Histoire générale*, VI, 629, note.

[8] R. Jagadowitsch, *Das Leben des Protopopen Avvakums von ihm selbst niedergeschrieben: Übersetzung aus dem altrussischen nebst Einleitung und Kommentar* (Königsberg-Berlin, 1930), *passim.*

[9] Paul Miliukov, *Outlines of Russian Culture, Part I, "Religion and the Church,"* 36.

[10] *Ibid.,* 35.

on the other, the Zealots, supported by the mass of the Russian people, who had been taught and were being taught by the extraordinarily successful preaching of the Zealots that the Russian church was infallible and the holy books literally sacred. Almost all the lower clergy, the monks and the common people were disturbed by the changes of the familiar words and of the gestures, which were like incantations, the least change of which would destroy their force. They were hostile to any innovation. Intellectual justification was irrelevant. In Holy Russia demons had been put to flight for centuries by the sign of the cross made with two fingers: why should that be changed at the behest of Little Russians tinged with Latin heresies and of Greeks, slaves of the Turk, who had their books printed at heretic Venice? The opposition far exceeded anything that Nikon or the tsar could have foreseen.

For twenty years the Zealots hoped that the work of Nikon might be undone but, despite Nikon's loss of favor with the tsar, the decision stood. In 1666 a council condemned the opponents of revision and in the following year they were formally anathematized by the eastern patriarchs. Avvakum was exiled to Siberia.

In the controversies that continued to rage the defenders of the official doctrines, like Simeon Polotsky (d. 1680) and his more radical disciple Sylvester Medvedev, utilized the arguments of western theology, which they had learned at Kiev. By the eighteenth century the warring theologians were speaking Latin and arguing the issues of faith and good works upon the authority of western Catholic and Protestant theologians. The conservatives within the church and the Raskolniks (schismatics) attacked both as representative of a rationalism that to their minds had no place in Orthodoxy, in principle historically defined and final.

The Zealots refused to accept the decree of the council of 1666 as the decision of the church. Alexis became a persecutor and the Raskolniks fled to the forests. The Solovetski monastery became the center of resistance. After several sieges it was taken in 1676. Persecution only increased the fanaticism of the Zealots. When some of them were threatened with capture, they created great communal pyres and burned themselves to death in hundreds and even thousands.

In spite (or because) of persecution, the Raskolniks grew in numbers. The original defenders of the ancient rites developed a whole series of sects generally characterized by anticlericalism and ranging over the whole scale of religious variation. Some merely repudiated the episcopate; some abolished the priesthood. The schism also seemed to be the starting point of various renewals of ancient Christian heresies and even of pagan revivals. Although minimized in official reports and even in the last census of the tsarist regime, the Raskolniks constituted altogether a considerable fraction of the Russian population, perhaps a sixth in the early twentieth century. The schism was intellectually retrogressive but it was a great step forward in the religious consciousness of the masses. From the standpoint of the Slavophiles, the victory of the revisionists meant a breach between the intellectuals and the masses. In that sense it was a pattern many times repeated in other fields with the general result that Russia was attached to Europe rather than permeated by it, linked by the head rather than by the heart.

The problem of education raised again the issue of westernism. By 1660 the importance of developing schools was recognized, but for twenty years a debate raged over the issue whether the schools should follow eastern or western models. A compromise was finally achieved by enlarging the program to include both Latin and Greek studies. The teachers were to be Greeks, but in 1687 the first appointments were given to Greeks who had been educated in Venice. Mathematics was ignored and indeed viewed with suspicion. In 1676 a mob invaded the house of Artamon Matyeev to search for a book alleged to contain Arabic numerals. No geometry was taught. It is part of the legend of Peter the Great that he was the first Russian to pronounce the name of Newton.[11]

The arts also felt the impact of the west. In painting Russia had already nationalized its inheritance from Byzantium. In the fourteenth and fifteenth centuries the brilliant final upsurge of Byzantine art had had its repercussions in Russia, where a distinctively Russian character began to manifest itself. Novgorod and Suzdal became centers where highly trained artists produced icons of a simplicity and directness that sets them apart from the Byzantine tradition. In the sixteenth century the Council of the Hundred Chapters attempted to impose orthodoxy in art as it had done in ritual. A manual of the established patterns, the "Illuminated Original," was set as the standard to which the icon painters were to conform. Nevertheless, during the seventeenth century painters developed their own ideas to an unprecedented degree.

Moscow centralized the painters by requiring each of them to do a period of service there. At the same time the work of German, Flemish and, in the latter part of the seventeenth century, Dutch painters abounded in the palaces of the tsar and of wealthy nobles. Originally purely secular, their influence spread to icon-painting. Nikon, the revisionist, and

[11] P. Miliukov, in P. Miliukov, C. Seignobos, and L. Eisenmann, *op. cit.*, I, 244.

Avvakum, the Old Believer, as well as the church council of 1666 which condemned both, united in protest against the western modes. Nonetheless, the "tsar's isographers" resolutely proceeded with the introduction of western naturalism instead of following the conventionalized formalism of the "Original." The mastery of the interior achieved in the west during this period was promptly imitated in Russia (even though perspective was still ignored). The Bible of Piscator (Johann Fischer), a German illustrated version, itself a hundred years behind the times, added the Italian style of the fifteenth century to the Netherlands baroque as an effective influence in the last quarter of the century.

In theory the victory of the modernizing western forces was complete. The "Critical Original" liberated the artists to deal with themes taken from church literature. In actuality, however, the cause of the modernizers and the possibility of a real revival of religious painting was lost because it failed to keep touch with the majority of the faithful, who would have nothing to do with iconographic innovation. Russian painting at the higher levels meekly surrendered itself as apprentice to the western masters.

Russian music was likewise marked by an intrusion of western influence. By the seventeenth century the Russians had developed a high musical tradition. Part of it was associated with the ritual inherited from the Greek church. Like the verbal part of the ritual, it was holy and immutable, the more so since it was written down in a fairly well developed distinctive system of notation, the semeionic. "You must know," wrote Samuel Collins, an English physician to Alexis, "they have musick schools, where children are brought up with much diligence and in much severity. Their notes are very strange, borrowed, I suppose, of the Greeks or the Sclavonians." [12]

In spite of this solid basis of teaching, Russian music began to yield to western music. Russia acquired from the west both the lineal notation and polyphonic choral singing. These innovations, like so many others, were introduced to Moscow by Kiev, which had already learned them from Poland. Kievan and Polish singers were imported by nobles and officials and they and their methods were introduced into the churches. Avvakum, the leader of the movement against revision of the ritual, represented the conservative protest: "In many of the churches at Moscow, they sing songs instead of sacred chants, they wave their hands, shake

[12] Samuel Collins, *The Present State of Russia* (London, 1671), 32.

their heads, and stamp their feet as do the Latin organists." [13] Composers
and theorists were also attracted to Moscow. P. Duletsky, a Lithuanian,
was made director of the Royal Chapter of Singers by Tsar Fedor and
published in Russian his *Idea on the Grammar of Music* (1679) and a
Grammar of Musical Singing, which were the basis of a much elaborated
polyphony.[14]

The ballet and the opera were more directly imported from their
western centers. The Muscovite ambasador at Florence brought back
reports of the Italian ballet that "astounded" the court and led to attempts
to secure musicians and dancers. The German colony in 1672 gave a play,
written by one of its pastors, to celebrate the birth of a tsarevitch. It was
a great success and led Pastor Gregory to further efforts, culminating in
the first Russian opera, *How Judith Cut Off the Head of Holofernes.*
The first ballet performance seems to have been a divertissement based
on some of the music of Heinrich Schütz, presented as prologue to one
of Pastor Gregory's plays. Thus the most distinctive of Russian arts was
imported outright from the west.[15]

In architecture, likewise, the baroque was imported through the familiar
channel, from Poland through Kiev to Moscow. By the latter half of the
seventeenth century Kiev had become a baroque town. Kievan architects
were promptly summoned to Moscow. It was, however, more directly
from the west that Peter the Great brought the architects who imposed
the baroque on St. Petersburg and upon eighteenth-century Russia.[16]

Political reorganization under the Romanovs carried Russia far along
the road to absolutism. Western influence and example are suggested in
many details, but it cannot be demonstrated that they were important in
this development. When Alexis came to the throne, he was confronted by
a turbulent and insubordinate nobility, the boyars, a fierce communal
spirit in the great towns, and the antagonism of the Cossacks on the
steppe frontier to any authority.

The government began to take on the character of a bureaucratic
service. Alexis established a department (*prikaz*) of secret affairs. In
effect, this was the ancestor of the secret police of Peter the Great and
later governments of Russia. With the aid of an assembly of notables, he
formulated a legal code, which, if it was not very advanced, nevertheless

---

[13] Quoted by Paul Miliukov, *Outlines of Russian Culture,* Part III, "Architecture, Painting and Music."
[14] *Ibid.,* 60.
[15] Cyril Beaumont, *The Ballet in Russia* (London, 1930), 2–5.
[16] Paul Miliukov, *Outlines of Russian Culture,* Part III, 13–17.

functioned as common law. A nobility of service was created to compete with the boyars and ultimately to displace them.

The great towns were reduced to obedience by the ruthless application of military force. In 1648 an uprising at Moscow had forced the tsar to surrender three hated administrators, two of whom were lynched while the third, Morazov, his tutor and principal adviser, managed to escape. In 1662, when Moscow rose again because of a flood of counterfeit money, the tsar's men-at-arms fired on the mob; hundreds were killed, drowned or hanged. Risings at Pskov and Novgorod had been similarly repressed by the simple application of military force.

The subjection of the church was achieved by the degradation of the Patriarch Nikon. The first Romanov had permitted the Patriarch Philaret, his father, to use titles and authority substantially equal to his own. Nikon had assumed a similar authority and, when the rather oblique countermeasures of Alexis frustrated him, renounced the patriarchate and retired to a monastery (1658). When Alexis did not recall him, as he had hoped, he returned of his own accord and was thereupon ignominiously expelled. The tsar, however, did not assume final power in the matter. It was referred to a council sanctioned by the presence of Macarius, patriarch of Antioch and the patriarch of Alexandria, who had been summoned for the purpose.[17] The tsar appeared as prosecutor of Nikon and recognized the patriarchs as judges. Nikon was degraded from the patriarchate and even from the priesthood and was then confined in a monastery. Alexis made several attempts at a reconciliation, but Nikon refused any terms short of his re-establishment as patriarch. The western issue was obviously implicit in the situation, but it was resolved in a definitely nonwestern way.

The subjection of the Cossack republics to Moscow was a difficult problem for the poorly organized Russian state, but in various ways they were reduced to some degree of obedience. The Cossacks were simply the frontier settlers of the southern steppes, in the valleys of the Dnieper, the Don, the Volga and the Ural. Some were "Settlement Cossacks" with grants of land and subsidies. The more serious problem was presented by the "Free Cossacks," who, to defend themselves against Tartar raids and, as their strength developed, to carry on raids of their own, had organized themselves in military fashion. Far from Moscow, democratic, somewhat communal, they were wholly disinclined to accept authority.

[17] *The Travels of Macarius*, extracts selected and arranged by Lady Laura Riding, New York, 1936.

The Ukrainian Cossacks had a rather highly developed organization under a hetman (or ataman), and dreamed of independence. In the middle of the seventeenth century, under the Hetman Bogdan Khmelnitsky, they had rebelled against Polish landlord controls. Defeated, they turned to Russia, which succeeded in wresting the eastern Ukraine and Kiev from Poland (Treaty of Andrusovo, 1667). In the western Ukraine the Cossacks retained some freedom by playing off the Poles against the Turks, but after the smashing defeats of the Turks by the Austrian and Polish forces they lost their semi-independence and merged with the rest of the peasantry. The Cossacks in the Russian Ukraine retained their rights of self-government until 1783.

The Zaporogian Cossacks, who were the most military of all, openly resisted all efforts of Moscow to establish its authority until in 1775 they fled across the Danube into Turkey.

The Don Cossacks had played a considerable part in the early ventures of the Stroganovs in Siberia, in support of various of the pretenders in the Time of Troubles, in the expulsion of the Poles and in the elevation of Michael Romanov. Although they were subsidized by Moscow, they were as hostile as the Cossacks of the Dnieper to governmental authority. Under the famous Stenka Razin they rose in a rebellion (1678) that threatened to subvert the whole Moscow system and bring about a generalization of the Cossack system. Razin concentrated all the vague resentments of the populace against the manifestations of authority, including the reform of the liturgy. His power rested in part on the legends of his severity with the rich and powerful and his generosity to the poor. He was also the "wonderman," invulnerable and unbeatable. His first defeat, when he was wounded, cost him all his supporters. His own people arrested him and turned him over to the tsarist authorities. He was carried to Moscow, tortured and dismembered joint by joint (1690).

The Cossack system, that is, military service with special land grants, continued to be used by the autocracy. At the close of the century there were still eleven Cossack units, comprising about 2,500,000 people. These units were governed by an appointive bureaucracy, with only a few vestiges of the original democracy remaining at the lower levels of the administration. They were brought into subjection by a policy of converting their leaders into administrators of the Moscow government, with privileges of lordship over the peasantry. Socially and politically the protected peasants became serfs long before the ukase of Catherine II, to which the reduction of serfdom is commonly ascribed but which only legalized the state of affairs already existing.[18] With the decline of personal freedom, the institutions of self-government, local as well as national, lost all meaning and fell into disuse. On the other hand, the governors (*voyvods*), like the French intendants, developed increased power and responsibility.

Meanwhile, the Russians were extending their domination over the primitive tribes of Siberia. By the middle of the century they had reached the Amur and established contact with the Chinese empire. For the Chinese they were merely one more of the numerous barbarian tribes to be contained on the frontier. In 1658 the Chinese imperial forces wiped out a Russian settlement near the mouth of the Sungari. The Chinese made repeated attempts to induce Moscow to repress the lawless bands of Cossacks who managed to maintain themselves in the region, but Moscow was quite helpless. About 1682 the Chinese prepared to act. They organized the Mongol tribes, who were suffering from Russian depredations, and with what seemed to be finality destroyed Albasin, a new fort which, with the aid of a German engineer, the Russians had established on the Amur. The Russian government was prepared to withdraw but the local expansionists could not be controlled. Albasin was rebuilt, the Chinese attacked again and, after a long siege, forced the Russians to accept a treaty (September 7, 1689) by which they withdrew from the Amur and accepted the ridge of the Stanovoi Mountains as the boundary line. Meanwhile, far to the north, restless fur traders, pushing further each year into the country of the Yakuts, reached the Kolima and the Anadir rivers which took them to the Bering Sea, although they were far from realizing at the time the import of their discovery.[19]

The last years of Alexis were dominated by several statesmen who, more than he, were precursors of Peter the Great, especially in that they were effectively in touch with western civilization. Such were the Boyar Fedor Artychev, who carried on a sustained propaganda for the modernization of education, Ordin-Nashokin, the first real Russian diplomat, and Artamon Matyeev, who was influenced both by a Polish wife and by the European merchants. When Alexis died in 1676, he was

---

[18] A. Miller, "Considerations sur le développement des institutions agraires de l'Ukraine au 17e et au 18e siècles," *Revue internationale de sociologie*, 36 (1928), 495–530; *Éssai sur l'histoire des institutions agraires de la Russie centrale du 16e au 18e siécles* (Paris, 1926); I. Polosin, "Le servage russe et son origine," *Revue internationale de sociologie*, 36 (1928), 605 ff. Polosin asserts that serfdom arose in the area northwest of Novgorod in the course of the wars of Ivan the Terrible.

[19] F. A. Golder, *Russian Expansion on the Pacific, 1641–1850* (Cleveland, 1914), chs. 1, 2, 3. Cf. also, A. Lobanov-Rostowsky, *Russia and Asia* (New York, 1933), 33–69.

succeeded by his son Fedor, who had received a European education. European and, in particular, Polish influences from Kiev overran Moscow. The last sanction of the ancient nobility was removed by the formal burning of the "books of rank." Nobility became identified with the state.[20]

The death of Fedor (1682) without issue brought the succession into question. After a complicated struggle Sofia, the daughter of Alexis, was established as regent for her feeble-minded brother Ivan and their half-brother Peter as joint tsars. Sofia's victory represented a further advance of the westernizing tendency and Peter, who overthrew the regency in 1689, carried it to lengths hitherto undreamed of.

II. THE RECOVERY OF THE DANUBE

The great, truly world-historical action of these years developed not in the arena of Louis XIV but along the roads which with all their limitations the Austrian monarchy and its allies trod. Here were achievements begun, relations established, which outlasted the centuries.[21]

In these decades of the seventeenth century, while Europe was spreading over all the seas and continents, it was confronted by its final and most serious threat from Islam. In spite of its apparently hopeless disruption and anarchy, it met and surmounted the crisis. The defeat of the Turks before Vienna in 1683 meant that for centuries to come Europe was supreme in its world, without effective external challenge.

Europe could carry on its conquest of the world in security. The nationalistic prepossessions, markedly baroque, with which the Europeans have made their picture of the past, have focused attention on the record of internal conflicts for power and perquisites. Yet at the time Europeans were fully conscious of the greatness of their salvation. The wars against the Turks, and notably the liberation of Vienna and the recovery of Buda, were celebrated in chronicles and relations, gazettes and geographical descriptions, panegyrics and poems, addressed to the pope, the emperor, the generals and the twenty-seven cardinals elevated in honor of the event. The municipal library of Budapest compiled a bibliography, *Litteratura contemporanea della reconquista el Buda e Pest, 1686-1718;* no less than sixteen hundred of such items are still extant.[22]

Since the Turks had crossed into Europe, they had expanded their conquests until they faced the Russia of the Romanovs, the Hungary of

---

[20] P. Miliukov in P. Miliukov, C. Seignobos and L. Eisenmann, *op. cit.,* I, 198.

[21] Erdmannsdörfer, *Deutsche Geschichte,* I, 695.

[22] Marc Jarič, "Bibliographies et instruments de travail," *Revue d'histoire moderne,* 12 (1937), 161.

the Hapsburgs, and the Poland of the Jagellons. They controlled all of the lower Danube, the entire shores of the Black Sea and the Caspian, and disputed the Ukraine with Poland and Russia, Podolia with Poland and Transylvania and the valley of the Theiss with the Hapsburgs. Throughout the Balkans and southern Russia they exercised an imperial authority that did not merely exploit the subject populations as passive victims but organized them to contribute positively to the strength of the empire in wealth, in soldiery and in brains. The harem, the Janizaries, the civil service and the councils utilized this cosmopolitan power, if not without regard to race and religion, at least with a high degree of flexibility and intelligence.

The haremlik, which in the sixteenth century could produce a Soleiman the Magnificent, in the seventeenth was producing petty and unmanly specimens such as Mohammed IV. This padishah, under whose reign Christendom was to tremble for the last time before the Turks, left the command of his armies to his grand vizier and spent his days hunting. While he was yet a child, his mother as regent had initiated a revival of Turkish vigor. Mohammed Kuprili, the first of a dynasty of strong grand viziers furnished by his family, was called to power in 1656 at the age of seventy. With an administration and an army disciplined to complete responsibility, he made the Turkish empire once more a threat to Europe.[23]

The problem from the Turkish point of view was twofold, to thrust back the advanced position of Venice in the Mediterranean and to utilize the restless Magyars as a base for advance up the Danube at the expense of the Hapsburgs and into the Ukraine and White Russia at the expense of the Poles and the Russians.

On the Danube the Magyars were as unsatisfactory allies for the Turks as they were for the Hapsburgs. When Mohammed Kuprili removed George II Rákóczy for involving himself and the Empire in a war with Poland, Rákóczy rose in rebellion. Kuprili II Ahmed, the son of Mohammed, sent an army into Transylvania and Hungary which was so successful that Ahmed himself entered the campaign with an army of nearly 250,000. Not only Hungary but Moravia and Silesia were devastated. Eighty thousand Christians were carried off into slavery.[24] The Emperor Leopold seemed wholly unable to repulse such forces. Pope Alexander VII bestirred himself to form a Holy League among the

Christian princes. Louis XIV was the first to adhere to the League, but his proposal to furnish 30,000 French soldiers and, as the principal member of the Rheinbund, another 30,000 alarmed Leopold more than did the Turkish threat. The pope and the Emperor induced Louis to reduce his offer to a corps of 9,000 French soldiers.[25] With an Imperial army of 20,000 reinforced by these 9,000 French, Montecuccoli, the Hapsburg general, defeated Kuprili's 240,000 Turks at Saint Gotthard (1664), where they had crossed the Raab. The Turks were glad to accept the Treaty of Vasvár. The Empire, on its part, was equally content to have its hands free to meet the rising threat of France in the Netherlands and along the Rhine.[26] Transylvania was evacuated by both Turkish and Imperial forces, but the Turkish candidate, Apaffy, was recognized as prince, with an obligation of tribute to the sultan. Of the seven palatine counties between the Theiss and Transylvania, three were assigned to the emperor and four to the sultan. Austria was then free to turn its attention to the French danger. The French troops were dismissed with little show of gratitude. They used their contact with the Hungarians to initiate cooperation against the Hapsburg.[27]

Louis XIV refused to become involved in a Holy Alliance against the Turks and turned his attention to his own crusade in the western Mediterranean. The position of the Venetians on Crete, where they had been under intermittent attack since 1648, was growing more difficult. Except from France they were unable to secure any help from Christian Europe. French aid, in spite of the attempt to keep up the traditional friendship with the sultan, was substantial at times but intermittent. Repeatedly French contingents failed to get along with Francesco Morosini, the Venetian commander, and withdrew after some brief and meaningless activity. Thus when Kuprili II came in person to conduct the siege (May, 1667), the garrison of Candia was reduced to 4,000 men and Morosini had to surrender. The attack on Crete had lasted twenty-one years. The last siege of sixteen months had cost the Venetians 30,000 men and the Turks 100,000. By the surrender (1669) Crete passed into the hands of the Turkish empire, there to remain for over two centuries.[28]

The Mohammedan population of Algiers and Tunis had elevated the

[25] A. Saint-Léger and P. Sagnac, *op. cit.,* 88–89, give the number as 6,000, but D. Kosáry, "Les français en Hongrie au 1664," *Revue d'histoire comparée,* IV (1946), 29–65, shows the figure to have been not less than 9,000.

[26] See above, p. 176.

[27] D. Kosáry, *op. cit.,* 29–65.

[28] A. de Saint-Léger and P. Sagnac, *op. cit.,* 116–17.

holy war against the infidel into a profitable industry of piracy. The *reis,* the pirate chiefs, constituted a powerful corporation, the *Taif,* and elected deys who gave purely nominal recognition to the suzerainty of the Turkish sultan. The Knights of Malta fought the pirates or, alternatively, redeemed their captives by purchase. St. Vincent de Paul's Fathers of the Mission maintained a hospital at the French consulate in Algiers to facilitate redemption. The Redemptorist fathers took Christian slaves to Leghorn to be there redeemed if funds were available, and otherwise to be returned to their owners.

In spite of the old alliance of the French king with the sultan, the piratical subjects of the Porte raided the Mediterranean coasts of France without compunction. The French navy, reorganized by Colbert, began a series of punitive expeditions which, without ending piracy, did establish French predominance in the western Mediterranean. As Franco-Turkish relations grew more embittered, the grand vizier and the French ambassador on one occasion came to blows. The campaigns against the pirates grew more effective and revived the consideration of the plan of Leibniz for the conquest of Egypt. When in 1681 Abraham Duquesne chased eight Tripolitan corsairs into the harbor of Chio, bombarded the forts, and threatened to blow the Turkish fleet out of the water, war was avoided only by a renewal of the capitulations, including the French privileges in the holy places.[29]

Meanwhile, the uncertainties of the Ukrainian situation involved Turkey in wars with Poland and Russia. The hetman Dourochenko of the western Ukraine, in rebellion against Poland, recognized Turkish suzerainty and brought the Turks into war with the Poles, out of which they won possession of Podolia (1672, 1676). When Dourochenko was driven out by the Muscovite party (1677), war with Russia resulted finally in the surrender by the Turks of Kiev and eastern Ukraine (1681). The peace left Kara Mustapha, the pupil and son-in-law of Kuprili I and third in this dynasty of effective grand viziers, free to take advantage of the rebellion of Emmerich Tököli against the Hapsburgs (1682) to attack Austria. He invaded Hapsburg Hungary with 100,000 troops, won some easy victories and resolved to march directly on Vienna, sure of succeeding where Suleiman the Magnificent had failed a century and a half before.[30]

---

[29] A. Rambaud, *op. cit.,* VI, 839.

[30] H. Hantsch, *Die Entwicklung Österreich-Hungarn zur Grossmacht* (Freiburg, 1933), 73-74; R. Lorenz, *Türkenjahr 1683. Das Reich im Kampf um den Ostraum* (Vienna, 1933); H. Kadbedo, *Bibliographie zur Geschichte der beiden Türkenbelagerungen Wiens*

The situation was wholly favorable to the Turkish hopes. Under Ahmed Kuprili, Crete had been recovered and Podolia conquered from the Poles. Under his successor, Kara Mustapha, peace had been made with Russia by surrendering Turkish claims to the Ukraine. In spite of the conciliatory diet of 1681, Hungary was in rebellion. Tököli had refused the settlement that made an Esterhazy the palatine and had offered the Turks suzerainty over Hungary. Europe was divided. Not only was France actively aiding the Hungarian rebels with money and recruits from Warsaw; the French king had defeated the statesman-like plan of Sobieski to organize a European defense against the Turks by refusing a truce in his cold war against the Empire. His troops had beseiged Luxemburg in full peace and had thus paralyzed the German states to which Leopold might look for assistance. Spain, Austria's natural ally, could hardly provide for the defense of the Netherlands. The United Provinces, torn by the divergences of policy between the estates-general and William of Orange, raised not a hand to save from destruction an ally whose loss would have been fatal to themselves. Frederick William of Brandenburg, betrayed as he believed at Nimwegen, had allied himself with France. His offer of twelve thousand troops was declined at Vienna.[31]

On the other hand, the pope succeeded in rendering effective assistance in the organization of European public opinion in response to the danger. At Vienna and Warsaw the papal diplomats played an important part. For a few years, however, the central figure in the organization of the defense was John III Sobieski, king of Poland.[32] As hetman he had made his reputation by defeating the Turks in Podolia. As king he undertook a statesman-like program: peace between Russia and Poland, truce between the Bourbon and the Hapburg, alliance between Poland and Austria.

Sobieski's program was crippled from the start by the refusal of Louis XIV to commit himself to a truce. Although France had favored his election, Sobieski gradually drew away from France and undertook a rapprochement with Austria. When French diplomats attempted by bribes to bring about the dissolution of the diet, Sobieski exposed them and for the time ended French influence. The emperor, meanwhile, was not

(Vienna, 1876); *Bibliographie zur Geschichte und Stadtkunde von Wien nebst Quellen und Literaturhinweisen* (Verein für Landeskunde von Niederösterreich und Wien, Vienna, 1947), Vol. I.

[31] A. W. Ward, "The Origin of the Kingdom of Prussia," *Cambridge Modern History,* V, 653.

[32] O. Forst de Battaglia, "Jan Sobieski, 1674–1696," in *The Cambridge History of Poland from the Origins to Sobieski* (Cambridge, 1950), 540–49.

eager for the alliance. The Hungarian rebels had received assistance from Poland and had even offered Sobieski the suzerainty of Hungary. It was not until the threatened invasion had become actual that terms were arrived at by which Sobieski was to receive a subsidy of 1,200,000 florins and furnish 40,000 men to make up a force of 100,000. When Louis XIV, under what was made to seem a response to public opinion, volunteered to raise the siege of Luxemburg, the German states responded to the emperor's appeals with respectable contingents.

In December, 1682, Kara Mustapha in effect declared war by demanding impossible conditions for the renewal of the truce which an Imperial mission had been seeking. An attack on the Empire had been the focus of the grand vizier's policy since the beginning of his career. In 1676 his announcement of this intention had been noted with satisfaction in the French council of state. War with Poland and then with Russia had prevented its execution. Now, at peace with both, he formally recognized Emmerich Tököli as vassal king of Hungary and organized an army at Adrianople. As it advanced through the Balkans reinforcements from the vassal states joined until it amounted to about 250,000 men, a very large proportion of which was service forces.[33]

Charles of Lorraine, in command of the Imperial forces, had only about thirty thousand men and was obliged to adopt a Fabian policy until reinforcements could reach him from the German states and Poland. By defeating the attempt of Tököli to take Pressburg, he was enabled to effect a junction with the Poles at Hollabrun and with the Germans at Tuln. The whole Christian force, numbering about seventy thousand, crossed the Danube and, without interference by the Turks, marched along the south bank to the Kahlenberg, a height that looked down on Vienna and the plain to the east.

The siege had begun on July 16, 1683. The heroic story of the defense has become the keystone of Vienna's legend. Under Count Rüdiger von Stahremberg some thirteen thousand regular troops, reinforced by all the able-bodied citizenry, maintained an obstinate resistance in spite of the ravages of famine, disease and bombardment. More than once Kara Mustapha might have taken the city by storm. He chose to wait until the rigors of the siege would compel surrender. The limit of human endurance was almost reached when, on September 11, the relieving army appeared on the slopes of the Kahlenberg.

Under the command of Sobieski, the European forces took advantage

[33] H. Hantsch, *op. cit.*, 73–74.

of the unpreparedness of the besiegers and promptly attacked on September 12. The result was a surprisingly easy victory. The Moldavian and Wallachian auxiliaries on the Turkish right were overrun by the Imperial forces. The whole line then threw itself on the Turkish camp and routed its guards. The Janizaries were caught in the siege trenches between the defenders and the vanguard of the relieving army and cut to pieces. In eight hours' combat the relief of Vienna had been accomplished.

The galvanic spasm of delight that shook Europe and found expression in hundreds of retellings of the story and eulogies of the leaders [34] was not matched by a corresponding resolution of the political issues. The participants in the battle themselves fell at once into jealous conflicts over their relative merits. The Imperials complained because they had borne the brunt of the battle and the Poles got the glory and most of the booty. The Polish king in turn was aggrieved because Leopold failed to show adequate gratitude and recognition. Louis XIV ordered the siege of Luxemburg re-established. The Spanish, hopeful of Dutch and Imperial support, declared war on France. The Imperial government faced again the same issue it had faced when the Turkish threat was developing, whether its principal interest was in the east or in the west. After a long debate, Leopold followed the urging of the pope and his victorious generals, rather than that of Spain, and entered upon a Holy League with Poland, Venice and the Knights of Malta to fight "the thirteenth crusade" (March 5, 1684) and developed the campaign against the Turks. France held off to pursue its own campaign against the Barbary pirates, but Russia adhered in 1686.

The exploitation of the Turkish defeat developed rapidly to such a degree of success that eastern Europe was transformed. Kara Mustapha laid the responsibility for the defeat on Ibrahim, pasha of Buda, and had him executed, but a few days later, by order of the sultan, was himself executed at Belgrade. The Turks were unable to find a point of resistance. In 1684 Pest was taken, Buda besieged and a Turkish army destroyed in Croatia. In 1685 the Imperial forces recovered Gran and Neuhaüsel. Tököli was chased into exile. On the famous battlefield of Mohács another destructive defeat was inflicted on the Turks. Buda was finally taken in 1687. Apaffy did homage to the emperor and a Hungarian diet at Pressburg declared the crown of Hungary hereditary in the house of Austria. The Venetians under Morosini, the hero of Candia, made their

---

[34] *Litteratura contemporanea della reconquista de Buda é Pest, 1686–1718;* see above, p. 237.

way into the Morea and besieged Athens, destroying the Parthenon, which the Turks had turned into a powder magazine (1687). The Turks at last sought to negotiate peace, but the demands of the Imperials were such that the Turks determined to continue the war. They were saved by Louis XIV. In September, 1688, the War of the League of Augsburg began. In spite of the mediatory efforts of England and Holland, the war in the Balkans dragged on until 1699, when Turkey had to give up Hungary and Transylvania to the Empire, Podolia and the western Ukraine to the Poles, Dalmatia and the Peloponnesus (less Corinth) to the Venetians as well as the islands of Aegina and Saint Maur, and to the Russians, Azov.[35]

In spite of division, conflict and confusion, Europe had ended the threat of conquest by Islam. It had preserved not only its system of power but its secularism and segmentation. The Balkans continued to be governed from Constantinople but the powerful forces of economic and technological advance and of intellectual adventure at first slowly and then, with the French Revolution, more rapidly penetrated the areas where once Islam had brought a civilization of a different order. Europe's conquest in cultural terms was never complete. Not only Islam but Byzantium still differentiates the southeast section of the European peninsula from the north and west. Nevertheless, the essential condition of European advance was established. Europe was still capable of suicide, but it was secure against catastrophe from the outside.

III. THE EXPANSION OVERSEAS

In 1660 the Europeans were traversing all the seas and had established themselves in controlling positions on all their shores. They were masters of the western coast of Africa from Gibraltar to the Cape of Good Hope. In India they held effective control of Bombay and Goa, and had privileged positions in Chandernagor and Madras. They ruled in Ceylon, in the Sunda Islands and in the Philippines. They had at least a foothold on the margins of the Chinese empire, at Canton and Macao. Nagasaki was a privileged western trading post and Formosa almost a European possession. In the western hemisphere European populations and European institutions were established and operating in Brazil, in the valley of the Rio de la Plata, in the ancient empire of the Incas and in the valleys of the Cauca and the Orinoco. Europeans controlled the Isthmus of Panama and the lands of Central America. Mexico was a sub-

---

[35] A. de Saint-Léger and P. Sagnac, *op. cit.*, 408–9.

metropolitan center of European culture, from which military, religious and economic enterprise was pushing the frontier far to the north. The islands of the Caribbean were rapidly being organized as sources of goods-capital for an expanding Europe. Florida was a northern bastion of the Spanish possessions. Along the eastern coast of North America North European peoples of diverse origins had settled in considerable numbers from the Kennebec to Albemarle Sound and were establishing urban centers of considerable vigor. In the St. Lawrence Valley, Quebec and Montreal were centers of French trade, religious enterprise and exploration that had already extended over the whole Great Lakes region.

This unparalleled dispersion of a culture, which is generally looked at from the standpoint of European state conflicts, requires attention as a unique phenomenon of European culture as a whole. To no other society in history had a whole world been opened for its exploitation.[36]

Of the relatively small population of Europe some hundreds of thousands (less than 1 per cent) were abroad, on the sea in ships, in foreign trading stations, in military establishments, in ecclesiastical positions, in mines and plantations, exploiting in one way or another the favorable economic opportunities assured them by the fact that they were either of a conquering group or able to deal with governments on an equal basis. In New England and New France immigrants wrested from the soil a hard living, but elsewhere labor was the function of unfree, native populations subject to the lordship or landlordship of Europeans, deported criminals and poor immigrants bound to labor as indentured servants, or Negro slaves brought from Africa in the growing slave trade of the Dutch, the French and the English. The slave trade was enriching towns like Nantes, Saint-Malo, Rotterdam and Bristol and sustaining a great increase in the number of the seagoing vessels and sailors of the northern nations. From the mines of Mexico and Peru came a river of silver and gold that flooded Spain with disastrous effect and overflowed into the northern countries, where it evoked an immense upsurge of productive activity and mercantile enterprise as well as of illegal activity like piracy and smuggling. In the long run much of this bullion found its way to the lands of the east, where Europe had nothing in the way of goods to offer in exchange for either their industrial products or their specialized agricultural products. Forced trade in India and the Dutch islands and the development of the Asian trade, especially between India and China,

---

[36] Georg Friederici, *Der Charakter der Entdeckung und Eroberung Amerikas durch die Europäer: Einleitung zur Geschichte der Besiedlung Amerikas durch die Völker der alten Welt* (3 vols., Stuttgart, 1925–1936).

mitigated the "imbalance" of the trade but it did not end it until late in the eighteenth century.

The goods-capital of Europe was greatly increased. As material for transport, for processing, for trading, for credit, the increasing flow of mass-produced colonial goods made opportunities for the economic energies of Europeans in areas thitherto close to the subsistence level. The old personal character of production and delivery was being overlaid and even displaced by a new system in which men ate food grown on land they never saw and sold the products of their industry to distant strangers. It is perhaps unnecessary to say that this increase in goods-capital and its exploitation did not produce an immediate rise in the general standard of living, though it does seem to have been a necessary step to later advances. The process could be dimly observed in the upsurge of urbanism in the Atlantic towns. The growth of Madrid, Lisbon, Bordeaux, London, Le Havre, Amsterdam, Rotterdam, Hamburg, Gothenburg, Copenhagen, was evidence not only of a vast importation of products from beyond the seas, but of a vast increase in the production and marketing of European products to pay for them.

When all is said, the net increase of Europe's stock of precious metals combined with the steady improvement of its banking and credit systems to provide fairly well for the expansion of its production and exchange. The increase of goods-capital, which the addition of new lands and new labor force made possible, was a basic element in modern European development. Sugar and spices, tobacco and rum, chocolate and dyewoods, and a host of other products involved a whole new pattern of production and marketing.

Over the northern and western coasts of South America, over the whole of Central America and Mexico, over Cuba, Puerto Rico and Hispaniola (Santo Domingo), European culture as power, as language, as religion, had been spread by Spanish settlers, soldiers, officials and, above all, by the Spanish church. In every little barrio the priest was known and in every region, some form of monastic institution. From Paraguay and Chile to California and Texas frontier missions multiplied and thousands of Indians were organized in patterns intermediate between primitive barbarism and European civilization.[37] In the more settled regions the Indians generally lived in their own villages or in "reduc-

[37] H. S Bolton, "The Mission as Frontier Institution in the Spanish-American Colonies," *American Historical Review*, 23 (1917), 42–61; W. W. Sweet, "Religious Enthusiasm as a Motive Force in Spanish Colonization," *Methodist Review*, 3 (1928), 569–80.

tions" brought about by the Spaniards. The Indians generally accepted the ritual of Christianity (and, willy-nilly, its code) and combined it with strong survivals of their native nature worship.

The Spanish production system in the colonies was based almost wholly on the forced wage labor of Indians and on Negro slavery. Planters and mineowners requiring labor secured from the government *repartimientos*, which in effect entitled them to the services of Indians put at their disposition for limited periods up to three months. Negro slaves were generally used in the islands, where the Caribs were being exterminated, and in mainland regions of high temperature.

The spirit of Las Casas, who in the sixteenth century had established Christian morality as the law for the treatment of the Indians, was by no means dead in the seventeenth century. In 1657 an official at Lima, Juan de Padilla, appealed for reform of the conditions of Indian labor in the silver mines. New regulations were made and a new viceroy sent out to enforce them. In 1684 two Capuchin missionaries in Lima challenged the legality of slavery, but were silenced and sent back to Spain, where their protest was submitted by the king to juntas of theologians and jurists.[38] The legitimacy of slavery was upheld, but it was something that the missionaries were able to make their protest and get a hearing. The *Recopilacion de los Leyes de los Reynos de los Indias* was not of very high order as a legal code, but it did provide a relatively high standard of protection for Indian rights. The Indians had access to the courts and were provided with legal assistance. The local social legislation in regard to labor regulation, land distribution, charity and religious culture, taken as a whole, makes an impressive showing. Much of it was derived from Inca precedents.[39] In spite of much greed and cruelty, the Spanish regime permitted no extermination and even encouraged cultural amalgamation. "Purity of race" remained a requirement only for official position. *Hispanidad* was indelibly implanted on a whole society.[40]

Urban centers like Mexico, Bogotá, Lima and Havana manifested a lively creative and reflective power. Schools were numerous, although education remained aristocratic. The universities of Mexico and San Marcos (Peru) produced scholars of European rank, such as Carlos de Si-

---

[38] G. Scellé, *La traite negrière aux Indes de Castille* (2 vols., Paris, 1906), I, 708–10.

[39] Carmelo Viña May, "Legislacion social ibero-americana durante la colonizacion," *Boletin del Museo social Argentino*, 20 (1932), 3–19.

[40] Nicolas Matias del Campo, *Memorial . . . en repuesto de otra . . . contra el repartimiento de indios en Potosi* (s.l.n.d.) and *Memorial historico y juridico, que refiere el origen de oficio de protector general de los Indios de Peru* (Madrid, 1671).

guenza y Góngora (1645–1702),[41] one of the most illustrious savants of Mexico, and Pedro de Peralta Barnuevo (1663–1743), who without leaving his native Lima became a famous mathematician. European books were imported in shiploads. The first edition of *Don Quixote* was absorbed almost entirely by the American trade. Lope de Vega's plays were not only read in America, but were used as the stock of the numerous theaters that attracted the entire communities, regardless of class. Descartes, Newton and Leibniz were well known in the New World within a few years of their publication.

The creole literary tradition was strong and produced at least one great lyric poet, Sor Iñez de la Cruz (1651–1695), and one great satirist, Juan del Valle y Caviedes (Lima, late seventeenth century). European painting, especially the work of Murillo and Zurbarán, was brought to America. Native artists, themselves not exactly primitive, responded sympathetically to the baroque ideal, as numerous churches and, above all, the church of the Jesuits in Cuzco, still demonstrate. Occasionally an isolated artist, virtually self-taught, managed to achieve genuine distinction, like Gregorio Vasquez de Arce y Ceballos (1638–1711) in Bogotá. Colonial art reached its highest levels in the schools of Cuzco and Quito.[42]

Economically, the function of Spain was to serve rather passively as the channel for the exchange of goods between Europe and America. Even in this passive function Spain was largely by-passed. A vast structure of regulations designed to prevent the intrusion of foreigners and to restrict colonial trade to the port of Cadiz was eroded by a flourishing illicit trade, sometimes at Seville and Cadiz, where the professional smugglers charged a modest 1 to 1½ per cent, sometimes in the ports of America, where goods-hungry settlers and pliant governors made such transactions easy. Spain lacked the economic organization necessary to provide an adequate supply of goods. Foreign capitalists, in our period especially Dutch, frequently secured government contracts (*asientos*) to supply Negroes and used their entry to smuggle manufactured goods into the colonies and bullion out from them.[43] A document of 1691 reported Frenchmen leading in the trade through Cadiz, with returns from America of thirteen or fourteen million *livres*, and the Genoese, Dutch and English following, in that order.[44]

[41] Irving A. Leonard, *Don Carlos Siguenza y Góngora, a Mexican Savant of the Seventeenth Century* (University of California Publications in History, No. 18 (1929), 287).

[42] C. H. Haring, *The Spanish Empire in America* (New York, 1947), 249.

[43] R. D. Hussey, "Antecedents of the Spanish Monopolistic Overseas Trading Companies, 1624–1728," *Hispanic-American Historical Review*, 9 (1929), 1–30.

[44] H. Sée, *Documents sur le commerce de Cadiz* (Paris, 1927), 21 ff. Reference from Haring, *op. cit.*, 315, note.

The Caribbean islands and Buenos Aires were the principal centers of the direct trade. Both the English and the French supplemented peaceful trade by organizing the buccaneers, who used bases at Jamaica and Santo Domingo for very profitable, if brutal, raids on peaceful Spanish communities such as Maracaibo, Panama, Santiago de los Caballeros and even Vera Cruz. Nevertheless, when Louis XIV in 1683 attempted to secure the legalization of at least some of the trade "beyond the line," the Spanish refused to make any concession from their nominally exclusive position.

The Spanish regarded the advances of the French, English and Dutch in the West Indies, the English settlements on the Atlantic Coast of the continent and the exploration of the Mississippi as so many violations of their empire, sanctioned by right of discovery, papal authority and the prescription of a century and a half. To meet these aggressions, they extended their governmental establishments to the north and east, far beyond any actual occupation, to east Texas, Mobile, Florida and Georgia. The powerful Indian tribes such as the Creeks and the Cherokees aligned themselves on one side or the other. As the English and the French grew more powerful, the Spanish were obliged to accept (if not to recognize) the existence of these competitors. In their attempts to organize the Indians on the Georgia coast, they aroused more hostility than friendship and were driven back to Florida by the English and Yamassees (1685). About the same time, a Spanish attempt to drive out the English fur traders from among the Creeks failed. Thus, at the end of the period the existence of English and French power in the Caribbean region had to be accepted as a fact. The Spanish formally recognized the English possessions in the islands in 1670, but even in 1683 refused similar recognition to the French.

In spite of the inertia and decay apparent in Spain, the expansionist impulse was far from spent on the margins of the empire. From Caracas and Mexico, the Spanish, with the aid of the missionaries of the Propaganda, were pushing into the interior of Venezuela and Yucatán and northward into the wilds of Texas, New Mexico and Arizona.[45] Portugal, too, showed some of its old vigor and recovered Brazil from the Dutch.

The West Indies, where Spain had effectively occupied Cuba, Puerto Rico and the eastern two-thirds of Hispaniola, suffered the vigorous intrusion of all three northern powers. The Dutch, who had been driven out of the Amazon valley by the Portuguese, dominated the West Indies

[45] H. E. Bolton and T. H. Marshall, *The Colonization of North America*, 223–25.

trade from two small bases, Curaçao off the Spanish mainland, and Saint Eustatius at the northern end of the Leeward Islands. Across the Atlantic they momentarily monopolized the slave trade centers along the African coast, which they had conquered from the Portuguese. Although this exclusive position was gradually lost in the stresses of international conflict during the latter decades of the century, the Dutch retained an easy predominance. Both their principal islands were great warehouses of European goods, and Curaçao was also a concentration point for their slave cargoes from Africa. With adequate capital and a good credit system, and, after 1648, a friendly relation with Spain, the Dutch maintained agents in all the Spanish ports and through legal and illegal channels introduced slaves and European goods almost at will. After the Portuguese rebellion in 1640, the Spanish had had to turn to the Dutch for slaves. In 1664 a Genoese firm was induced to undertake an asiento or contract to deliver slaves, but apparently lacked financial backing and in 1684 had to admit participation by the Amsterdam firm of Coymans. The Dutch introduced the Portuguese techniques of sugar production which they had learned in Brazil to the French and English planters, and financed the shift from tobacco-raising to sugar-planting, upon which the significance of the islands in the European economic system came to depend.[46]

During the earlier decades of the century the French had established themselves at Saint-Christophe (which they shared with the English) and from that base had extended their occupation over Martinique, Guadeloupe, Grenada and a number of smaller islands. The companies organized by Richelieu and the Company of the West Indies, which Colbert founded in 1664, all failed to function as aids to colonization. The Dutch War of 1665-1667 bankrupted the French West India Company and the next war (1672-1678) bankrupted the Dutch Company. Nevertheless, under two able governors, Ogeron (1663-1675) and Paul Tarin de Cussy (1683-1691), the rapid settlement of the Windward Islands, the conquest of western Hispaniola (Santo Domingo) and, above all, the domestication of the buccaneers of Tortuga opened the way to the great role of the Antilles in the economic life of France and Europe in the next century. Immigrants from France were coming in at the rate of about a thousand a year. In 1685 the population of the French islands was estimated at 52,000, of which two-thirds or more were Negro slaves. Martinique was still the principal island with a population of about 16,500.[47] The

[46] A. P. Newton, *The European Nations in the West Indies, 1493-1688* (1933), 196.
[47] W. A. Roberts, *The French In the West Indies* (New York, 1942), 75.

Colonial Code of 1685, generally known as the *code noir,* gave the slave a standing as a moral entity. It did not end the horrors of slavery, but it did make it possible for the Negroes to enter into the heritage of French culture.

The English were established on Barbados, Jamaica and, with the French, on Saint Kitts. Both the larger islands prospered, especially after new sugar-refining methods were introduced by the Dutch. By the end of the century the sugar business had so expanded that the islands had become wholly dependent on the northern colonies for food, work animals, lumber and staves for their sugar casks.[48] Some attempt was made to build them up with white indentured labor, but the whites escaped to join the pirates or to settle in the French or Dutch islands which were regarded as freer for trade and for persons.[49]

The English colonies, like the others, quickly became dependent on slave labor. Both islands lodged many complaints that the Royal African Company ignored them in order to furnish slaves to the *asientistas* who came to Kingston with hard money. The Royal African Company did some business with the English planters on credit on very hard terms, but found itself impeded by legislation hostile to creditors and collectors.[50] In 1670 Sir Thomas Modyford declared that Barbados had prospered before the days of the company only because the slave trade and immigration had been unrestricted.[51]

During the decades after 1660 the West Indies were partially brought under international law. The Spanish doctrine that the Caribbean was a *mare clausum* and that prior discovery gave Spain exclusive rights in the whole area had long before proved unenforceable. The intruding powers, Holland, England and France, disregarded outside of Europe any of the treaties made in Europe, either in regard to Spain or in regard to each other. Complete anarchy reigned.

During the late seventeenth century foreigners were supplying five-sixths of the manufactures consumed in Spain itself and engrossing nine-tenths of that American trade which the Spaniards had sought so carefully to monopolize.[52] The French had developed an extensive system by which the names of Spaniards were used to cover the business

[48] C. Nettels, *Money Supply in the American Colonies* (Madison, 1934), 135.

[49] E. D. Collins, "Studies in the Colonial Policy of England," *American Historical Association Report,* 1900, I, 143.

[50] *Ibid.,* I, 160.

[51] *Ibid.,* I, 144.

[52] G. Weiss, *L'Espagne depuis Philip II jusqu'aux Bourbons,* II, 204–15; C. H. Haring, *The Buccaneers in the West Indies in the Seventeenth Century* (London, 1910), 8.

financed, managed and controlled by French principals and French agents. In 1680 the Comte d'Estrées was instructed to visit with his fleet all the ports in the West Indies and the Main, especially Cartagena and Santo Domingo, to remind the Spaniards that justice must be done the French merchants.

Thus, the Spaniards by persisting, both at home and in their colonies, in an exclusionist policy which was fatally inconsistent with their powers and resources, saw their commerce rapidly extinguished by the foreign interloper and their tropical possessions fall prey to marauding bands of buccaneers. The buccaneers were a manifestation of the low state of governmental organization. The Spanish had transferred to the islands and the mainland the administrative organization which in the sixteenth century they had developed beyond the standard of any other European nation, but they had not at any time furnished the machine with adequate power either to move, to defend or to control it. Indeed, the long peaceful acceptance of Spanish monopoly in America, hardly qualified by the casual exploits of Hawkins, Drake and Raleigh, had permitted an establishment to grow up that would be difficult to defend under modern conditions and that could not be defended in the seventeenth century even by the most advanced administration of the time.[53]

In the anarchy of the period the relatively high organization of Spanish America proved a handicap rather than a source of strength. The non-possessing powers, France, England and Holland, less able to control their agents or their subjects at such distances, were obliged, in spite of substantial considerations to the contrary, to adapt their policy to the demands of the remote and unmanageable colonists and to insist repeatedly, in face of plain terms, that treaties which they had signed did not have any validity "beyond the line." The settlement of the Windward and Leeward Islands by the English, French and Dutch, and the conquest of Jamaica by the English (1655) gave a new impulse to contraband trade. Jamaica became an important center. The buccaneers down to 1680 claimed a priority for their labor-saving methods of exploiting Spanish wealth. The planters demanded slaves of the Royal African Company and a ready channel for their own products to the Spanish ports. On the other hand, the English government, when Spain conceded recognition of its possessions (1670), had agreed to permit the "asiento" ships to be supplied with slaves from the Royal African Company. The market for

---

[53] C. H. Haring, *Trade and Navigation between Spain and the Indies* (Cambridge, 1918), 249–57.

slaves grew so large that it required both the company and the interlopers to supply it. The English government made the trade free in law as it was in fact. Although the picturesquely brutal achievements of Sir Henry Morgan at Porto Bello (1670) and at Panama (1671) were left unpunished, the English did begin to repress buccaneering.[54]

The Spanish, unwisely, did not co-operate. Instead, they resorted to retaliation upon the settlements and drove many of the islanders to join the pirates in the Carolinas and Bahamas. A characteristic venture of such a group was the startlingly successful attack on Vera Cruz in 1683. It was led by two Dutchmen, Van Horn and Laurens de Graff. Of the other six captains, three were Dutch, one French and two English. As restrictions grew more effective, the pirates turned in great numbers to the North American colonies, where they concealed themselves in the shoal waters and inlets of the Carolinas and swaggered in the streets of Boston, New York and Philadelphia. There they continued to be welcomed long after they had ceased to have any official protection. "Our laws against privateers," wrote Sir Thomas Modyford, "neither discourage or lessen them while they have such retreats as New England and the other colonies." [55]

For the Spaniards the buccaneers were a terrible scourge. Between the years 1655 and 1671 alone the corsairs sacked eighteen cities, four towns and more than thirty-five villages—Panama once, Cumanagote twice, Maracaibo and Gibraltar twice, Rio de la Hasha five times, Santa Marta three times, Tolu eight times, Porto Bello once, Chagre twice, Santa Catalina twice, Granada in Nicaragua twice, Campeche three times, Saint Jago de Cuba, once, and other towns and villages in Cuba and Hispaniola for thirty leagues inland innumerable times. In 1685 the marquis de Barinas estimated the losses of the Spanish at the hands of buccaneers since 1665 at sixty million crowns. The cost to the English was correspondingly great in another form. Between 1668 and 1671 it was estimated that buccaneering expeditions had absorbed 2,600 men from Jamaica. In 1684 Sir Thomas Lynch wrote, "All servants that can, run away and turn pirates." [56] The usefulness of Jamaica as a base from which to compete with the French and the Dutch in the trade with the Spanish colonies was lost. Even directly, in view of the effectively inter-

[54] C. Nettels, "England and the Spanish American Trade, 1680–1715," *Journal of Modern History*, III (1931), 1–32.

[55] *Calendar of State Papers, America and the West Indies, 1684–5*, No. 1425; reference from E. D. Collins, *op. cit.*, I, 152.

[56] *Ibid.*

national and non-Spanish character of the cargoes that moved between Porto Bello and Vera Cruz and Cadiz and Seville, the capture of a galleon or the wrecking of a city on the Main meant loss to the English, French and Dutch merchants.[57]

French and English colonies, still comparatively unproductive, had grown up in North America. In the course of the early seventeenth century the French had established substantial settlements at Quebec and Montreal. The French advance, like the Spanish, was carried on with a considerable apparatus of government and with the useful and effective missionary organizations of the church. The Jesuits had become the leading element among the missionaries, but they worked in close harmony with the Society for Foreign Missions and with the Sulpicians. Between 1607 and 1660 the missionaries and the *coureurs de bois* (fur traders) had pushed their way to the head of the Great Lakes. Ontario and Erie, however, were but slightly known, as the Ottawa route to Lake Nipissing and Lake Huron was first developed.

The government under Richelieu and Mazarin had made various unsuccessful attempts to organize companies to carry the burden of colonial enterprise. They had all failed for one reason and another. When Colbert came to power, the currently existing Company of New France was ready to surrender its nominal powers. The West Indies Company was to combine the monopoly of all the trade of New France with the monopoly of the African slave trade and the trade with the mainland of South America from La Plata to the Amazon. In Canada an intendant, Talon, injected considerable vigor into the administration, and in spite of constant quarrels with Frontenac, the royal governor, and Laval, the bishop of Quebec, built up trade with the West Indies, brought wives for the settlers from France and promoted the building of mills, breweries and tanneries. By 1671 the population, which was 3,418 in 1666, had risen to 6,000. To aid in defense and colonization, Talon established a seignorial system along the Richelieu and the St. Lawrence, the remnants of which are only now disappearing.[58]

From the St. Lawrence basin the missionaries and the *coureurs de bois* spread far and wide over the upper Great Lakes region and the Mississippi valley. In spite of the catastrophic attack of the Iroquois on the French missions among the Hurons (1649), the Jesuits extended their field of operations to the shores of Lake Superior and Lake Michigan. In

[57] C. H. Haring, *The Buccaneers in the West Indies*, 8.

[58] G. M. Wrong, *The Rise and Fall of New France* (2 vols., New York, 1928), I, 381–417.

1665 Allouez established a mission at the western end of Lake Superior. In 1673 Joliet, a fur trader, and Father Marquette penetrated to the Mississippi and explored it to the mouth of the Arkansas. In 1682 in a brilliantly organized and well-executed expedition, the Chevalier de La Salle and his lieutenant, Tonti, an Italian, reached the delta of the great river, while another part of the expedition explored northward from Illinois, reaching Duluth. The attempt of La Salle in succeeding years to establish a colony on the Gulf of Mexico ended in disaster, but Tonti established a solid base for later advance at the mouth of the Arkansas. By 1683 Le Sueur, a prominent fur trader, had established a post at Saint Anthony's Falls (Minneapolis) for trade with the Sioux, and within a few years had a protected rout to Lake Superior. Anonymous French traders made their way up the Tennessee and the Cumberland to the Cherokees and even across the mountains into South Carolina. The later development of the control of the mouth of the Mississippi by the establishment of Biloxi in 1699 and New Orleans in 1718 assured the French an easy predominance among the southwestern Indians.[59]

On the Atlantic seaboard of North America Englishmen had established themselves along the coasts of New England and the shores of Chesapeake Bay. Boston was already the metropolitan center of a group of settlements scattered from the Connecticut River to the Penobscot. Their economy was basically a sustenance economy, but a small fur trade with the Indians and fishing and lumber industries had begun, and a substantial shipbuilding industry served as a basis for an expanding commerce with England and the developing West Indies. Massachusetts already had more good ships than Scotland and Ireland combined. In 1700, 350 Bostonians had money invested in shipping. Ownership was widely distributed in the forms of shares, which obviated the need of insurance. Many of the ships were sold with their cargoes in foreign ports.[60] An offshoot of the Massachusetts Bay Colony had been established in the form of several independent towns along the Connecticut River. Along the shores of the Chesapeake and especially along the estuaries reaching well inland, a wholly different economy had developed on the basis of an export crop, tobacco, which involved dependence on an imported labor supply in the form of Negro slaves from Africa and imported food supply from the Bahamas and the northern colonies.

The English settlers brought to their new homes a cultural apparatus on the whole slighter than had the Spanish or even the French colonists.

[59] *Ibid.*, chs. 18, 20.
[60] C. Nettels, *Money Supply in the American Colonies*, 69, 102, 106–7.

Neither government nor church functioned effectively, as did the Spanish and French government and church. The movement to the New World was essentially an escape from controls and was carried out by groups which, however highly they themselves valued their differentiation from the dominant elements in English and other societies, lacked the positive support and the positive orientation of an imperial purpose. In general they were concerned with the saving of their own souls and not of the souls of others. They did not seek to convert the Indians or to acquire them as subjects for the king, but rather to eliminate them as obstacles to their own pursuit of profit and possessions. In the pursuit of individual advantage they maximized the difficulties, already large, that were implicit in the low stage of English administrative organization, so that the best intentions of the crown (like the worst) were readily defeated.

The dealings of the New Englanders with the Indians were at first not unfriendly. The settlers on the Connecticut, however, got involved in a war with the Pequots (1637) which promptly set the pattern. The tribe was exterminated. John Eliot and the Mayhews made an earnest and partially successful effort to Christianize the Indians, but the Indians began to suspect, not without reason, that conversion meant subjection to the white man. On the other hand, the decline of the fur trade led the New Englanders to regard the Indians as useless. When disorder in Rhode Island led to the death of a settler, Massachusetts, Plymouth and Connecticut joined forces and attacked not only the Wampanoags, who were suspected of the disturbance, but also the Narragansetts, who were suspected of an intention to join the Wampanoags. This was known as "King Philip's War." By August, 1676, the process of extermination had broken the power of the tribes and cleared the way for the further advancement of the frontier.

In Virginia the closer relation of the colony to the royal government made it possible for the crown and the governor to maintain a more scrupulous standard of dealing with the Indians. When the native tribes, reinforced by Susquehannas, retaliated upon squatters who had disregarded the bounds set for settlement by whites, the planters were, of course, outraged and demanded military action against them. When Governor Berkeley refused even to allow a group of willing volunteers under Nathaniel Bacon to act, they rebelled. They succeeded in driving Berkeley to the Eastern Shore, but when he had been reinforced by troops from England, the rebellion collapsed. Bacon had died, but in spite of a royal pardon for the rebels, Berkeley had many of them hung—as Charles

II remarked, more than had been executed for the death of his father.[61]

The Second Dutch War, unfortunate for England in its European aspects, enabled the English to seize the Dutch colony of New Amsterdam, which had become a substantial settlement of ten thousand. The colony was granted as an appanage to the duke of York, who regranted the region between the Hudson and the Delaware to two of his supporters, George Carteret and Lord Berkeley. New York, as it came to be called, remained Dutch and cosmopolitan in its make-up. The Jerseys—East and West—were rapidly settled with a conglomerate population. In West Jersey, which passed to Penn by purchase, the Quaker settlers pursued a very humane policy toward the Indians and escaped the usual round of Indian troubles.

Meanwhile William Penn, the most prominent English Quaker, as heir of Admiral George Penn, secured from Charles II, in payment of a debt owed his father, a grant of the lands that came to be known by his name. As a result of an industrious publicity policy on Penn's part, the solid attractiveness of the land, and the religious freedom which Quaker auspices assured, Pennsylvania attracted a diverse population. In addition to Quakers from England and Wales, German Mennonites, French Huguenots, Scotch Presbyterians, Irish from Ulster and Swedes made up a population of eight thousand by 1685, three years after the settlement began.

From Virginia, the founding of which had been regarded as a hazardous intrusion upon the Spanish territory of Axacan,[62] the obvious weakness of the Spanish regime invited a further extension of English settlement to the southward.[63] Eight proprietors, under the leadership of Anthony Ashley Cooper, later earl of Shaftesbury, were granted a charter to promote the settlement of the region, to which they gave the name Carolina (now North and South Carolina) under a half-feudal scheme of government devised by John Locke. The actual settlement, however, was made under circumstances that bore little relation to Locke's project. From Virginia a group of settlers, largely Quakers, independently established themselves around Albemarle Sound and by 1682 had reached the respectable number of 2,500. This colony was essentially an extension of the Virginia tobacco economy. Far to the south, after several false starts, a number of settlers from England and from Barbados established another settlement at the junction of the Ashley and Cooper rivers, the beginning

[61] T. J. Wertenbaker, *Torchbearer of the Revolution; the Story of Bacon's Rebellion and its Leader* (Princeton, 1940), 74–84.

[62] H. E. Bolton and T. H. Marshall, *op. cit.*, 117.

[63] Cf. above, p. 249.

of Charleston. One of the principal elements in the population was a group of Huguenot emigrants ranging from capitalists to indentured servants. The movement continued well into the eighteenth century and contributed valuable elements of strength to the new colony.[64] Combined with the Bahamas in 1670, Carolina served as a base for aggression against Spanish settlements on the Florida coast and against the Spanish monopoly of trade with the Creeks of western Georgia and Alabama. It also became a base for the pirates and buccaneers who were being expelled from the islands.

In 1670 the Hudson's Bay Company was organized. Two outlawed French traders and a British captain made their way to Hudson Bay and, on the basis of their information, organized a stock company and founded a fort on Rupert's River. From that center they developed a large and extremely profitable trade that aroused the aggressive competition of the French traders from the St. Lawrence.[65] It was only after our period that the Hudson's Bay Company began the expansion into the interior that carried it to the Pacific coast and made it for so long the principal form of European action in the north and far west of the continent.

In the Far East the Europeans stood in a wholly different relationship to the ancient cultures which they found there. Social patterns, power organizations and production systems were fully developed and, except in military efficiency, superior in general to their European counterparts. The Portuguese had early destroyed the Arab naval power in the Indian Ocean and the Bay of Bengal and, in turn, had been themselves eliminated by the Dutch.[66] The latter had established themselves as the ruling power in the Spice Islands and in Ceylon, and held at Cape Town the only proper refitting station between Europe and India. A second war with Portugal gave the Dutch exclusive control of the Ceylon coast and the ports of southern India. Ceylon became the Dutch East India Company's "cinnamon garden" and Malabar supplied the cloth which was one of the principal materials of trade in the Malay Archipelago. The Dutch monopoly in the Spice Islands was completed by the conquest of Macassar on Celebes and the extinction of the Portuguese, French and English factories there.

On the other hand Formosa, where the Dutch had built up a Christian

---

[64] A. H. Hirsch, *The Huguenots of South Carolina* (Durham, N.C., 1928), 25.

[65] G. B. Tyrrell, "Documents Relating to the Early History of Hudson Bay," Champlain Society *Publications*, 18 (1931), 419.

[66] A. Hyma, *The Dutch in the Far East* (Ann Arbor, 1942).

community of some thousands, was lost to Chinese refugees from the Manchus under the leadership of Koxinga (1661). In spite of this loss, the empire of the Dutch East India Company flourished. Between 1650 and 1680 all the major Indonesian states disintegrated.[67] The Dutch combined with the lesser princes to exploit the subject populations. The company secured the exclusive right to buy at customary prices; an additional small tax took care of the princes.[68] Under an able governor general, John Maetsuijcker (1653–1678), an industrious bureaucracy, wholly responsive to him and the company, served to establish a broadly tolerant regime, notable for its thoroughgoing secularism, its legal system and its encouragement of some remarkable scientific work. Batavia, the seat of the company's government in the east, became a magnificent city of canals, broad avenues and tropical comfort. Like the other towns of Dutch foundation, New York, Pernambuco, Cape Town, it was thoroughly cosmopolitan. The wars and anarchic violence that disturbed the West Indies here had no counterpart.[69]

The Dutch East India Company soon learned to overcome the drain on the precious metal reserves of Europe. The vast international trade which went on among the Asiatic countries offered an opportunity to secure the same ascendency in this field as the Dutch enjoyed in the carrying trade in Europe. Batavia became the center of a great system that ranged far beyond Dutch military control—from Nagasaki in Japan to Ormuz and Isfahan in Persia. That such a system could be organized at all was due to the ability of the company to secure credit to the extent of ten million guilders. The profits of this trade came to exceed the profits from the areas of agricultural exploitation, where the Dutch monopoly had to be maintained by ships and troops. By 1685 the inter-Asiatic trade had not only earned large dividends for the company, but had also made possible the accumulation of a reserve fund in the Indies of some twenty million guilders.

The English had early undertaken to emulate the Dutch in the Far East, but had neither achieved the territorial solidity nor the commercial and financial importance of the Dutch. The English East India Company, founded in 1600, had prospered intermittently, but chiefly during its first decades, and on a purely commercial basis. In 1660 the company owned no territory in India, though as tenant it held a number of factories at Surat, at Madras, at Mazulipatam and three other places on the

[67] B. Van Vlekke, *Nusantara* (Cambridge, 1943), 149.
[68] Pierre Gonnaud, *La colonisation hollandaise à Java* (Paris, 1905), 328.
[69] A. Hyma, *op. cit.*

Coromandel coast, and at Balasore, Orissa and Hugli in the Ganges Delta. Somewhat similar establishments were maintained at Basora in the Persian Gulf, at Mokha on the Red Sea and at Bantam in Java.

The acquisition of Bombay and its transfer to the East India Company in 1668 imposed on the company the responsibility of governing. Disorder and rebellion forced its hand. The company became involved in war so serious that only its sea power enabled it to escape with its holdings intact and to obtain in addition Calcutta, destined to become the effective center of the company's empire in India.[70]

The French also tried to rival and even destroy the power of the Dutch in the Indies. The result fell far short of their hopes. The Company of the Indies, which Colbert founded (1664) with such large views, was never adequately financed even for its relatively small operations. After some decades of fitful life, it was absorbed by the more grandiose organization of John Law (1719). Diplomatic relations were established with the shah of Persia and with the grand mogul and even with the nawab of Calicut, who hated the Dutch. Attempts were made to found refitting establishments at Madagascar and at the Ile de Bourbon, but without success. However, François Martin (d. 1706), a great servant of the company, succeeded in establishing a firm foothold at Surat and created the city of Pondichéry: before his death Pondichéry had grown from nothing to a powerfully defended city of fifty thousand. In 1690 he created new French establishments at Chandernagor and Mazulipatam (1690). French missionaries paved the way for French commerce and political action beyond the Bay of Bengal. Bangkok was a possession of the French until they were driven out in 1689.[71]

[70] G. M. Clark, *The Later Stuarts*, 335–38.
[71] H. Blét, *Histoire de la colonisation française*, 177–80.

BIBLIOGRAPHY

Limitation of space permits only a select list of books. The plan has been to include all the important bibliographical instruments and the secondary works of importance in western European languages, with a certain relaxation of the standard for recent books and books in English. Accounting of the large body of source materials has not been undertaken at all. The books listed are classed in the order of the chapters.

BIBLIOGRAPHICAL AIDS

There is no bibliographical guide for the history of Europe as a whole. Of truly oecumenical scope, the *Guide to Historical Literature* (New York, 1931), edited by a committee of the American Historical Association, serves remarkably well to lead to the published sources, the basic general works and a large number of the special works in English. *The International Bibliography of the Historical Sciences,* 1927—— (Zürich and New York, 1930 ff.) presents annually the whole effort of the scholarly world in all fields of history. For the years 1878–1913 a similar function was performed by the *Jahresberichte der Geschichtswissenschaft* (Berlin, 1880–1916). More specialized bibliographies will be named in connection with the particular fields to which they refer.

GENERAL HISTORIES

The *Histoire générale du 4e siècle à nos jours,* edited by E. Lavisse and A. Rambaud (twelve volumes, Paris, 1893–1901), is ably edited, but now somewhat antiquated. *The Cambridge Modern History,* planned by Lord Acton, edited by Sir A. W. Ward, Sir G. W. Prothero and Stanley Leathes (fourteen volumes, Cambridge, Eng., and New York, 1902–1912), is less satisfactorily organized, but Volume V, *The Age of Louis XIV,* contains some valuable chapters. The worldwide scope of the papacy's concerns makes L. Pastor's *History of the Popes from the Close of the Middle Ages* (translated from the German under the editorship of T. Antrobus, thirty-four volumes, London, 1891–1941) peculiarly valuable. A. de Saint-Léger and P. Sagnac, *La prépondérance française: Louis XIV, 1661–1715* (*Peuples et civilisations,* edited by L. Halphen and P. Sagnac, Paris, 1935), is emphatically French, but substantially complete and equipped with excellent bibliographies. K. Kaser, *Geschichte Europas im Zeitalter des Absolutismus und der Vollendung des modernen Staatensystems* (Stuttgart, 1923), is intentionally popular in style. Volume VI of *Propyläen Weltegeschichte, Das Zeitalter des Absolutismus* by W. Goetz and others (Berlin, s.d.) lacks organization. Two English one-volume works, G. N. Clark, *The Seventeenth Century* (Oxford, 1929), and D. Ogg, *Europe in the Seventeenth Century* (London, 1925), both emphasize social and intellectual aspects.

THE INTELLECTUAL REVOLUTION

The best guide to the scholarly work of the past generation in the whole field of intellectual history is the series of "critical bibliographies" appearing each year in *Isis,* edited by G. Sarton, recently collected and published as *Horus: A Guide to the History of Science* (Waltham, Mass., 1952). A. Wolf, *A History of Science, Technology and Philosophy in the Sixteenth and Seventeenth Centuries* (New York, 1935) not only has good bibliographies but is a uniquely compendious history of the sciences.

The new scholarship is well portrayed in the single volume by J. H. Randall, *The Making of the Modern Mind* (revised edition, New York, 1940). Preserved Smith, *A History of Modern Culture,* Volume I, *The Great Renewal, 1543–1687* (New York, 1930), perpetuates some of the old myths and misconceptions. Older works, such as J. M. Robertson, *Short History of Free Thought, Ancient and Modern* (London, revised edition, 1936), are more concerned with controls than with the functions of thought itself.

In the field of philosophy proper, an important guide is E. Gilson, *Index Scholastico-Cartésien* (Paris, 1912). The general histories of philosophy are all of some use. Bertrand Russell, in his *History of Western Philosophy and Its Connection with Political and Social Circumstances from the Earliest Times to the Present Day* (New York, 1945), is brief but dynamic.

More specifically relevant to this period, of a vast literature, are E. Boutroux, *Les prédecesseurs de Leibniz: Bacon, Descartes, Hobbes, Spinoza, Malebranche, Locke et la philosophie de Leibniz* (Paris, 1929), and the somewhat more popular work of S. H. Mellone, *The Dawn of Modern Thought: Descartes, Spinoza, Leibniz* (London, 1930), which, like Cay von Brockdorff, *Descartes und die Fortbildung der kartesischen Lehre* (Berlin, 1923), portrays the influence of Descartes on his time. A good biography of Descartes is that of J. Chevalier (Paris, 1921). M. Leroy, *Descartes, le philosophe en masque* (two volumes, Paris, 1929), supports with a wealth of learning the thesis that Descartes was a *libertin.* H. A. Wolfson, *The Philosophy of Spinoza, Unfolding the Processes of His Reasoning* (two volumes, Cambridge, 1934), is one of the most exhaustive studies of any philosopher. R. McKeon, *The Philosophy of Spinoza* (New York, 1928), is a keen analysis. L. Brunschvicg's *Spinoza et ses contemporains* (Paris, 1923) is brief but pregnant.

The new problem of science in our time has produced some significant reexaminations of seventeenth-century beginnings. E. A. Burtt, *The Metaphysical*

Foundations of Modern Physical Science (London, 1932), somewhat criticized by E. W. Strong, *Procedures and Metaphysics* (Berkeley, 1936); A. N. Whitehead, *Science and the Modern World* (New York, 1948) and *Adventures of Ideas* (New York, 1933); and John Dewey, *The Quest for Certainty* (New York, 1929), each contribute valuable definitions to "what happened" in the seventeenth century. K. B. Collier, *Cosmogonies of our Fathers* (New York, 1934), is primarily descriptive rather than critical. J. B. Conant, *On Understanding Science: An Historical Approach* (New Haven, 1947), is the starting point of a movement likely to have great significance for history as well as for science. E. Whittaker, *From Euclid to Eddington: A study of Conceptions of the Physical World* (Cambridge, Eng., 1949), and A. d'Abro, *The Evolution of Scientific Thought from Newton to Einstein* (New York, 1950), are superior works of popularization. B. Ginzburg, *The Adventure of Science* (New York, 1930), has a particularly valuable formulation of the relations of Newtonianism and Cartesianism. H. Butterfield, *The Origins of Modern Science, 1300–1800* (London, 1949), minimizes the part of Aristotle and of the Renaissance. M. R. Cohen explodes "The Myth about Bacon and the Inductive Method" in *Scientific Monthly,* 23 (1926), 504–08.

General histories of science are now facing the problem of science as a social (rather than technical) fact. A. Wolf (cited above), W. C. Dampier-Whetman, *A History of Science and Its Relations with Philosophy and Religion* (New York, 1931), F. Dannemann, *Die Naturwissenschaften in ihrer Entwicklung und in ihrer Zusammenhängen* (two volumes, Leipzig, 1920–1923), and C. Singer, *A Short History of Science* (revised edition, New York, 1943), are more concerned with science than with society. R. H. Shryock, *The Development of Modern Science: An Interpretation of the Social and Scientific Factors Involved* (New York, 1947), represents the newer tendency. The small volume of H. T. Pledge, *Science since 1500* (London, 1940; reissue, New York, 1947), is full of significant ideas. *Science and Social Welfare* (New York, 1937) by G. N. Clark explicitly faces the social problem. It is in part an answer to the Marxist interpretation of B. Hessen, "The Social and Economic Roots of Newton's *Principia,*" in *Science at the Crossroads* (London, 1931).

Of national histories, R. T. T. Gunther, *Early Science at Oxford* (twelve volumes, Oxford, 1920 ff.), has a more than local import with its large documentation. C. S. Duncan, *The New Science and English Literature in the Classical Period* (Menasha, Wis., 1913), is a valuable if incomplete analysis. M. Caullery, *La science française depuis le XVII\e siècle* (Paris, 1933), brings out the conditions under which science developed. Dorothy Stimson, *The Gradual Acceptance of the Copernican Theory* (New York, 1917), still stands alone in this field.

The history of scientific organizations has been the subject of many books. Martha Ornstein, however, broke a new path with *The Role of Scientific Societies in the Seventeenth Century* (Chicago, 1928); Cay von Brockdorff,

Gelehrte Gesellschaften im XVII. Jahrhundert (Kiel, 1940), embodies the result of recent studies. C. Weld, *A History of the Royal Society with Memoirs of the Presidents* (two volumes, London, 1848), and H. Lyons, *The Royal Society, 1660–1940* (Cambridge, Eng., 1944), are organizational studies. Dorothy Stimson, *Scientists and Amateurs, a History of the Royal Society* (New York, 1948), is a good popular account. The early scientist is well studied in W. E. Houghton, "The English Virtuoso in the Seventeenth Century," *Journal of the History of Ideas* III (1942), 51–73, 190–219. The first history of the French Academy was J. B. Duhamel, *Regiae scientiarum academiae historia* (Paris, 1698). The "eulogies" of defunct members by Fontenelle, the permanent secretary, were published as *Histoire de l'Académie* (1666–1699) (two volumes, Paris, 1733). The antecedents of the Academy are the subject of G. Bigourdain, *Les premières sociétés savantes de Paris au XVIIᵉ siècle et les origines de l'Académie des Sciences* (Paris, 1919), and H. Brown, *Scientific Organizations in Seventeenth Century France 1620–1680* (Baltimore, 1934).

Of the many biographies of Newton, perhaps the best are those of L. T. More (New York, 1934) and J. W. N. Sullivan (New York, 1938); George J. Gray, *A Bibliography of the Works of Sir Isaac Newton* (second edition, Cambridge, 1907), is also of importance. L. T. More is also the author of the excellent *Life and Works of . . . Boyle* (London, 1944). J. F. Fulton has a *Bibliography of . . . Boyle* (Oxford, 1932; Addenda, 1934). F. J. Greenslet's early study, *Joseph Glanvill; A Study in English Thought and Letters of the Seventeenth Century* (New York, 1900), is still important, but hardly displaces the introductory essay of J. Owen in his edition of the *Scepsis scientifica* (London, 1885). The important introduction of C. H. Hull to his edition of the *Economic Writings of Sir William Petty* (two volumes, Cambridge, Eng., 1899) is the best account of Petty's achievement as economist.

The histories of particular sciences are too numerous to mention but, because of the central importance of physics, note must be taken of A. N. Whitehead, "The First Physical Synthesis," in F. S. Marvin, *Science and Civilization* (London, 1923), A. Einstein and L. Infeld, *The Evolution of Physics* (New York, 1938), and Sir James Jeans, *The Growth of Physical Science* (Cambridge, Eng., 1947); these gentlemen are much less certain, more tentative about what happened to physics in the seventeenth and the twentieth centuries than the historians! E. Nordenskiöld introduces some revolutionary ideas in *The History of Biology* (English translation, New York, 1928). The important advances in geographical knowledge are described in the densely compacted *History of Geographical Discovery in the Seventeenth and Eighteenth Centuries* (Cambridge, Eng., 1912) of E. Heawood. Lloyd A. Brown, *The Story of Maps* (Boston, 1949), is valuable for a brilliant account of the relevant activities of the Academy of Sciences. G. Atkinson, *Les relations de voyages du XVIIᵉ siècle et l'évolution des idées* (Paris, 1925), surveys the geographical literature, genuine and false, and its influence on the European mind. E. Roll, *A History of Economic Thought* (revised edition, New York, 1946), and E. A. Johnson, *Predecessors of Adam Smith* (New York, 1937), show the effect of quantitative thinking on economic thought.

THE BAROQUE

GENERAL

Although it does not develop the baroque as music and literature, one of the best general definitions of the concept is to be found in the article, "Arte barocco," in the *Enciclopedia italiana* by R. Papini and L. Serra. Probably the best definition of the baroque in English is provided by Gilbert Highet, *The Classical Tradition* (New York, 1949). Basic to the modern concept are A. Riegl, *Die Enstehung der Barockkunst in Rom* (Vienna, 1923), and H. Wölfflin, *Principles of Art History* (English translation, New York, 1932). W. Weisbach, *Der Barock als Kunst der Gegenreformation* (Berlin, 1921), is the best example of a point of view avoided in this work. O. Redlich, "Uber Kunst und Kultur des Barocks in Österreich," *Archiv für österreichische Geschichte,* 115 (1943), 331–79, is particularly valuable for its formulation of the social setting. Eleven pages of more than ordinary value in A. Weber, *Farewell to European History* (English translation, New Haven, 1948), connect and contrast Pascal and Rembrandt.

The general histories of art are too numerous and too easily accessible to be listed here. To understand what has happened to art concepts in the last half-century, it is worth while to examine any two good art manuals, say, S. Reinach, *Apollo* (Paris, 1904), and H. Gardner, *Art through the Ages* (New York, 1926), and note the contrast in the treatment of El Greco and Murillo.

Of the more specialized works, the most satisfactory are W. Weisbach, *Die Kunst des Barocks in Italien, Frankreich, Deutschland und Spanien* (*Propyläen Kunstgeschichte,* Berlin, 1924), and *Spanish Baroque Art* (English translation, Cambridge, Eng., 1941). In spite of incompleteness and inaccuracy, S. Sitwell, *Southern Baroque Art* (London, 1924), *German Baroque Art* (London, 1927) and *Spanish Baroque Art* (London, 1931), are worth using for their author's poetic insight. René Schneider, *L'art français: dix-septième siècle* (Paris, 1925), and H. Lemonnier, *L'art français au temps de Louis XIV* (Paris, 1913), are both encyclopedic in range and objective.

ARCHITECTURE

Still showing some romanticist prudery, M. S. Briggs, *Baroque Architecture* (London, 1913), is nevertheless a competent all-over survey. A. E. Brinkmann, *Baukunst des 17. und 18. Jahrhunderts in den romanischen Ländern* (Berlin, 1930), more specialized, is somewhat fuller and better illustrated. The biographies of Bernini by S. Franchetti (Milan, 1900) and Marcel Reymond (Paris, 1910) and of Borromini by Ed. Hempel (Vienna, 1924) are useful because of the magisterial position of their subjects. L. Hautecour, *Histoire de l'architecture classique en France: II, Le règne de Louis XIV* (one volume in two, Paris, 1948), is dense with detail. M. S. Noel, *Arquitectura virreinal* (Buenos Aires, 1934), is representative of a lively school of writing on Spanish colonial and Mayan art. H. Inigo Triggs, *Garden Craft in Europe* (London, 1913), provides a good account of this important type of baroque architecture. P. de Nolhac is encyclopedic for *Les jardins de Versailles* (Paris, 1913); André Lenôtre, who created them, is worthily included in the *Collection des grands artistes* (J. J. Guiffrey, Paris, n.d.). A very important special phase of baroque is well treated and well illustrated in Helène Leclerc, *Les origines italiennes de l'architecture théatrale moderne* (Paris, 1946).

MUSIC

P. H. Lang, *Music and Western Civilization* (New York, 1941), H. Leichentritt, *Music, History and Ideas* (Cambridge, Mass., 1938), and M. F. Bukofzer, *Music in the Baroque Era* (New York, 1947), are all distinguished efforts to integrate the development of music with that of society and the other arts. Bukofzer provides an especially valuable bibliography. A. W. Ambros and H. Leichentritt, *Geschichte der Musik* (five volumes, Leipzig, 1911), is a valuable general history. C. H. H. Parry, *The Music of the Seventeenth Century*, the second edition of which appears as Volume III of the *Oxford History of Music* (New York, 1902), shows a complete lack of understanding of the musical developments of the period, but is useful as a catalogue. Two good manuals are W. S. Pratt, *History of Music* (New York, 1935), and Paul Landormy, *A History of Music* (English translation, New York, 1934). Romain Rolland, *Some Musicians of Former Days* (English translation, New York, 1915), is particularly good for the seventeenth century. A. della Corte analyzes the relations of "Il barocco e la musica" in *Mélanges de musicologie offerts à M. Lionel de la Laurencie* (Paris, 1933). A. Pirro, *Descartes et la musique* (Paris, 1907), connects music with the advancing technology.

On opera, R. Rolland, *Les origines de l'opéra en Europe avant Lully et Scarlatti* (Paris, 1895), still stands as an understanding and suggestive general history, but L. de La Laurencie, *Les créateurs de l'opéra français* (Paris, 1921), embodies the results of much research in musicology of which he was a leading spirit. See also his *Lully* (Paris, 1911). Good shorter manuals are those by R. A. Streatfield, *The Opera* (fifth edition, London, 1925), and W. F. Apthorp, *The Opera, Past and Present* (New York, 1901). E. J. Dent, *Foundations of English Opera* (Cambridge, Eng., 1928), and J. A. Westrup, *Purcell* (London, 1937), tell the story of that brilliant episode. André Pirro supplements the general histories with excellent studies of *Schütz* (Paris, 1913) and *Dietrich Buxtehude* (Paris, 1913).

Music as an interest of individuals and groups is the specific subject of Liselotte Krüger, *Die hamburgische Musikorganisation im 17. Jahrhundert*

(Strassburg, 1933), and is reflected in many items in T. Gerold, *L'art du chant en France* (Strassburg, 1921). A. Babeau, *Les académies de musique de Troyes au XVII° et XVIII° siècles* (Troyes, 1803), George Becker, *La musique en Suisse* Geneva, 1874), E. M. Fallet, *La vie musicale au pays de Neuchâtel* (Strassburg, 1936), are particularly valuable for the record of new forms of association. Roger North, *Memoirs of Musick* (edited by E. F. Rimbault, London, 1846), F. Bridge, *Samuel Pepys, Lover of Musique* (London, 1903), H. B. Wheatley, *Samuel Pepys and the World He Lived in* (New York, 1880), and Anthony Wood's *Life and Times* (edited by A. Clark, five volumes, Oxford, 1891–1900), reflect the much less organized but similarly active musical life of English society. A cosmopolitan, Constantin Huygens, left a similar record of wider range in his correspondence, published as *Musique et musiciens au XVII° siècle* by W. J. A. Jonckbloet and J. P. N. Land (Leyden, 1882). The impact of technical advance on the older gilds is shown in E. van der Straeten, *La musique aux Pays-Bas avant le XIX° siècle* (eight volumes, Brussels, 1867–1888), Volumes I and II. C. Beaumont, *A Bibliography of Dancing* (London, 1929), is a slim book which lists only books in the British Museum. The same author's story of *The Ballet in Russia* (London, 1930) indicates that the Russians did not invent it. An important phase of music is the subject of F. Blume, *Die evangelische Kirchenmusik* (Potsdam, 1933). For the development of baroque instruments, such as the organ and the violin, the most convenient accounts are to be found in G. R. Hayes, *Musical Instruments and Their Music, 1500–1750* (three volumes, London, 1928), and W. H., A. F. and A. E. Hill, *The Violin Makers of the Guarneri Family—1626–1737* (London, 1931).

PAINTING AND SCULPTURE

Rome as capital of the painters' world is reflected in A. Bertolotti, *Artisti belgi et olandesi a Roma nei secoli XVI e XVII* (Florence, 1880), and his *Giunte ogli artisti belgi . . .* (Rome, 1885), as also in J. Alazard, *L'abbé Luigi Strozzi, correspondant artistique de Mazarin, de Colbert, de Louvois et de La Tulerie* (Paris, 1924). W. Drost, *Barockmalerei in den germanischen Ländern* (Potsdam, 1927), and N. Pevsner and O. Grantoff, *Barockmalerei in den romanischen Ländern* (Potsdam, 1928), give excellent encyclopedic coverage. An interesting contemporary survey is André Félibien, *Entrétiens sur la vie et les ouvrages des plus excellentes peintres* (Paris, 1679–1685). A. McComb, *The Baroque Painters of Italy* (Cambridge, Mass., 1934), is a good account of the metropolitan influence of this group. Max J. Friedländer, *Die niederländischen Maler des 17. Jahrhunderts* (*Propyläen Kunstgeschichte* XII, Berlin, 1923), is distinguished in content and format. H. W. Van Loon, *R.v.R.: The Life of Rembrandt van Rijn* (New York, 1930, reissue, 1939), is fiction based on much learning and great comprehension. F. Schmidt-Degener, *Rembrandt und der holländische Barock* (Leipzig, 1928), connects the historical function of Vondel and Rembrandt. N. S. Trivas, *The Paintings of Franz Hals* (New York, 1941), is valuable principally for the complete reproduction of the known paintings. E. Plietzsch, *Vermeer van Delft* (Munich, 1939), also has many reproductions. W. Weisbach, *Französische Malerei des XVII Jahrhunderts im Rahmen von Kultur und Gesellschaft* (Berlin, 1932), justifies the program indicated in the title. A. Félibien, the contemporary critic, left an interesting *Description des peintures faits pour le Roi* (Paris, 1671). J. Jouin, *Le Brun et les arts sous Louis XIV* (Paris, 1889), and A. Leclerc, "Ch. Le Brun, son œuvre et son influence sur les arts au XVIIe siècle," in *Versailles illustré* (Paris, 1902, 1903), portray Le Brun as administrator and promoter rather than as painter. For sculpture, A. E. Brinckmann, *Barockskulptur . . . seit Michelangelo bis zum 18. Jahrhundert* (Berlin, 1919), is encyclopedic and intelligent.

LITERATURE

Still of major value as a comprehensive and learned integration of style values is G. E. B. Saintsbury, *A History of Criticism and Literary Taste in Europe from the Earliest Texts to the Present Day* (three volumes, Edinburgh and London, 1900–1904). L. Magnus, *A History of European Literature* (New York, 1934), is slight but significant as an essay in intellectual organization. P. van Tieghem, *Outline of the Literary History of Europe since the Renaissance* (English translation, New York, 1930), is statistical and conventional. G. Highet's *The Classical Tradition*, cited above, is superior to both. M. W. Croll, "The Baroque Style in Prose" (*Studies . . . in honor of Frederick Klaeber*, Minneapolis, 1939), and E. Ermatinger, *Barock und Rokoko in der deutschen Dichtung* (second edition, Leipzig, 1928), are important essays in the adaptation of the general terminology of art to literature. B. Willey, *The Seventeenth Century Background* (London, 1934), relates the whole intellectual and artistic pattern to the literature. R. F. Jones, "Science and English Prose Style in the Third Quarter of the Seventeenth Century," *Proceedings of the Modern Language Association,* 45 (1930), 977–1009, somewhat narrowly interprets the influence of the Royal Society's literary ideal. D. McCarthy, "The European Tradition in Literature from 1600 Onwards" in E. Eyre, *European Civilization,* VI, is a thoughtful essay in the same general sense.

The histories of literature are, of course, largely national in scope. It would be superfluous to list the distinguished histories of French literature. Among special studies, C. Sainte-Beuve, *Causeries de lundi* (15 vols., Paris, 1852–1862), and E. Faguet's *Dix-septième siècle: études littéraires* (twenty-eighth edition, Paris, 1903), contain many illuminating essays. A. Tilley, *From Montaigne to Molière* (London, 1908), is good for background. F. Brunot, *Histoire de la langue française des origines à 1900* (ten volumes, Paris, 1905–1943), is a mine of social data, on the seventeenth century especially valuable for the spread of the language and its contest with Latin. F. Masson, *L'académie française, 1629–*

1793 (Paris, 1912), is "lodge history," but useful in other ways. G. Ascoli, *La Grande Brétagne devant l'opinion française au XVIIe siècle* (two volumes, Paris, 1930), and A. F. B. Clark, *Boileau and the French Classical Critics in England* (Paris, 1925), are valuable studies of the interaction of the two segments of the culture. *The Cambridge History of English Literature* (fifteen volumes, Cambridge, Eng., 1919–1930), of which Volume 8 is devoted to *The Age of Dryden,* gathers together the results of recent scholarship in essays of uneven quality and in generally valuable bibliographies. Two recent special studies of value are J. G. Wilson, *Court Wits of the Restoration* (Princeton, 1948), and Montague Summers, *A Bibliography of the Restoration Drama* (London, 1950). There are many biographies of the principal literary characters of the period, but as yet no adequate account of John Bunyan and his masterpiece; but see J. Brown, *John Bunyan* (revised by F. M. Harrison, London, 1928). F. H. T. Vogt and M. Koch, *Geschichte der deutschen Literatur* (fifth edition, three volumes, Leipzig, 1934–1938), Volume 1, is very important for the striking development of literary societies (*Sprachgesellschaften*) in this period. G. Ticknor, *History of Spanish Literature* (fifth edition, three volumes, Boston, 1882), still retains authority but is largely displaced by J. Fitzmaurice-Kelly, *New History of Spanish Literature* (London and New York, 1926), and his indispensable *Bibliographie de l'histoire de la littérature espagnole* (Paris, 1913).

POLITICS

IDEOLOGY

The most convenient comprehensive accounts of political thought in English are W. A. Dunning, *A History of Political Theories from Luther to Montesquieu* (New York, 1903), C. E. Vaughan, *Studies in the History of Political Philosophy before and after Rousseau* (two volumes, Manchester, 1925) and, at a lower level, F. J. C. Hearnshaw (editor), *Social and Political Ideas of Some Great Thinkers of the 16th and 17th Centuries* (London, 1926). Somewhat more special and of great significance is O. Gierke, *Natural Law and the Theory of Society* (English translation, E. Barker, two volumes, Cambridge, Eng., 1934). F. Watkins, *The Political Tradition of the West* (Cambridge, Mass., 1948), usefully generalizes the political heritage. G. P. Gooch (with H. J. Laski), *Political Thought from Bacon to Halifax* (Cambridge, Eng., 1927), and H. Sée, *Les idées politiques en France au XVIIe siècle* (Paris, 1923), are rather pedestrian. H. Michel, *L'idée de l'état* (Paris, 1906), and especially F. Meinecke, *Die Idee der Staatsräson* (third edition, Munich, 1932), are important historians' comments on the ethical problem. The best books on Hobbes are F. Tönnies, *Thomas Hobbes, Leben und Lehre* (Stuttgart, 1925), and G. E. C. Catlin, *Thomas Hobbes as Philosopher, Publicist and Man of Letters* (Oxford, 1922). P. Laslett's edition of Sir R. Filmer, *Patriarcha, and other Political Works* (Oxford, 1949), goes far in defense of

Filmer against Locke. J. Toland's edition of James Harrington, *Oceana . . . and His Other Works with an Account of his Life Prefixed* (1737) is still the main treatment of the life of Harrington, but Miss A. E. Levett has a good article in the *Encyclopedia of the Social Sciences*. F. Bezold, E. Gothein and R. Koser made an unsuccessful attempt to formulate the history of *Staat und Gesellschaft der neueren Zeit* (Berlin, 1908). Ernest Barker, *The Development of Public Services in Western Europe* (London, 1944), is a too limited attempt to develop the theme of function.

MERCANTILISM

The general histories of economic thought, such as C. Gide and C. Rist, *History of Economic Doctrines* (English translation, London, 1915), and R. Gonnard, *Histoire des doctrines économiques* (three volumes, Paris, 1930), make little direct contribution to the history of mercantilism. G. F. von Schmoller, *The Mercantile System and Its Historical Significance* (English translation, W. J. Ashley, New York and London, 1896), is basic to all modern studies. E. P. Heckscher, *Mercantilism* (English translation, London, 1935), labors to make a system of what was unsystematic. P. W. Buck, *The Politics of Mercantilism* (New York, 1942), is less encyclopedic, but more acute in its analysis. J. Morini-Comby, *Mercantilisme et protectionnisme* (Paris, 1930), and L. Sommer, *Die österreichischen Kameralisten in dogmengeschichtlicher Darstellung* (two volumes, Vienna, 1920, 1925), portray mercantilism as a phase of absolutism. C. W. Cole, *French Mercantilist Doctrines before Colbert* (New York, 1931), *Colbert and a Century of French Mercantilism* (two volumes, New York, 1939), and *French Mercantilism 1683-1700* (New York, 1943) are encyclopedic collections without much synthesis. Paul Harsin, *Les doctrines monétaires en France aux XVIe et XVIIe siècles* (Paris, 1928), is primarily ideological. B. Suivaranta, *The Theory of the Balance of Trade in England: A Study in Mercantilism* (Helsingfors, 1923), is a thorough study from a limited point of view (good bibliography). In *The English Navigation Laws* (New York, 1939), L. A. Harper undertakes to demonstrate that the laws were beneficial to England. E. S. Furniss, *The Position of the Laborer in a System of Nationalism* (Boston, 1920), unfortunately remains alone in its field.

FRANCE

French history is provided with an extensive but unorganized set of bibliographical aids. E. Bourgeois and L. André, *Les sources de l'histoire de France, XVIIe siècle* (eight volumes, Paris, 1913–1935), is confined to secondary materials contemporary with the period and to printed collections of documents. E. Saulnier and A. Martin, *Bibliographie des travaux publiés de 1866 à 1897 sur l'histoire de France de 1500 à 1789,* of which five fascicules (out of eight) have been published, fills about the last gap. It was supplemented in advance for the years 1898 to 1913 by the *Répertoire méthodique de l'histoire moderne et contemporaine de la France* edited by G. Brière and P. Caron (Paris, 1899–1914). The *Bibliographie critique des principaux travaux parus sur l'histoire de 1600 à 1914* by the editors of *La révue d'histoire moderne* (Paris, 1927–1937) was originally intended to cover the field, but was soon restricted to French history by French authors. For the years 1920–1931, the *Répertoire bibliographique de l'histoire de France,* edited by P. Caron and H. Stein (Paris, 1923–1938), carries on the function of the *Répertoire methodique* listed above.

French history still owes something to Leopold Ranke, *Französische Geschichte, vornehmlich im sechzehnten und siebzehnten Jahrhundert* (five volumes, Leipzig, 1868–1874). E. Lavisse, *Louis XIV de 1643–1685,* Tome VII, 1 and 2, of *Histoire de France des origines à la Révolution* (Paris, 1911), is unsurpassed. G. Hanotaux (editor), *Histoire de la nation française* (ten volumes, Paris, 1920–1929), is divided topically: L. Madelin, *Histoire politique, 1515–1804,* falls below the best Madelin; G. Goyau, *Histoire religieuse,* admirably summarizes recent scholarship in that field; F. Réboul, *Histoire militaire et navale des croisades à la Révolution,* is good for military history but not for naval history; R. Pinon, *Histoire diplomatique,* is more than competent for the Louis XIV period. Two recent smaller works are clever summaries: A. Bailly, *La Règne de Louis XIV* (Paris, 1946), and M. Ashley, *Louis XIV and the Greatness of France* (London, 1946).

On the problem of absolutism in France, J. E. King, *Science and Rationalism in the Government of Louis XIV, 1661–1683* (Johns Hopkins *Studies in History and Political Science,* LXVI, No. 2, 1949), breaks new ground and is certainly the most important recent contribution to the history of power in society. G. Pagès, *La monarchie administrative en France sous Louis XIV et sous Louis XV* (Paris, 1934), is very general but suggestive. Basic to the work of the moderns are the old books of P. Clément, *Le gouvernement de Louis XIV . . . de 1683 à 1689* (Paris, 1848), *La police sous Louis XIV* (Paris, 1866), *Histoire de Colbert et son administration* (two volumes, third edition, Paris, 1892). P. Boissonade, *Colbert, le triomphe de l'étatisme . . . 1661–1683* (Paris, 1932), is oriented to the economic policy, as is also his study (with P. Charliat) of *Colbert et la compagnie du commerce du Nord, 1661–1789* (Paris, 1930). The legal and constitutional problems are magisterially handled in E. Glasson's general *Histoire du droit et des institutions de la France* (eight volumes, Paris, 1887–1903) and more particularly in *Le Parlement de Paris, son rôle politique depuis Charles VII jusqu'à la Révolution* (2 volumes, Paris, 1900). E. Fléchier, *Mémoires sur les grands jours d'Auvergne* (edited by P. A. Chéruel, Paris, 1856; English translation, W. W. Comfort, Philadelphia, 1937), illustrates concretely the application of royal justice.

On the development of the armed forces, C. Rousset, *Histoire de Louvois et de son administration politique et militaire depuis la paix de Nimègue* (four volumes, Paris, 1862–1863), is still important but has been valuably supplemented by L. André, *Michel Le Tellier et Louvois* (Paris, 1943). The brief essay of H. Guerlac, "Vauban: The Impact of Science on War," in *Makers of Modern Strategy,* edited by E. M. Earle (Princeton, 1944), is of great importance. See also C. Lecomte, *Les ingénieurs militaires en France sous le règne de Louis XIV* (Paris, 1904). Ch. de La Roncière, *Histoire de la marine française* (six volumes, Paris, 1899–1932), is a classic, but has not entirely displaced G. Lacour-Gayet, *La marine militaire sous les règnes de Louis XIII· et Louis XIV* (Tome I, Paris, 1911). J. Tramond, *Manuel d'histoire maritime de la France des origines à 1815* (Paris, 1927), is an effective summary. A. Anthiaume, *Évolution et enseignement de la science nautique en France* (two volumes, Paris, 1920), is an important contribution.

The establishment of central control over the provinces is best illustrated in A. Rébillon, *Les états de Bretagne de 1661 à 1789* (Paris, 1932), but A. Thomas, *Une province sous Louis XIV . . . Bourgogne de 1661–1715* (Paris, 1844), is also important. M. du Roux, *Louis XIV et les provinces conquises* (Paris, 1938), provides a useful form for the local history of central government. Louis Batiffol, "Les difficultés de Louis XIV avec les Alsatiens" (*Revue de Paris,* 37 (1930), 564–93, 843–71), brings out the combination of compulsion and tact used by the government.

On the government and the church, V. Martin, *Le gallicanisme et le clergé de France* (Paris, 1929), is a thorough and illuminating study. J. T. Loyson, *L'Assemblée du Clergé de France de 1682* (Paris, 1870), is still useful. T. Giraud, *Bossuet* (Paris, 1930), and M. Langlois, *Madame de Maintenon* (Paris, 1932), reflect the important activities of these two figures in this situation. The Company of the Holy Sacrament, that interesting symptom of religious feeling, is the subject of R. Allier, *La cabale des dévots, 1627–1666* (Paris, 1902), not a very scholarly work, and of the articles of A. Rébelliau, "Un épisode de l'histoire religieuse du XVIIᵉ siècle" (*Revue des deux mondes,* July 1, August 1, September 1, 1903, and August 15, October 15, November 1, 1909). R. P. Bessières, *Deux grands méconnus: Gaston de Renty et Henry Buch* (Paris, 1931), is valuable for its account of two truly religious souls who used the Company as an instrument of social action. On the revocation of the Edict of Nantes, numerous articles and current bibliographies are to be found in the *Bulletin de la société de l'histoire du protestantisme français* (1853 ff.). H. M. Baird, *The Huguenots and the Revocation of the Edict of Nantes* (two volumes, New York, 1895), is still the definitive work. F. Puaux and A. Sabatier, *Étude sur la révocation de l'édit de Nantes* (Paris, 1886), is less important. A. Rébelliau, *Bossuet, historien du protestantisme* (Paris, 1891), acutely defines the intellectual setting of the problem. R. Gachon, *Quelques préliminaires de la révocation . . . en Languedoc* (Toulouse, 1890), is a valuable local study. E. G. Leonard, "Les protestants français au XVIIIᵉ siècle" (*Annales d'histoire sociale,* II (1940), 5–20) is important both for the revocation and for the subsequent evolution of the Huguenot organization in France.

ENGLAND

The *Bibliography of British History: Stuart Period, 1603–1704,* edited by
G. Davies (Oxford, 1928), is poorly done. C. L. Grose, *A Select Bibliography
of British History, 1660–1760* (Chicago, 1939), is more satisfactory. It is well
supplemented by the annual *Writings on British History* (London, 1937 ff.)
compiled by A. T. Milne. E. R. Adair, *The Sources for the History of the
Council in the Sixteenth and Seventeenth Centuries* (New York, 1934), is a
thorough job which has particular relevance for this work. Like French
history, English history still owes something to L. Ranke, *History of England
Especially in the Sixteenth and Seventeenth Centuries* (English translation, 6
volumes, Oxford, 1875). The observation of three contemporaries has done
more than most to form the picture for later generations: Samuel Pepys, *Diary*
(best edition, H. B. Wheatly, nine volumes, London, 1893–1899), John Evelyn,
Diary . . . with introduction and notes by Austin Dobson (three volumes,
London, 1906), and Gilbert Burnet, *History of My Own Times* (edited by
O. Airy, two volumes, to 1685, Oxford, 1897). Of recent works, G. M. Trevelyan, *England under the Stuarts* (London, New York, 1904), is a brilliantly
written account, very Whiggish in politics but valuable for its rich social
sense. The latter aspect is beautifully supplemented by Volume II of his *Il-
lustrated English Social History* (London and New York, 1950). R. Lodge,
The Political History of England, 1660–1702 (London and New York, 1910),
is narrowly political but dense with data. Of more recent works, D. Ogg,
England in the Reign of Charles II (two volumes, Oxford, 1934), also rather
Whiggish, is notable for its utilization of the archives of Oxford, Cambridge,
Winchester and the Royal Society. G. N. Clark, *The Later Stuarts* (Oxford,
1934), emphasizes the social and intellectual atmosphere. One of the most
clarifying books on the problem of power organization is D. L. Keir, *The
Constitutional History of Modern Britain* (London, 1937). Keith Feiling, *A
History of the Tory Party* (Oxford, 1924), is even more important for this
period. E. L. Turner, *The Privy Council of England in the Seventeenth and
Eighteenth Centuries* (Baltimore, 1930), is more concerned with machinery
than with power as such. Administration and the local bearing of central
government is very slightly developed, but Florence M. G. Evans, *Principal
Secretary of State, a Survey of the Office from 1558 to 1680* (Manchester,
1923), is a good study in an area requiring extended research. Edward and
Annie Porritt, *The Unreformed House of Commons* (two volumes, Cambridge,
Eng., 1909), throws some light as well as serving greatly its own purpose.
Similarly J. W. Fortescue, *A History of the British Army* (thirteen volumes,
in twenty, London, 1899–1930), Volume 1 to 1713, and W. L. Clowes, *The
Royal Navy* (seven volumes, 1897–1903), are partly administrative. J. R.
Tanner, *Samuel Pepys and the Royal Navy* (Oxford, 1920), and his edition
of Pepys' *Naval Minutes* (1926) and his *Mr. Pepys* (London, 1925) are of
high value. Among other biographies, H. Craik, *The Life of Edward, Earl of*

Clarendon . . . (two volumes, London, 1911), is overeulogistic; Violet Barbour, *Henry Bennet, Earl of Arlington* . . . (Washington, 1914), is an acute political study; H. E. Woodbridge, *Sir William Temple: The Man and his Work* (New York, 1940), portrays a thoughtful man who did not "think through"; H. C. Foxcroft, *The Character of the Trimmer . . . the First Marquis of Halifax* (Cambridge, 1946), a politician whose reputation was wrecked in the strife of parties. The king himself is the subject of a very revisionary biography, A. Bryant, *King Charles II* (London, 1931), rather Tory, well documented. E. R. Turner, "Charles II's Part in Governing England" (*American Historical Review,* 34 (1928), 44–47), already showed him as a hard-working ruler; C. L. Grose, "Charles II of England" (*Ibid.,* 43 (1938) 553–41), defended the myth of the self-indulgent idler.

GERMANY

The *Quellenkunde der deutschen Geschichte* of F. C. Dahlmann and G. Waitz (ninth edition, H. Haering, Leipzig, 1931) is still the best of the national bibliographies. It is supplemented by the annual *Jahresberichte der deutschen Geschichte,* 1918 ff., edited by V. Loewe and others (Breslau, 1920 ff.).

The best general history of Germany in the last half of the seventeenth century is B. Erdmannsdörfer, *Deutsche Geschichte vom westphälischen Frieden bis zum Regierungsantritt Friedrichs des Grossen, 1648–1740* (two volumes, Berlin, 1892–1893). Karl Lamprecht, *Deutsche Geschichte zur jüngsten deutschen Vergangenheit* (two volumes, Berlin, 1905–1911), is lost in controversy over method. His influence persists in D. Schäfer, *Deutsche Geschichte* (ninth edition, two volumes, Jena, 1922), a general history with much social emphasis. Bruno Gebhardt, *Handbuch der deutschen Geschichte* (sixth edition, revised by A. Meister, three volumes, Berlin, 1922–1923), is a useful compendium with valuable bibliographies. E. F. Henderson, *A Short History of Germany* (two volumes, New York, 1902, revised edition, 1916), and G. Barraclough, *The Origins of Modern Germany* (Oxford, 1929), are useful summaries in English.

On the problem of the Empire, Paul Frischauer, *The Imperial Crown: The Story of the Rise and Fall of the Holy Roman and the Austrian Empires* (English translation, H. L. Farnell, London, 1939), is primarily biographical. One of the best books for understanding the complexities of Hapsburg politics of this period is A. F. G. Pribram, *Franz Paul, Freiherr von Lisola (1613–1674) und die Politik seiner Zeit* (Leipzig, 1894). H. F. Schwarz, *The Imperial Privy Council in the Seventeenth Century* (Cambridge, Mass., 1943), is a specifically constitutional study.

Guidance to the literature of Austrian history is well supplied by R. Charmatz, *Wegweiser durch die Literatur der österreichischen Geschichte* (Stuttgart, 1912), and K. and M. Uhlirz, *Handbuch der Geschichte Österreichs und seiner Nachbarländer Böhmen und Ungarn* (three volumes, in four parts, Graz, 1927–1941). For its period, Otto Brunner, "Ouvrages sur l'histoire moderne de l'Autriche, 1526–1918, parus de 1918 à 1929" (*Revue d'histoire moderne,* 5 (1930), 34–47, 131–42), is thorough. Of general histories, only the somewhat antiquated work of L. Léger, *History of Austria-Hungary* (English translation, Mrs. Birkbeck Hill, London, 1889), is available in English. Two important recent works are O. Redlich, *Geschichte Österreichs, 1648–1705* (Gotha, 1921), and H. Hantsch, *Die Entwicklung Österreichs-Ungarns zur Grossmacht* (Freiburg-i.-B., 1933).

Hungarian history is well provided with bibliographies in Magyar; the literature in western languages for the years 1861 to 1921 is covered by *Bibliographica Hungariae,* I: *Historia,* edited by R. Gragger for the Hungarian Institute of the University of Berlin (Berlin, 1923). The major general histories of Hungary are A. Szilagi (editor), *A Magyar Nemzet Története* (ten volumes, Budapest, 1895–1898), and B. Homan and J. Szefku, *Magyar Történet* (five volumes, Budapest, third edition, 1935–1936). E. Sayous, *Histoire générale des Hongrois* (two volumes, Paris, 1876), still has some value. C. M. Knatchbull-Hugessen, *The Political Evolution of the Hungarian Nation* (two volumes, London, 1908), is wholly partisan. P. Teleki, *The Evolution of Hungary and its place in European History,* is valuable for its geography and ethnography—and its considerable bibliography. F. Eckhardt, *A Short History of the Hungarian People* (London, 1931; in French, Paris, 1938), is an able, concise statement of the problems, well documented. D. G. Kosáry, *A History of Hungary* (Cleveland, 1941), is defensive propaganda, but still a useful compendium. The absolutism in Hungary is described by T. Mayer, *Verwaltungsreform in Ungarn nach der Türkenzeit* (Vienna, 1911). On Bohemia, E. Denis, *La Bohème depuis la Montagne-Blanche* (two volumes, Paris, 1903), is pro-Bohemian but scientific. S. H. Thomson, *Czecho-Slovakia in European History* (New York, 1943), is an excellent brief summary.

Of general works on Brandenburg-Prussia, L. Ranke's *Zwölf Bücher preussischer Geschichte* (five volumes, Berlin, 1874), stands at the beginning of the modern historiography. J. G. Droysen, *Geschichte der preussischen Politik* (fourteen volumes, Leipzig, 1855–1886), combined prodigious research with propaganda. H. Tuttle, *History of Prussia* (four volumes, Boston, 1884–1896), was dominated by the Germanophilism of his time. H. Prutz, *Preussische Geschichte* (four volumes, Stuttgart, 1900–1902), severely criticized the patriotic legend and punctured many myths. A. Waddington, *Histoire de Prusse* (two volumes, Paris, 1911, 1922), and O. Hintze, *Die Hohenzollern und ihr Werk* (Berlin, 1915), are both distinguished monuments of scholarship. M. Braubach, *Der Aufstieg Brandenburg-Preussens, 1640 bis 1815* (Freiburg-i.-B., 1933), is a product of the republican period. J. A. R. Marriott and C. G. Robertson, *The Evolution of Prussia* (Oxford, 1915, revised edition,

1946) is a capable summary with a working bibliography. F. Schevill, *The Great Elector* (Chicago, 1947), is a spirited popular account. H. Rachel, *Die Handels-, Zoll- und Aksizepolitik Brandenburg-Preussens* (three volumes, Berlin, 1911–1928), is rich in administrative detail. H. von Stephan, *Geschichte der preussischen Post* (new edition, K. Sautter, Berlin, 1928), is the story of one of the most creative efforts of the elector's machine. W. L. Dorn, "The Prussian Bureaucracy in the Eighteenth Century" (*Political Science Quarterly*, 46 (1931), 403–23; 47 (1932), 75–94, 259–73) throws light on the developments of the seventeenth century.

P. J. Blok, *History of the People of the Netherlands* (English translation, O. A. Bierstadt and Ruth Putnam, five volumes, New York and London, 1898–1912), is solid but not brilliant. G. Lefèvre-Pontalis, *John de Witt, Grand Pensionary of Holland, or, Twenty Years of a Parliamentary Republic* (English translation, S. E. and A. Stephenson, two volumes, London, 1885), is not a biography but a careful and thorough study of the period. H. Van Loon, *Fall of the Dutch Republic* (Boston, 1913, second edition, 1924), has a brilliant introductory section covering our period. B. H. M. Vlekke, *Evolution of the Dutch Nation* (New York, 1945), is a brief, crisply told story, especially valuable for reminders of "the other Holland." Marjorie Bowen, *William, Prince of Orange . . . up to his 24th year* (London, 1928), is devoutly Orangist. Mary C. Trevelyan, *William III and the Defense of Holland, 1672–1674* (London and New York, 1930), is a careful study of the great crisis.

The Cambridge History of Poland from the Origins to 1696 (edited by W. F. Reddaway, J. H. Penson, O. Halecki, and R. Dyboski, Cambridge, 1950), bears the marks of the harsh circumstances of the preceding decade. Although lacking all apparatus, it provides a complete and relatively detailed account of the whole political development and some of the cultural history. O. Loskowski, *Jan III Sobieski, King of Poland, 1629–1696* (London, 1941), is a competent biography. J. Dierauer, *Geschichte der schweizerischen Eidgenossenschaft* (five volumes, Gotha, 1887–1919), and E. Gagliardi, *Geschichte der Schweiz von den Anfängen bis auf die Gegenwart* (two volumes, Zürich, 1920), are standard, but for the purposes of this account, W. Rappard, *Cinq siècles de sécurité collective, 1291–1798: les expériences de la Suisse sous le regime de pactes de secours mutuel* (Paris and Geneva, 1945), was particularly valuable.

The history of Sweden is covered by the co-operative *Sveriges Historia til Vara Dagar,* edited by E. Hildebrand and L. Stavenow (thirteen volumes, Stockholm, 1919–1920). Three good one-volume histories in English, A. J. H. Hallendorf and A. Schück, *History of Sweden* (Stockholm, 1929), A. A. Stomberg, *A History of Sweden* (New York, 1931), and R. Svanstrom and C. F. Palmstierna, *A Short History of Sweden* (Oxford, 1934), have displaced the excellent but very brief *Scandinavia* (Cambridge, Eng., 1905) of R. Bain. K. Gjerset, *History of the Norwegian People* (two volumes, New York,

1915), and K. Larsen, *A History of Norway* (New York, 1948), both emphasize the more recent period.

For Spanish history in the Old World and the New, the best guide is R. Foulché-Delbosc and L. Barrau Dihigo, *Manuel de l'hispanisant* (two volumes, New York, 1920, 1926). The general histories of R. Altamira, *Historia de España y de la civilizacion española* (four volumes, third edition, Barcelona, 1913–1914), and of A. Ballesteros y Beretta, *Historia de España y de su influencia en la historia universal* (six volumes, Barcelona, 1918–1932), are less valuable for the period of this book than G. M. Desdevisses de Desert, *L'Espagne de l'ancien régime* (three volumes, Paris, 1897–1899). C. E. Chapman, *History of Spain* . . . (New York, 1918), is avowedly an abstract of Altamira's work. Ballesteros has also abbreviated his larger work in *Sintesis de historia d' España* (third edition, 1936). A. Canovas de Castillo, *Historia de la decadencia de España* . . . (Madrid, 1854, second edition, 1910), was the brilliant effort of a young man of genius. C. Petrie and L. Bertrand, *The History of Spain* (New York, 1934), is a good summary. H. Berindoague, *Le mercantilisme en Espagne* (Paris, 1929), is useful for indications of the operation of the decadent state. For Italy Carlo Morandi presents a compendious survey of recent work in a "Bulletin historique: histoire d'Italie du XVᵉ au XVIIIᵉ siècle" (*Revue historique*, 169 (1932), 159–81, 340–76). B. Croce, *Storia della età barocco in Italia* (Bari, 1929), is primarily literary and intellectual history.

THE ANARCHY

For international conflicts in general see the histories listed above. The bibliographies of A. de Saint-Lèger and P. Sagnac, *La préponderance française* (Paris, 1935), are particularly valuable for the history of international relations. E. Bourgeois, *Manuel historique de la politique étrangère* (four volumes, Paris, 1919–1926), of which the first volume *Les origines, 1610–1789* (seventh edition, Paris, 1919), relates to our period, gives complete coverage of the literature up to its date. D. J. Hill, *A History of Diplomacy in the International Development of Europe* (three volumes, New York, 1905–1914), is conventional but informative. The more popular *History of European Diplomacy 1451–1789* (London, 1928) of R. B. Mowat ignores the essential backgrounds. A. Vagts, *A History of Militarism* (New York, 1937), is a thoughtful general reconstruction of the problem. O. L. Spalding, H. Nickerson and J. W. Wright, *Warfare: A Study of Military Methods from the Earliest Times* (New York, 1925), is technical but useful. A. T. Mahan, *The Influence of Sea Power upon History, 1660–1783* (Boston, 1897, thirty-second edition, 1928), is almost biblical in authority. R. C. Anderson, *Naval Wars in the Baltic, 1522–1850* (London, 1910), is a regional study of tactics rather than strategy. M. Immich, *Geschichte des europäischen Staatensystems, 1660–1789* (Munich, 1905), assumes, i.e., does not define, the states of the system. In the Hanotaux series,

Histoire de la nation française, R. Pinon, *Histoire diplomatique,* is less useful for the period than A. Legrelle, *La diplomatie française et la succession d'Espagne* (four volumes, Paris, 1888–1892), or the very recent L. André, *Louis XIV et l'Europe* (Paris, 1950). C. A. Picavet, *La diplomatie française au temps de Louis XIV, 1661–1715* (Paris, 1930), describes the institutions, manners and customs of the service. Particular phases of French action in Europe are well treated by A. F. Pribram, *Beitrag zur Geschichte des Rheinbunds von 1658* (Vienna, 1888); G. Pagès, *Le Grand Electeur et Louis XIV* (Paris, 1905); S. de Gavestins, *Guillaume III et Louis XIV . . .* (eight volumes, Paris, 1868); and J. de Broglie, *Louis XIV et l'alliance suédoise* (Blois, 1905). E. Emerton, *Sir William Temple und die Tripelallianz vom Jahre 1668* (Berlin, 1877), is interestingly supplemented by *The First Triple Alliance: The Letters of Christopher Lindenov, Danish Envoy to London, 1668–1672,* edited by W. Westergaard (New Haven, 1947). The German public reaction is portrayed by H. Gillot, *Le règne de Louis XIV et l'opinion publique en Allemagne* (Nancy, 1914). E. Driault, *La question d'Orient depuis ses origines jusqu'à nos jours* (eighth edition, Paris, 1921), treats the eastern question from the point of view of the political decline of Islam. J. A. Marriott, *The Eastern Question: An Historical Study in European Diplomacy* (third revised edition, Oxford and New York, 1924), is a general survey but useful. J. Hudita, *Histoire des relations diplomatiques entre la France et la Transylvanie, 1635–1683* (Paris, 1924), expertly unravels a tangled skein. K. Keller, *Die orientalische Politik Ludwigs XIV, im Verhältniss zu dem Türkenkrieg vom 1683* (Leipzig, 1917), is less special but also revealing. C. L. Grose exposes "Louis XIV's Financial Relations with Charles II and the English Parliament," *Journal of Modern History,* I (1929), 177–204. K. Feiling, *British Foreign Policy, 1660–1672* (London, 1930), expertly analyzes the first phases of the French alliance. Paul Ritter, *Leibniz' aegyptischer Plan* (Darmstadt, 1930), explodes a myth.

RELIGION

A Bibliographical Guide to the History of Christianity (edited by S. J. Case, Chicago, 1931) is selective but highly useful. The best general work covering the period is K. Müller, *Kirchengeschichte* (two volumes in three, Tübingen, 1892–1902), Volume II, Part 2, dealing with the Counter Reformation to the end of the eighteenth century. L. A. Veit, *Die Kirche in Zeitalter des Individualismus, 1648–1800* (Freiburg-i.-B., 1930), is a valuable product of Catholic scholarship. J. W. C. Wand, *A History of the Modern Church from 1500 to the Present Day* (London, 1930), is a carefully done handbook, sensitive to the meaning of the issues and objective. A scholarly, complete and objective account of the missionary effort is presented by K. S. Latourette, *A History of the Expansion of Christianity,* Volume III, *Three Centuries of Advance,* A.D. 1500–A.D. 1800 (New York and London, 1939). E. Descamps and others,

Histoire générale et comparée des missions (Paris, 1932), is a convenient scholarly account in briefer form. A. Launay, *Histoire générale de la société des missions étrangères* (two volumes, Paris, 1915–1916), is an official history fully worthy of its subject. H. Brémond, *Histoire littéraire du sentiment religieux en France, depuis la fin des guerres de religion jusqu'à nos jours* (six volumes, Paris, 1916–1922, translated by the Society for Promoting Christian Knowledge, three volumes, London, 1928–1936), exemplifies purely religious history as distinguished from organizational history. Somewhat more concerned with machinery but in the same spirit, is Louis Prunel, *La renaissance catholique en France au XVIIe siècle* (Paris, 1921). C. Eckhardt, *The Papacy and World Affairs* (Chicago, 1937), is primarily political and very summary for our period. Very significant, however, is E. Troeltsch, *The Social Teaching of the Christian Church* (translated by Olive Wyon, New York, 1931), and *Die bedeutung des Protestantismus für die Entstehung der modernen Welt* (third edition, Munich, 1924). Troeltsch shows more religious insight than Max Weber, *The Protestant Ethic and the Spirit of Capitalism* (English translation, Talcott Parsons, New York, 1930). H. M. Robertson, *Aspects of the Rise of Economic Individualism* (Cambridge, Eng., 1934) is an unsuccessful criticism of Weber (see Brodrick, *Economic Morals,* below). V. Carrière, "Bossuet au XXe siècle. Les travaux de l'abbé Urbain relatifs à Bossuet" (*Revue d'histoire de l'église de France,* 17 (1931), 464–87) is a useful index of the recent revival of Bossuet studies. G. Truc, *Bossuet et le classicisme religieux* (Paris, 1927), and P. Souday, *Bossuet* (Paris, 1931), are useful biographical studies. The standard work on Jansenism is A. Gazier, *Histoire générale du mouvement janseniste* (two volumes, Paris, 1922). Racine's act of piety toward his old masters, *Abrégé de l'histoire de Port Royal,* written after his return to Jansenism, has been edited by A. Gazier (Paris, 1908) and is interesting as a document of lay Jansenism. Charles Augustin Saint-Beuve, *Port Royal* (six volumes, plus an index volume, Paris, 1840; seventh edition, Paris, 1922), is political rather than religious; nevertheless, a work of highest order. W. Deinhardt, *Der Jansenismus in deutschen Landen. Ein Beitrag zur Kirchengeschichte des 18. Jahrhundert* (Munich, 1929), and Ruth Clark, *Strangers and Sojourners at Port Royal; Being an Account of the Connections between the British Isles and the Jansenists of France and Holland* (Cambridge, Eng., 1932), are valuable for Jansenism as a European influence. P. Honigsheim, *Die Staats- und Soziallehren der französischen Jansenisten im 17. Jahrhundert* (Heidelberg, 1914), and Arturo Carlo Jemolo, *Il giansenismo prima della rivoluzione* (Bari, 1928), are concerned with the political and social influence of Jansenism.

The *Bibliographie générale des oeuvres de Blaise Pascal,* compiled by A. Maire (five volumes, Paris, 1925–1927), is definitive. Probably the best biography is that of F. Strowski, *Histoire du sentiment religieux en France au xviie siècle, Pascal et son temps* (three volumes, Paris, 1922–1929). The introductory essay of H. F. Stewart to his edition of *Les lettres provinciales* (New York, 1920) raises some interesting issues which are debated by J. Brodrick, *The Economic Morals of the Jesuits* (Oxford, 1934), a reply to H. M. Robertson (above) and also to Stewart and to Pascal.

On Richard Simon and his *Critical History of the Old Testament* (London, 1682), the most satisfactory general study is H. Margival, *Essai sur Richard Simon et la critique biblique au XVIIe siècle* (Paris, 1900), but important additions to the story are made by H. Fréville, "Richard Simon et les protestantes d'après sa correspondance" (*Revue d'histoire moderne*, VI (1931), 30–55), and Albert Monod, *La controverse de Bossuet et de Richard Simon, au sujet de la version de Trévoux* (Strassburg, 1922). On the Cambridge Platonists, J. Tulloch, *Rational Theology and Christian Philosophy in England during the 17th Century* (two volumes, Edinburgh, 1872), has been superseded by F. J. Powicke, *The Cambridge Platonists* (1928), and by E. Cassirer, *Die platonische Renaissance in England und die Schule von Cambridge* (Berlin, 1932). M. Nicolson's edition of the *Conway Letters; the Correspondence of Anne, Viscountess Conway, Henry More and Their Friends, 1642–1684* (New Haven, 1930), has an important introduction and notes. G. V. Lechler, *Geschichte des englischen Deismus* (Tübingen, 1841), is old, but still important. A. A. Seaton, *The Theory of Toleration under the Later Stuarts* (Cambridge, Eng., 1911), is a useful but not very profound study.

The only full-length study of the principal Quietist is P. Dudon, *Le quiétiste Michel Molinos, 1628–1696* (Paris, 1921), but more important is A. Chéruel, *Fénelon, ou la religion du pur amour* (Paris, 1934). Albrecht Ritschl, *Geschichte des Pietismus* (three volumes, Bonn, 1880–1886), is the best general history of the movement but is usefully supplemented by H. Heppe, *Geschichte des Pietismus und der Mystik in der reformierten Kirche, namentlich der Niederlanden* (Leiden, 1879). Hilding Pleijel, *Der swedische Pietismus in seinen Beziehungen zu Deutschland* (Lund, 1935), reflects the cosmopolitan character of the movement. J. T. Mueller, *Geschichte der Böhmischen Brüder* (three volumes, 1922–1931), is the story of one of the most interesting Pietistic developments. Arthur Nagler, *Pietism and Methodism* (Nashville, Tenn., 1918), is disappointing. A scholarly biography of the great German Pietist is provided by P. Grünberg, *Philipp Jakob Spener* (three volumes, Göttingen, 1893–1906). A. Salomon defines the indistinct relation to the Pietist movement of "Jean de Labadie," in the *Bulletin* of the *Société de l'histoire du protestantisme français*, 68 (1929), 7–41, 229–37. W. T. Whitley has ably edited *A Baptist Bibliography* (two volumes, London, 1916, 1922). F. Catron, *Histoire des Anabaptistes* . . . (Amsterdam, 1699), shows a wide acquaintance with its diverse forms. H. Dosker, *The Dutch Anabaptists* (Philadelphia, 1921), is a scholarly, sympathetic monograph.

G. R. Cragg, *From Puritanism to the Age of Reason* (Cambridge, 1950), is a thoughtful analysis of changes in religious thought in the English church.

H. G. Plum, *Restoration Puritanism: A Study of the Growth of English Liberty* (Chapel Hill, N.C., 1943), is primarily concerned with use of the church as a political instrument. H. M. Dexter, *The Congregationalism of the Last Three Hundred Years, as Seen in Its Literature* (two volumes, London, 1879, 1880), is more important for bibliography than for content. F. J. Powicke, *Life of the Reverend Richard Baxter* (two volumes, London, 1924, 1927), is not only sympathetic but devout. A. L. Lodell, *Richard Baxter, Puritan and Mystic* (New York and Toronto, 1925), is more objective. The works of W. C. Braithwaite, *The Beginnings of Quakerism* (London, 1923) and *The Second Period of Quakerism* (London, 1921), are thorough and authoritative. The biographical studies of Rachel Knight, *The Founder of Quakerism, a Psychological Study of the Mysticism of George Fox* (London, 1922), and of Bonamy Dobree, *William Penn* (London, s.d.), are excellent analyses. W. I. Hull, *Benjamin Furly and Quakerism in Rotterdam* (Swarthmore, 1941), illustrates Quaker missionary method. Luella M. Wright, *The Literary Life of the Early Friends* (New York, 1923), Arnold Lloyd, *Quaker Social History 1669–1783* (London, 1950), and Isabel Grubb, *Quakerism and Industry before 1800* (London, 1930), are three good books on special aspects of Quakerism.

ECONOMIC LIFE

Two important special bibliographical works, A. Grandin, *Bibliographie générale des sciences juridiques, politiques, économiques et sociale de 1800 à 1925–1926*, with successive annual supplements (three volumes, Paris, 1926, 1927), and H. Higgs, *Economic Bibliography* (London, 1935), are concerned with economics, incidentally with economic history. V. Porri, "Storia economica europea, età medioevale e moderna: Rassegna degli studi pubblicati fra il 1919 ed il 1929," *Rivista storica italiana*, 47 (1930), 135–54, 408–43, and 48 (1931), 41–87, is of high value for the limited period. M. M. Kovalevskii, *Die oekonomische Entwicklung Europas bis zum Beginn der kapitalischen Wirtschaftsform* (German translation, seven volumes, Berlin, 1901–1914), treats all of geographical Europe to, roughly, the nineteenth century, with rich detail but only in conventional categories. W. Sombart, *Der moderne Kapitalismus: historisch-systematische Darstellung des gesamteuropäischen Wirtschaftslebens von seinen Anfängen bis zur Gegenwart* (nominally second edition, three volumes in six, Munich, 1916–1927), is a model for European history as history of Europe. An indulgent reader may recognize in the present volume the attempt to emulate Sombart's organization. An excellent analysis, economic rather than historical, is supplied by T. Parsons, "Capitalism in Recent German Literature: Sombart and Weber," (*Journal of Political Economy*, Volumes 36 and 37). F. L. Nussbaum, "The Economic History of Renaissance Europe," (*Journal of Modern History*, 13 (1941), 527–45) attempts to explain the connections of Sombart's work. The excellent article of O. Hintze, "Der moderne

Kapitalismus als historisches Individuum" (*Historische Zeitschrift*, 1929), is a criticism of Sombart's historical method.

G. von Below, "Die Entstehung des modernen Kapitalismus und die Hauptstädte" (*Schmollers Jahrbuch*, 43 (1919), Part 1) is definitely anti-Sombart. F. L. Nussbaum, *A History of the Economic Institutions of Modern Europe. An introduction to* Der moderne Kapitalismus *of Werner Sombart* (New York, 1933), is a textbookish summary which Sombart approved. M. Dobb, *Studies in the Development of Capitalism* (London, 1946), has some useful monographic essays.

H. Sieveking, *Grundzüge der neueren Wirtschaftsgeschichte vom 17. Jahrhundert bis zur Gegenwart* (fifth edition, Leipzig, 1928), and J. M. Kulischer, *Allgemeine Wirtschaftsgeschichte des Mittelalters und der Neuzeit* (two volumes, Munich, 1928–1929), are admirable examples of the German manual. Three useful English manuals are H. Heaton, *Economic History of Europe* (revised edition, New York, 1948), M. M. Knight, H. E. Barnes and F. Flugel, *Economic History of Europe in Modern Times* (Boston, 1928), and S. B. Clough and C. W. Cole, *Economic History of Europe* (revised edition, Boston, 1946). H. M. Robertson, *Aspects of the Rise of Economic Individualism* (Cambridge, Eng., 1933), is a criticism of Max Weber which fails, but has important seventeenth-century material. J. Brodrick, *The Economic Morals of the Jesuits: An Answer to H. M. Robertson* (Oxford, 1934), pretty well demolishes Robertson.

The general advance of the bourgeois is the theme of two good books, B. Groethuysen, *Origines de l'esprit bourgeois en France* (Paris, 1927), and R. N. Gretton, *The English Middle Class* (London, 1917). E. Levasseur, *Histoire des classes ouvrières et de l'industrie en France avant 1789* (second edition, Paris, 1900–1901), and *Histoire du commerce de la France* (two volumes, Paris, 1911–1912), are fundamental for French economic history. M. Germain Martin, *Histoire économique et financière de la France* (*Histoire de la nation française*, G. Hanotaux X, Paris, 1927), is particularly valuable for the period of Louis XIV. Henry Sée, *Histoire économique de la France: Le moyen âge et l'ancien régime* (edited by R. Schnerb, Paris, 1939), serves to bring out gaps in the record and has superior bibliographies. One of those gaps is the study of Jacques Savary; but see J. Trouller, "Jacques Savary, le parfait négociant" (*Economie nouvelle*, 27 (1930), 367–85), and the chapter on Savary in H. Hauser, *Les débuts du capitalisme* (Paris, 1916). The useful article of F. Artz, "Les débuts de l'éducation technique en France" (*Revue d'histoire moderne*, 12 (1937), 469–519), shows France ahead of England in technical education.

The pioneer work of W. Cunningham, *The Growth of English Industry and Commerce in Modern Times* (Cambridge, Eng., 1892), has been largely displaced by E. Lipson, *The Economic History of England* (three volumes, London, 1937; seventh edition of Volume I, third edition of Volumes II, III).

The most convenient manual of Dutch economic history is E. Baasch, *Holländische Wirtschaftsgeschichte* (Jena, 1927). N. W. Posthumus, *Inquiry into the History of Prices in Holland* (Leiden, 1946), is a significant index from the point of view of prices. L. Dechesne, *Histoire économique et sociale de la Belgique depuis les origines jusqu'en 1914* (Paris, 1932), and J. Rutkowski, *Une esquisse de l'histoire économique de la Pologne jusqu'à les partages* (Paris, 1927), are convenient one-volume summaries. The importance of Sweden in this period gives more than ordinary importance to E. P. Heckscher, *Sveriges Ekonomiska Historia fran Gustav Vasa* (two volumes, Stockholm, 1935, 1936), which is usefully summarized by the author, "The Place of Sweden in Economic History" (*Economic History Review*, 4: 1932, 1 ff.). O. A. Johnsen, *Norwegische Wirtschaftsgeschichte* (Jena, 1939), shows some agricultural advance in the seventeenth century.

On urbanism, G. Botero, *A Treatise Concerning the Causes of the Magnificence and Greatness of Cities* (translated from the Italian, London, 1606), has unhappily not been emulated by modern writers. J. Beloch, "Antike und moderne Grossstädte" (*Zeitschrift für Sozialwissenschaft*, 1898), is an important formulation of the problem. P. Lavedon, *Histoire de l'urbanisme. Renaissance et temps modernes* (Paris, 1946), is valuable as a beginning, but views the problem too narrowly and strangely ignores the Dutch towns. V. Barbour, *Capitalism in Amsterdam in the Seventeenth Century* (*The Johns Hopkins University Studies in History and Political Science*, Series LXVII, No. 1, Baltimore, 1950), is a superior accounting of the development of Amsterdam's metropolitan function as economic capital. Among the books about Amsterdam as a vessel, A. E. d'Ailly, *Die groote Stadsuitbreidigen* (in *Zeven Eeuwen Amsterdam*, edited by A. E. d'Ailly, six volumes, Amsterdam, s.d., Volume II, *De Zeventiende Eeuw*), and A. Bredius and others, *Amsterdam in de Zeventiende Eeuw* (three volumes, 'sGravenhage, 1897–1904), are impressive in format and richly illustrated, but monumental rather than functional in approach. J. P. Hazewinkel, "Le développement d'Amsterdam" (*Annales de géographie*, 35 (1926), 322–29), is an important study of the physical setting and its adjustments. H. I. Bloom, *The Economic Activities of the Jews of Amsterdam in the Seventeenth and the Eighteenth Centuries* (Williamsport, Pa., 1937), indicates that the Jews were a minor element in the city. The financial aspect of Amsterdam's development is portrayed in the important article of J. Van Dillen, "Amsterdam, marché mondial des métaux précieux au XVIIe et au XVIIIe siècle" (*Revue historique*, 152 (1926), 194–201).

M. Poète, *Une vie de cité: Paris de sa naissance à nos jours* (three volumes, and album, Paris, 1924–1931), is also monumental rather than economic; the album has significant material. A. Maquet, *Paris sous Louis XIV* (Paris, 1883), shows the growth and reorganization of the city. W. G. Bell, *The Great Fire of London in 1666* (London, 1920), and *The Great Plague of London in 1665* (London, 1924), are useful accounts of these great disasters.

The social unit emerges more clearly from T. F. Reddaway, *The Rebuilding of London after the Great Fire* (London, 1940). G. S. Thomson, *The Russells in Bloomsbury, 1669–1771* (London, 1940), and *Life in a Noble Household, 1641–1700* (New York, 1937), have much about the real-estate operations of the Russells and the extension of London into Bloomsbury. M. D. George, *London Life in the Eighteenth Century* (New York, 1925), reflects some light on the preceding century. For Vienna, *Bibliographie zur Geschichte und Stadtkunde von Wien nebst Quellen- und Literaturhinweisen,* Volume I (Vienna, 1947) is the best of town bibliographies. *Wien, sein Boden und seine Geschichte* (edited by O. Abel, Vienna, 1924), is the most recent general history. Paul Burckhardt, *Geschichte der Stadt Basel* (Basle, 1942), is political rather than urban history. A. P. Usher, *History of the Grain Trade in France, 1400–1710* (Cambridge, Mass., 1913), and N. S. B. Gras, *The Evolution of the English Corn Market* (Cambridge, Mass., 1915), portray the impact of developing urbanism upon traditional markets.

A. Girard, *Le commerce à Seville et Cadix au temps des Habsbourgs: contribution à l'étude du commerce étranger en Espagne aux XVIᵉ et XVIIᵉ siècles* (Paris, 1932) and *La rivalité commerciale et maritime entre Seville et Cadix, jusqu'à la fin du XVIIIᵉ siècle* (Paris, 1932); C. H. Haring, *Trade and Navigation between Spain and the Indies in the Time of the Habsburgs* (Cambridge, Mass., 1918), and Jean O. McLachlan, *Trade and Peace with Old Spain, 1667–1750, a Study of the Influence of Trade on Diplomacy* (Cambridge, Eng., 1940), portray the channeling of European interest in South America through Spain. G. Scellé, *Histoire politique de la trait negrière aux Indes de Castille* (two volumes, Paris, 1906), is a work of the first order. P. Masson, *Histoire du commerce français dans le Levant au XVIIᵉ siècle* (two volumes, Paris, 1896), is the central work of several in which the author has covered the Mediterranean trade of France. L. J. P. M. Bonnassieux, *Les grandes compagnies de commerce* (Paris, 1892), is good for the French companies, but not much else. The local bearing of a great company emerges from G. Martin, *Nantes et la compagnie des Indes, 1664–1789* (Paris, 1927). Two good general surveys of England's East India trade are J. F. Hamilton, *Trade Relations between England and India, 1660–1806* (Calcutta, 1919), and B. N. Krisna, *Commercial Relations between India and England* (London, 1924). V. M. Godinho, "Le Portugal, les flottes du sucre et les flottes d'or" (*Annales, 5* (1950), 184–97), and Curtis Nettels, "The Economic Relations of Boston, Philadelphia, and New York, 1680–1715" (*Journal of Economic and Business History,* 3 (1931), 185–215), are useful articles of a type of which there should be more. Violet Barbour, "Dutch and English Merchant Shipping in the Seventeenth Century" (*Economic History Review,* 2 (1928), 261–90), shows that Dutch shipping reached its highest point in the last half of the century and explains why.

In the field of financial history, J. G. Van Dillen edits the *History of the*

Principal Public Banks (The Hague, 1934), which brings together the whole picture of early banking in a useful perspective. G. Martin and M. Bezançon, *L'histoire du credit en France sous le règne de Louis XIV* (Paris, 1913), shows the nobles as investors in industry and insurance, and as money-lenders. P. Harsin, *Credit public et banque d'état en France du XVIᵉ au XVIIIᵉ siècle* (Paris, 1933), brings out the small development in our period. G. d'Avenel, *Histoire de la fortune française à travers sept siècles* (Paris, 1927), is statistically weak but has good social indications. G. N. Clark, *The Wealth of England from 1496 to 1760* (London, 1947), is better based. Earl J. Hamilton, *War and Prices in Spain, 1650–1800* (Cambridge, Mass., 1947), is a learned study of inflation and deflation. C. Nettels, *Money Supply in the American Colonies* (University of Wisconsin *Studies in the Social Sciences and History,* No. 20, Madison, Wis., 1934), is an important "export-of-capital" study. V. Barbour, "Marine Risks and Insurance in the Seventeenth Century" (*Journal of Economic and Business History,* I (1929), 561–96), shows the still unformed character of the business. C. Wright and C. E. Foyle, *A History of Lloyd's: from the Founding of Lloyd's Coffee House to the Present Day* (London, 1928), reflects part of the preceding situation. D. Houtzager, *Hollands Lijf- en Los-Renteleningen vóór 1672* (Schiedam, 1950), is a workman-like dissertation on the introduction of mathematical concepts. J. U. Nef, *The Rise of the British Coal Industry* (two volumes, London, 1932), sets a high standard as a comprehensive study of a single business. H. Heaton, *The Yorkshire Woolen and Worsted Industries* (Oxford, 1920), has fewer data but is hardly less illuminating. R. B. Westerfield, *Middlemen in English Business* (New Haven, 1915), analyzes the patterns of various businesses. G. Unwin, *Industrial Organization in the Sixteenth and Seventeenth Centuries* (Oxford, 1904), is primarily early seventeenth century but throws some light on the latter half. W. R. Scott, *The Constitution and Finance of English, Scottish and Irish Joint-Stock Companies to 1720* (three volumes, Cambridge, Eng., 1910–1912), is the most important work on the early history of this form of co-operative enterprise.

INDUSTRY AND AGRICULTURE

La grande industrie sous la règne de Louis XIV (Paris, 1898) of Germain Martin is specifically industrial. Ch. Ballot, *L'introduction du machinisme dans l'industrie française* (Paris, 1923), is mainly eighteenth-century material. J. Kulischer, "La grande industrie au XVIIᵉ et XVIIIᵉ siècles: France, Allemagne, Russie" (*Annales d'histoire économique et sociale,* 5 (1931), 11–46), is a very general article useful as integration of the problem. F. Bacquié, *Les inspecteurs de manufactures sous l'Ancien Régime, 1669–1791* (Paris, 1930), shows the inspectors as valuable influences for the improvement of techniques. W. A. Young, "Works Organization in the Seventeenth Century: Some Account of Ambrose and John Crowley" (*Transactions of the Newcomen Society,* Vol. IV (1923–1924), 73–101), is a picture of an organization very "modern" for its time. Alice Clark, *The Working Life of Women in the Seventeenth Century* (London, 1919), is useful as one of the rare attempts to show the conditions of labor. Two general surveys, H. Sée, *Esquisse d'une histoire du régime agraire en Europe aux XVIIIᵉ et XIXᵉ siècles* (Paris, 1921), and N. S. B. Gras, *History of Agriculture in Europe and America* (New York, 1925), are significant general essays which bring out the fact that the history of agriculture in the seventeenth century is still a neglected field. R. Dion, *Essai sur la formation du paysage rural français* (Tours, 1934), and G. Roupnel, *Histoire de la campagne française* (Paris, 1932), are brilliant social studies. Paul Raveau, *L'agriculture et les classes paysannes dans l'Haut-Poitou* (Paris, 1926), pushes back to the sixteenth and seventeenth centuries the acquisition of lands by the bourgeois, the process long regarded as peculiar to the eighteenth century. Somewhat in the same manner as Roupnel and Dion, Mrs. Mabel Seebohm has described *The Evolution of an English Farm* (London, 1927). R. E. Prothero, *English Farming, Past and Present* (fourth edition, London and New York, 1927), is the most comprehensive history of farming in any European country. R. M. Garnier, *History of the English Landed Interest* (two volumes, London, 1892–1893), and F. Luetge, *Die mitteldeutsche Grundherrschaft* (Jena, 1934), are valuable histories of landlordship. In *The Enclosure and Redistribution of Our Land* (Oxford, 1920), W. H. R. Curtler covers the whole story with special reference to our period. J. Klein, *The Mesta: A Study in Spanish Economic History, 1273–1836* (Cambridge, Mass., 1920), is a brilliant study of the powerful sheep growers association. The various articles of G. E. Russell, for example, "Eighteenth Century Agricultural Dictionaries" (*Bulletin of the Institute of Historical Research,* 7 (1930), 144–48) and "The First English Book on Potatoes" *Scottish Farmer,* 40 (1932), 509–10), are important contributions to the history of this neglected period.

THE EXPANSION PROCESS

THE EUROPEANIZATION OF RUSSIA

R. J. Kerner, *Slavic Europe, a Selected Bibliography in the Western European Languages, Comprising History, Languages and Literature* (Cambridge, Mass., 1918), is excellent within the limit of its date. The important general surveys available in Western languages are V. Kliuchevsky, *Kurs russkoi istorii* (five parts, Moscow, 1904–1921; English translation, *History of Russia,* five volumes, London and New York, 1911–1931), K. Stählin, *Geschichte Russlands von den Anfängen bis zur Gegenwart* (four volumes, Stuttgart, 1923–1939), probably the best history by a western scholar, and P. Miliukov, C. Seignobos and L. Eisenmann, *Histoire de Russie* (three volumes, Paris, 1932–33). M. N. Pokrovsky, *History of Russia from the Earliest Times to the Rise of Commercial Capitalism* (translated by J. D. Clarkson and M. R. M. Griffiths, New

York, 1931), is a Marxist interpretation. D. S. Mirsky, *Russia, a Social History* (London, 1901), is a brilliant general sketch, but for the seventeenth century, P. Miliukov, *Outlines of Russian Culture* (three volumes, Philadelphia, 1942), is most valuable. K. Waliszewski, *Le berceau d'une dynastie; les premiers Romanov, 1613–1682* (Paris, 1909), is a valuable work by a Polish historian. For the eastward expansion of Russia, A. Lobanov-Rostovsky, *Russia and Asia* (New York, 1933), is a comprehensive survey; F. A. Golder, *Russian Expansion on the Pacific, 1641–1850* (Cleveland, 1914), is usefully supplemented by R. H. Fisher, *The Russian Fur Trade* (Berkeley, 1943), and G. V. Lantzeff, *Siberia in the Seventeenth Century* (Berkeley, 1943). Alexandre Miller, *Essai sur l'histoire des institutions agraires de la Russie centrale du 16ᵉ au 18ᵉ siècle* (Paris, 1926), is central to the continuing controversy over the origins of serfdom. S. Konovalov, *Russo-Polish Relations: An Historical Survey* (London, 1945), presents a Russian view of that dismal story.

THE END OF THE TURKISH THREAT

Bibliographie zur Geschichte von Wien, listed above, has 40 pages, 526 numbers, on the two attacks on Vienna. H. Kadbebo, *Bibliographie zur Geschichte der beiden Türkenbelagerungen Wiens* (Vienna, 1876), is still useful for the earlier literature. O. Klopp, *Das Jahr 1683* —— (Graz, 1882), is as thorough as any later work. R. Lorenz, *Türkenjahr 1683. Das Reich im Kampf um den Ostraum* (Vienna, 1933), is regional rather than local in its purpose. O. Laskowski, *Jan III Sobieski (King of Poland), 1629–1696* (London, 1941), is valuable for Sobieski's large part in the repulse of the Turks. An important and interesting contemporary account, apparently widespread at the time as propaganda, has been translated by F. H. Marshall: J. Kakabelos, *The Siege of Vienna* (Cambridge, Eng., 1925).

OVERSEAS EXPANSION

Bibliographie d'histoire coloniale, 1900–1930 (edited by A. Martineau, A. Roussier, and J. Tramond, commissioned by the First International Congress of Colonial History 1931, Paris, 1932), is composite, international and incomplete. W. G. F. Roscher, *Kolonien, Kolonialpolitik und Auswanderung* (third edition, Leipzig, 1885), is a thoughtful work that deserves attention. P. Leroy-Beaulieu, *De la colonisation chez les peuples modernes* (sixth edition, two volumes, Paris, 1908), is generally regarded as "standard." A. G. Keller, *Colonization, a Study of the Founding of New Societies* (Boston, 1908), is a sociological formulation of interest. H. C. Morris, *History of Colonization from the Earliest Times to the Present Day* (two volumes, New York and London, 1900), is generally condemned for its errors of fact but is valuable as a unique attempt at a general history. C. de Lannoy and H. Van der Linden, *Histoire de l'expansion coloniale des peuples européens* (three volumes, Brussels, 1907–1921), is more scholarly, but uncompleted because of the loss of materials in the First World War. Georg Friederici, *Der Charakter der*

Entdeckung und Eroberung Amerikas durch die Europäer: Einleitung zur Geschichte der Besiedlung Amerikas durch die Völker der alten Welt (three volumes, Stuttgart, 1925–1936), a product of the modern conscience, bitterly attacks the Europeans.

LATIN-AMERICA

Latin-America is well supplied with bibliographical instruments: Cecil Knight Jones, *Bibliography of Latin-American Bibliographies* (second edition, Washington, 1942); H. L. Hoskins, *Guide to Latin American History* (Boston, 1922); *Handbook of Latin American Studies* (annual, Harvard University Press, 1935——).

C. H. Haring, *The Spanish Empire in America* (New York, 1947), is the most recent and one of the best general histories. B. Moses, *Spanish Colonial Literature in South America* (London and New York, 1922), is a useful reminder of the strength of Spanish-American culture. V. G. Quesada, *La vida intellectual en la America española durante los siglos XVI, XVII y XVIII* (Buenos Aires, 1910), is also an important contribution. At long last the treatment of the historical development of European art forms in South America is under way, a result, in part at least, of the rationalization of the concept of the baroque. Three major works representative of the movement are: R. C. Smith, *The Colonial Art of Latin America* (Washington, 1945), P. Kelemen, *Baroque and Rococo in Latin America* (New York, 1951), which has a magnificent apparatus of illustration, as well as a good bibliography, and M. S. Noel, *Téoria historica de la arquitectura virreinal* (Buenos Aires, 1932). The religious aspect of Spanish colonization is well represented in general works such as Haring, *The Spanish Empire,* and Latourette, *Three Centuries of Expansion,* listed above, but R. K. Wyllys, *Pioneer Padre: The Life of Eusebio Francisco Kino* (Dallas, 1935), is valuable as a specific account.

WEST AND EAST INDIES

A. P. Newton, *The European Nations in the West Indies* (London, 1933), is the best general work. J. Tramond, "Les études historiques françaises sur les Antilles depuis 1900" (*Revue de l'histoire des colonies françaises,* 19 (1931), 409–18), is an excellent brief book list. The *Histoire des colonies françaises et l'expansion de la France dans le monde,* under the editorship of Gabriel Hanotaux and A. Martineau (Paris, 1930), has not been carried beyond Volume I, devoted to French expansion in America. H. I. Priestley, *France Overseas through the Old Regime* (New York, 1939), is a brief, useful survey. H. Blét, *Histoire de la colonisation française: naissance et déclin d'un empire, des origines à 1789* (Paris, 1946), and Georges Hardy, *Histoire de la colonisation française* (Paris, 1928), are scholarly summaries. W. A. Roberts, *The French in the West Indies* (New York, 1942), is popular but competent. Henri Malo, *Les îles d'aventure* (Paris, 1928), emphasizes the picturesque. C. H. Haring,

The Buccaneers in the West Indies in the Seventeenth Century (London, 1910) is a thoroughgoing study of the lawlessness "beyond the line." F. Parkman, *Count Frontenac and New France under Louis XIV* (1877), and *La Salle and the Discovery of the Great West* (1869) in his *Works* (twelve volumes, Boston, 1893), in spite of the passage of time remain as great literary monuments. G. M. Wrong, *The Rise and Fall of New France* (two volumes, New York, 1928), is a more objective and more systematic account from the standpoint of a Canadian. On the Dutch in the East, E. S. De Klerck, *History of the Netherlands East Indies* (two volumes, Rotterdam, 1938), is largely a story of the military aspect of the conquest. J. S. Furnivall, *An Introduction to the History of Netherlands India* (Rangoon, 1934), is hardly more than a pamphlet but excellent for its illustrative documents. B. H. M. Van Vlekke, *Nusantara: A History of the East Indian Archipelago* (Cambridge, Mass., 1943), represents the new tendency in Dutch (and other) scholarship. A. Hyma, *The Dutch in the Far East* (Ann Arbor, 1942), is apologetic but solidly based. P. Gonnaud, *La colonisation hollandaise à Java* (Paris, 1905), is an excellent older book.

THE ENGLISH IN INDIA AND NORTH AMERICA

J. R. Seeley, *The Expansion of England* (London, 1883—— many times reprinted, to 1911), is an interesting document of the empire's better days. The first volume of *The Cambridge History of the British Empire* (Cambridge, 1929) is compendious, with good bibliographies, and is well supplemented by the fifth volume of *The Cambridge History of India* (1910). W. W. Hunter, *History of British India* (two volumes, New York and London, 1899–1900), is an authoritative history of the Company rule. P. E. Roberts, *History of British India under the Company and the Crown* (Oxford, 1923), is soundly based on documentary material. C. S. S. Higham, *Development of the Leeward Islands under the Restoration, 1660–1688* (Cambridge, 1921), marks an important step in laying foundations for a really scientific history of the West Indies. R. C. Dutt, *Economic History of British India* (fourth edition, London, 1916), sets a new standard in an area where much loose writing has been done. H. Weber, *La compagnie française des Indes, 1604–1875* (Paris, 1904), is rather formal and political, and definitely lacking in economic sense. P. Koeppelin, *La compagnie des Indes Orientales et François Martin* (Paris, 1908), tells the story of a great servant of the French company. As a part of United States history, the history of the North American colonies has been written mainly by Americans. With valuable results, H. E. Bolton and T. H. Marshall, *The Colonization of North America, 1492–1783* (New York, 1920), transcends the purely English point of view of works such as H. L. Osgood, *American Colonies in the Seventeenth Century* (three volumes, New York, 1904–1907), which is definitive history of the North American English colonies in their legal, institutional and administrative relations. C. M. Andrews, *The*

Colonial Background of the American Revolution (New Haven, 1931), embodies the results of a very active period of scholarship in which Andrews' part was a leading one. A. B. Faust, *German Element in the United States with Special Reference to Its Political, Moral, Social and Educational Influence* (new edition, two volumes in one, New York, 1927), G. Chinard, *Les réfugiés huguenots en Amérique* (Paris, 1925), and A. H. Hirsch, *The Huguenots of South Carolina* (Durham, N.C., 1928), are useful studies of non-English elements in the United States.

THE NEW WORLD AND EUROPE

A. Reichwein, *China and Europe; Intellectual and Artistic Contacts in the Eighteenth Century* (English translation, London and New York, 1925), is a comprehensive and well-documented study. Belevitch Stankevitch, *La Chine en France au temps de Louis XIV* (Paris, 1910), is a valuable treatment of the more limited area and period. J. E. Gillespie, *The Influence of Overseas Expansion on England to 1700* (New York, 1920), is less cultural, more concerned with economic influence. G. Chinard, *L'Amérique et le rêve éxotique dans la littérature au XVIIe et au XVIIIe siècle* (Paris, 1913), is a brilliant essay.

INDEX

HARPER TORCHBOOKS / The University Library
[Selected Titles]

John R. Alden	THE AMERICAN REVOLUTION: 1775–1783. Illus. TB/3011
Ray A. Billington	THE FAR WESTERN FRONTIER: 1830–1860. Illus. TB/3012
J. Bronowski & Bruce Mazlish	THE WESTERN INTELLECTUAL TRADITION: From Leonardo to Hegel TB/3001
Edward P. Cheyney	THE DAWN OF A NEW ERA: 1250–1453. Illus. TB/3002
Carl J. Friedrich	THE AGE OF THE BAROQUE: 1610–1660. Illus. TB/3004
Myron P. Gilmore	THE WORLD OF HUMANISM: 1453–1517. Illus. TB/3003
Lawrence Henry Gipson	THE COMING OF THE [AMERICAN] REVOLUTION: 1763–1775. Illus. TB/3007
Wallace Notestein	THE ENGLISH PEOPLE ON THE EVE OF COLONIZATION: 1603–1630. Illus. TB/3006
Joseph A. Schumpeter	CAPITALISM, SOCIALISM AND DEMOCRACY. Third edition. TB/3008
Frederick L. Nussbaum	THE TRIUMPH OF SCIENCE AND REASON: 1660–1685. Illus. TB/3009
Louis B. Wright	THE CULTURAL LIFE OF THE AMERICAN COLONIES: 1607–1763. Illus. TB/3005
M. D. Zabel, Ed.	LITERARY OPINION IN AMERICA. 3rd Edition. Vol. I, TB/3013; Vol. II, TB/3014

HARPER TORCHBOOKS / The Academy Library
[Selected Titles]

Jacques Barzun	THE HOUSE OF INTELLECT TB/1051
Jeremy Bentham	THE HANDBOOK OF POLITICAL FALLACIES. Intro. by Crane Brinton TB/1069
Henri Bergson	TIME AND FREE WILL: The Immediate Data of Consciousness TB/1021
H. J. Blackham	SIX EXISTENTIALIST THINKERS TB/1002
Crane Brinton	ENGLISH POLITICAL THOUGHT IN THE NINETEENTH CENTURY TB/1071
Joseph Charles	THE ORIGINS OF THE AMERICAN PARTY SYSTEM TB/1049
Thomas C. Cochran	THE AMERICAN BUSINESS SYSTEM: A Historical Perspective TB/1080
Cochran & Miller	THE AGE OF ENTERPRISE: A Social History of Industrial America TB/1054
G. G. Coulton	MEDIEVAL VILLAGE, MANOR, AND MONASTERY TB/1022
Wilhelm Dilthey	PATTERN AND MEANING IN HISTORY TB/1075
St. Clair Drake & Horace Cayton	BLACK METROPOLIS: A Study of Negro Life in a Northern City. Introductions by Richard Wright and Everett C. Hughes. Revised edition. Vol. I, TB/1086; Vol. II, TB/1087
Peter F. Drucker	THE NEW SOCIETY: The Anatomy of Industrial Order TB/1082
W. K. Ferguson, et al.	THE RENAISSANCE: Six Essays TB/1084
F. L. Ganshof	FEUDALISM TB/1058
W. K. C. Guthrie	THE GREEK PHILOSOPHERS: From Thales to Aristotle TB/1008
John Higham, Ed.	THE RECONSTRUCTION OF AMERICAN HISTORY TB/1068
Dan N. Jacobs, Ed.	THE NEW COMMUNIST MANIFESTO and related documents TB/1078
Henry James	THE PRINCESS CASAMASSIMA. A novel. Intro. by Clinton Oliver TB/1005
Hans Kohn, Ed.	THE MIND OF MODERN RUSSIA TB/1065
Samuel Noah Kramer	SUMERIAN MYTHOLOGY. Illustrated TB/1055
Paul Oskar Kristeller	RENAISSANCE THOUGHT: Classic, Scholastic, Humanist Strains TB/1048
Arthur O. Lovejoy	THE GREAT CHAIN OF BEING: A Study of the History of an Idea TB/1009
Paul Mantoux	THE INDUSTRIAL REVOLUTION IN THE EIGHTEENTH CENTURY TB/1079
William Miller, Ed.	MEN IN BUSINESS: The Historical Role of the Entrepreneur TB/1081
J. E. Neale	THE AGE OF CATHERINE DE MEDICI TB/1085
Erwin Panofsky	STUDIES IN ICONOLOGY: Humanistic Themes in Renaissance Art. Illus. TB/1077
Parsons & Shils, Eds.	TOWARD A GENERAL THEORY OF ACTION TB/1083
Priscilla Robertson	REVOLUTIONS OF 1848: A Social History TB/1025
Ferdinand Schevill	THE MEDICI. Illustrated TB/1010
C. P. Snow	TIME OF HOPE. A novel. TB/1040
N. N. Sukhanov	THE RUSSIAN REVOLUTION, 1917: Eyewitness Account Vol. I, TB/1066; Vol. II, TB/1067
Dorothy Van Ghent	THE ENGLISH NOVEL: Form and Function TB/1050
W. Lloyd Warner	SOCIAL CLASS IN AMERICA: The Evaluation of Status TB/1013
Alfred N. Whitehead	PROCESS AND REALITY: An Essay in Cosmology TB/1033

HARPER TORCHBOOKS / The Bollingen Library
[Selected Titles]

Rachel Bespaloff	ON THE ILIAD. Introduction by Hermann Broch TB/2006
Joseph Campbell, Ed.	PAGAN AND CHRISTIAN MYSTERIES: Papers from Eranos Yearbooks. Illus. TB/2013
Elliott Coleman, Ed.	LECTURES IN CRITICISM TB/2003

C. G. Jung	PSYCHOLOGICAL REFLECTIONS. Edited by Jolande Jacobi TB/2001
C. G. Jung	SYMBOLS OF TRANSFORMATION. Illustrated. *Vol. I*, TB/2009; *Vol. II*, TB/2010
C. G. Jung & Carl Kerényi	ESSAYS ON A SCIENCE OF MYTHOLOGY: *The Myth of the Divine Child and the Divine Maiden*. Illus. TB/2014
Erich Neumann	AMOR AND PSYCHE: *A Commentary on the Tale by Apuleius* TB/2012
Erich Neumann	ORIGINS AND HISTORY OF CONSCIOUSNESS. *Vol. I*, illus. TB/2007; *Vol. II*, TB/2008
St.-John Perse	SEAMARKS. Translated by Wallace Fowlie TB/2002
A. Piankoff	THE SHRINES OF TUT-ANKH-AMON. Ed. by N. Rambova. Illus. TB/2011
Jean Seznec	SURVIVAL OF THE PAGAN GODS. Illus. TB/2004
Heinrich Zimmer	MYTHS AND SYMBOLS IN INDIAN ART AND CIVILIZATION. Illus. TB/2005

HARPER TORCHBOOKS / The Cloister Library

[*Selected Titles*]

W. F. Albright	THE BIBLICAL PERIOD FROM ABRAHAM TO EZRA TB/102
C. K. Barrett, *Ed.*	THE NEW TESTAMENT BACKGROUND: *Selected Documents* TB/86
Karl Barth	CHURCH DOGMATICS: *A Selection*. Edited by G. W. Bromiley TB/95
Martin Buber	ECLIPSE OF GOD: *The Relation Between Religion and Philosophy* TB/12
R. Bultmann	HISTORY AND ESCHATOLOGY: *The Presence of Eternity* TB/91
Jacob Burckhardt	THE CIVILIZATION OF THE RENAISSANCE IN ITALY. Illustrated Edition. Introduction by B. Nelson and C. Trinkaus. *Vol. I*, TB/40; *Vol. II*, TB/41
Edward Conze	BUDDHISM: *Its Essence and Development*. Foreword by Arthur Waley TB/58
Frederick Copleston	MEDIEVAL PHILOSOPHY TB/76
Mircea Eliade	COSMOS AND HISTORY: *The Myth of the Eternal Return* TB/50
Sigmund Freud	ON CREATIVITY AND THE UNCONSCIOUS: *Papers on the Psychology of Art, Literature, Love, Religion*. Edited by Benjamin Nelson TB/45
F. H. Heinemann	EXISTENTIALISM AND THE MODERN PREDICAMENT TB/28
Winthrop Hudson	THE GREAT TRADITION OF THE AMERICAN CHURCHES TB/98
Johan Huizinga	ERASMUS AND THE AGE OF REFORMATION. Illustrated TB/19
Søren Kierkegaard	THE PRESENT AGE. Intro. by W. Kaufmann TB/94
Søren Kierkegaard	PURITY OF HEART TB/4
Kenneth B. Murdock	LITERATURE AND THEOLOGY IN COLONIAL NEW ENGLAND TB/99
H. Richard Niebuhr	CHRIST AND CULTURE TB/3
P. Teilhard de Chardin	THE PHENOMENON OF MAN TB/83
D. W. Thomas, *Ed.*	DOCUMENTS FROM OLD TESTAMENT TIMES TB/85
Paul Tillich	DYNAMICS OF FAITH TB/42
Ernst Troeltsch	SOCIAL TEACHING OF CHRISTIAN CHURCHES. *Vol. I*, TB/71; *Vol. II*, TB/72
G. van der Leeuw	RELIGION IN ESSENCE AND MANIFESTATION: *A Study in Phenomenology*. Appendices by Hans H. Penner. *Vol. I*, TB/100; *Vol. II*, TB/101
Wilhelm Windelband	A HISTORY OF PHILOSOPHY I: *Greek, Roman, Medieval* TB/38
Wilhelm Windelband	A HISTORY OF PHILOSOPHY II: *Renaissance, Enlightenment, Modern* TB/39

HARPER TORCHBOOKS / The Science Library

[*Selected Titles*]

Harold F. Blum	TIME'S ARROW AND EVOLUTION. Illustrated TB/555
R. B. Braithwaite	SCIENTIFIC EXPLANATION TB/515
Louis de Broglie	PHYSICS AND MICROPHYSICS. Foreword by Albert Einstein TB/514
J. Bronowski	SCIENCE AND HUMAN VALUES TB/505
W. E. Le Gros Clark	ANTECEDENTS OF MAN: *Intro. to Evolution of Primates*. Illus. TB/559
R. E. Coker	THIS GREAT AND WIDE SEA: *Oceanography & Marine Biology*. Illus. TB/551
A. C. Crombie, *Ed.*	TURNING POINTS IN PHYSICS TB/535
W. C. Dampier, *Ed.*	READINGS IN THE LITERATURE OF SCIENCE. Illustrated TB/512
C. V. Durell	READABLE RELATIVITY. Foreword by Freeman J. Dyson. Illus. TB/530
F. K. Hare	THE RESTLESS ATMOSPHERE. Illus. TB/560
Werner Heisenberg	PHYSICS AND PHILOSOPHY: *The Revolution in Modern Science*. Intro. by F. S. C. Northrop TB/549
Max Jammer	CONCEPTS OF FORCE: *A Study in the Foundations of Dynamics* TB/550
J. M. Keynes	A TREATISE ON PROBABILITY. Foreword by N. R. Hanson TB/557
S. Körner	THE PHILOSOPHY OF MATHEMATICS: *An Introduction* TB/547
J. R. Partington	A SHORT HISTORY OF CHEMISTRY. Illustrated TB/522
H. T. Pledge	SCIENCE SINCE 1500: *A Short History of Mathematics, Physics, Chemistry, and Biology*. Illustrated TB/506
Paul A. Schilpp, *Ed.*	ALBERT EINSTEIN: *Philosopher-Scientist*. *Vol. I*, TB/502; *Vol. II*, TB/503